C000132185

500 **DOG FRIENDLY PLACES TO STAY**

Published 2009 © AA Media Limited 2009.

AA Media Limited retains the copyright in the current edition © 2009 and in all subsequent editions, reprints and amendments to editions. The information contained in this directory is taken from AA Pet Friendly Places to Stay 2010 and the data is sourced entirely from the AA's establishment database, AA Lifestyle Guides. The contents of this publication are believed correct at the time of printing. Nevertheless, the publishers cannot be held responsible for any errors or omissions or for changes in the details given in this guide or for the consequences of any reliance on the information provided by the same. This does not affect your statutory rights. Assessments of AA inspected establishments are based on the experience of the Hotel and Restaurant Inspectors on the occasion(s) of their visit(s) and therefore descriptions given in this guide necessarily contain an element of subjective opinion which may not reflect or dictate a reader's own opinion on another occasion.

The AA strives to ensure accuracy in this guide at the time of printing. Due to the constantly evolving nature of the subject matter the information is subject to change. The AA will gratefully receive any advice from our readers of any necessary updated information.

Editorial Department: lifestyleguides@theaa.com
AA Hotel & Guest Accommodation enquiries:
01256 844455

Cover photography: (top) The Tollgate Inn & Restaurant, Kingham, Oxfordshire; (middle) Leona Mundin; (bottom) Corinne Moore

All other photos: 1 & 3 Sarah Montgomery

Printed in China by Leo Paper Products

www.theaa.com/shop

Directory compiled by the AA Lifestyle Guides Department and managed in the Librios Information Management System and generated from the AA establishment database system.

Published by AA Publishing, a trading name of AA Media Limited, whose registered office is Fanum House, Basing View, Basingstoke, Hampshire RG21 4EA.

Registered number 06112600

A CIP catalogue record for this book is available from the British Library

ISBN: 978 0 7495 6461 2

A04301

Welcome to the Guide.

This guide is perfect for dog owners who want to take their pets on holiday wth them.

AA Classifications & Awards

The establishments in this guide have all been inspected by the AA's professional inspectors.

HOTELS

The following designators indicate an establishment is rated as a Hotel by the AA: Hotel;Town House Hotel; Country House Hotel; Small Hotel; Metro Hotel; Budget Hotel. The AA's top hotels in Britain and Ireland are usually identified by red stars. Because this guide is printed with only two colours they are shown as green stars in this guide.

GUEST ACCOMMODATION

These designators indicate that an establishment is rated as Guest accommodation by the AA: Bed & Breakfast; Guest House; Farmhouse; Restaurant with Rooms; Guest Accommodation; Inn. The very best establishments in the Guest Accommodation scheme in the 3, 4 and 5 star ratings are usually indicated by yellow stars. In this guide these are also shown as green stars.

For an explanation of AA food & accommodation ratings see www.theaa.com

Contents

① HUNGERFORD

Bear Hotel

② ★★★ 80% ⊛⊛ HOTEL

③ ☎ 01488 682512 📠 01488 684357
41 Charnham St RG17 0EL
e-mail: info@thebearhotelhungerford.co.uk
web: www.thebearhotelhungerford.co.uk

④ dir: M4 junct 14, A338 to Hungerford for 3m, left
at T-junct onto A4, hotel on left

⑤ PETS: Bedrooms unattended Public areas
Grounds Exercise area canal & common nearby
Resident Pet: Bear (cat)

⑥ Situated five miles south of the M4 this hotel
dates back as far as early 13th century and
was once owned by King Henry VIII. It now has
a contemporary feel throughout. Bedrooms are
split between the main house, the courtyard and
Bear Island. The award-winning restaurant is
open for lunch and dinner, and lighter snacks
are available in the bar and lounge. Guests can
enjoy the sun terrace in the summer and log fires
in the winter.

⑦ Rooms 39 (26 annexe) (2 fmly) (24 GF)
S £82.50-£150; D £92.50-£185* Facilities FTV
Xmas New Year Wi-fi Conf Class 35 Board 34
Thtr 80 Del from £125 to £165* Parking 68
Notes LB Civ Wed 80

① **Location** The guide is divided into countries.
Each country is listed in county order and
then alphabetically in town/village order
within a county. Within each location hotels
are listed first, in descending order of stars
and % score, followed by B&Bs in descending
orders of stars.

② **Establishment rating & name** For further
information on AA ratings and awards see
theAA.com. If the establishment name
appears in italics, the establishment have
not provided us with up-to-date information
this year.

③ **Contact details**

④ **Directions** Short details of how to find the
establishment.

⑤ **Pet facilities (PETS:)**
Bedrooms GF Ground floor bedrooms;
unattended indicates that you can leave your
pet unattended in the bedroom; sign indicates
that a sign is provided to hang on the door
stating an animal is in the room.
Public areas & Grounds indicates that
pets are allowed in the gounds and public
areas. Any exceptions are as stated. Most
establishments in the guide request that dogs
should be kept on leads in public areas and
in the grounds.

Charges This might indcate a charge for damage only.

Exercise area The type of area available (i.e. fields, beach, coastal path etc.) and the distance from the establishment (i.e. 100yds).

Facilities Information and specific facilities that guests who are staying with their pets might find useful.

Other Additional information supplied by the establishment.

Restrictions Certain establishments have rules on the number of pets, or the size or the breed of dog allowed.* We strongly advise readers to check with the hotel or B&B at the time of booking that their pet will be permitted to accompany them during their stay.

*Some establishments have stated that they do not accept 'dangerous dogs'. The following breeds are covered under the Dangerous Dogs Act 1991 – Pit Bull Terrier, Japanese Tosa, Dogo Argentino and Fila Brazilierio.

Resident Pets Lists the names and breeds of the proprietors' own pets.

❻ **Description** This is written by the AA Inspector at the time of their visit.

❼ **Rooms** The number of bedrooms, and whether they are en suite, family or ground floor rooms. **Prices** These are per room per night, and are indications only, not firm quotations (

∗ indicates 2009 prices). Please check the AA website **theAA.com** for current information.

Facilities Leisure facilities are as stated in the entries. .

Parking Shows the numbers of spaces available for the use of guests.

Notes This section can include the following:
No Children followed by an age indicates that a minimum age is required (i.e. No children 4yrs)

RS (Restricted Service) Some establishments have a restricted service during quieter months and some of the listed facilities may not be available.

LB Some establishments offer leisure breaks.
Dinner (**B&Bs only**) indicates that an evening meal is available, although prior notice may be needed. **Licensed** (**B&Bs only**) indicates that the establishment is licensed to serve alcohol.
Payment The majority of establishments in this guide accept credit and debit cards. ☺ This symbols indicates those that don't.

Although all the establishments in this guide have told us they welcome dogs, things can change, and you should always check when you book that your chosen establishment will accommodate your pet.

Key to symbols

★	Hotel and B&B rating
%	Merit score (hotels only)
[U]	AA Rating not confirmed
⊛	AA Rosette Award for quality of food
⊜	No credit cards
✳	2009 prices
◔	Indoor swimming pool (heated or unheated)
◝	Outdoor swimming pool (heated or unheated)
⊋	Tennis court/s
⚐	Croquet lawn
⚴	Golf course
♫	Entertainment

Bed & Breakfast only

⚱	A very special breakfast, with an emphasis on freshly prepared local ingredients
⚰	A very special dinner, with an emphasis on freshly prepared local ingredients

Key to abbreviations

Air con	Air conditioning
BH/bank hols	Bank Holidays
D	Double bedroom
Etr	Easter
Fmly	Family bedroom
Fr	From
FTV	Freeview television in bedrooms
GF	Ground floor bedroom
hrs	Hours
incl. bkfst	Including breakfast
LB	Special leisure breaks
m	Miles
mtrs	Metres
mdnt	Midnight
New Year	Special New Year programme
No Children	No children can be accommodated
rdbt	Roundabout
RS/rs	Restricted services
S	Single bedroom
STV	Satellite television in bedrooms
Spa	Establishment has own spa facilities
Whit	Whitsun Bank Holiday
Wi-fi	Wireless network access
wk	Week
wkend	Weekend
Xmas	Special Christmas programme

Bed & Breakfast only

Cen ht	Full central heating
pri facs	Bedroom with separate, private facilities
rms	Bedrooms in main building
Tea/coffee	Tea & coffee making facilities
TVB	Television in bedrooms
TVL	Television lounge

ASCOT

Macdonald Berystede Hotel & Spa
★★★★ 78% ® HOTEL

☎ 0844 879 9104 🖷 01344 872301
Bagshot Rd, Sunninghill SL5 9JH
e-mail:
general.berystede@macdonald-hotels.co.uk
web: www.macdonald-hotels.co.uk/berystede
dir: A30/B3020 (Windmill Pub). Continue 1.25m
to hotel on left just before junct with A330

PETS: Bedrooms unattended Charges Public
areas except restaurant Grounds Exercise area
0.5m Restrictions small & medium size dogs
only

This impressive Victorian mansion, close to Ascot
Racecourse, offers executive bedrooms that
are spacious, comfortable and particularly well
equipped. Public rooms include a cosy bar and an
elegant restaurant in which creative dishes are
served. There is an impressive conference centre
and spa facility.

Rooms 126 (61 fmly) (33 GF) S £80-£150;
D £90-£160 (incl. bkfst) Facilities Spa STV 🛇
🌂 Gym Leisure complex inc thermal & beauty
treatment suites Outdoor garden spa Xmas New
Year Wi-fi Conf Class 220 Board 150 Thtr 330
Del from £160 to £290 Services Lift Parking 200
Notes LB Civ Wed 300

HUNGERFORD

Bear Hotel
★★★ 80% ®® HOTEL

☎ 01488 682512 🖷 01488 684357
41 Charnham St RG17 0EL
e-mail: info@thebearhotelhungerford.co.uk
web: www.thebearhotelhungerford.co.uk
dir: M4 junct 14, A338 to Hungerford for 3m, left
at T-junct onto A4, hotel on left

PETS: Bedrooms unattended Public areas
Grounds Exercise area canal & common nearby
Resident Pet: Bear (cat)

Situated five miles south of the M4 this hotel
dates back as far as early 13th century and
was once owned by King Henry VIII. It now has
a contemporary feel throughout. Bedrooms are
split between the main house, the courtyard and
Bear Island. The award-winning restaurant is
open for lunch and dinner, and lighter snacks
are available in the bar and lounge. Guests can
enjoy the sun terrace in the summer and log fires
in the winter.

Rooms 39 (26 annexe) (2 fmly) (24 GF)
S £82.50-£150; D £92.50-£185* Facilities FTV
Xmas New Year Wi-fi Conf Class 35 Board 34
Thtr 80 Del from £125 to £165* Parking 68
Notes LB Civ Wed 80

HUNGERFORD

Three Swans

★★★ 70% HOTEL

☎ 01488 682721 📠 01488 681708
117 High St RG17 0LZ
e-mail: info@threeswans.net
web: www.threeswans.net
dir: M4 junct 14 follow signs to Hungerford. Hotel half way along High St on left

PETS: **Bedrooms** unattended **Charges Public areas** only in public bar **Grounds**

Centrally located in the bustling market town of Hungerford this charming former inn, dating back some 700 years, has been renovated in a fresh and airy style. Visitors will still see the original arch under which the horse-drawn carriages once passed. There is a wood panelled bar, a spacious lounge and attractive rear garden to relax in. The informal restaurant is decorated with a range of artwork by local artists. Bedrooms are well appointed and comfortable.

Rooms 25 (10 annexe) (1 fmly) (5 GF) (3 smoking) **Facilities** FTV Access to local private gym Xmas New Year Wi-fi **Conf** Class 40 Board 30 Thtr 55 **Parking** 30

PANGBOURNE

Elephant at Pangbourne

★★★ 78% ⊛ HOTEL

☎ 0118 984 2244 & 07770 268359
📠 0118 976 7346
Church Rd RG8 7AR
e-mail: annica@elephanthotel.co.uk
web: www.elephanthotel.co.uk
dir: A4 Theale/Newbury, right at 2nd rdbt signed Pangbourne. Hotel on left

PETS: **Bedrooms** unattended **Charges Public areas** only reception & bar **Grounds Exercise area Other** dogs allowed in one bedroom only

Centrally located in this bustling village, just a short drive from Reading. Bedrooms are individual in style but identical in the attention to detail, with handcrafted Indian furniture and rich oriental rugs. Guests can enjoy award-winning cuisine in the restaurant or bistro-style dining in the bar area.

Rooms 22 (8 annexe) (2 fmly) (4 GF) **S** £100; **D** £140 (incl. bkfst)* **Facilities** FTV ⤴ Xmas New Year Wi-fi **Conf** Class 40 Board 30 Thtr 60 **Parking** 10 **Notes** ⊗ Civ Wed 60

STREATLEY

The Swan at Streatley
★★★★ 75% ◉◉ HOTEL

☎ 01491 878800 📠 01491 872554
High St RG8 9HR
e-mail: sales@swan-at-streatley.co.uk
web: www.swanatstreatley.co.uk
dir: From S right at lights in Streatley, hotel on left before bridge

PETS: Bedrooms unattended **Charges Public areas** except restaurant **Grounds**

A stunning location set beside the Thames, ideal for an English summer's day. The bedrooms are well appointed and many enjoy the lovely views. The hotel offers a range of facilities including meeting rooms, and the Magdalen Barge is moored beside the hotel making an unusual, yet perfect meeting venue. A motor launch is available for hire from April to October. The spa includes an indoor heated mineral pool and offers a range of treatments. Cuisine is accomplished and dining here should not be missed.

Rooms 45 (12 GF) **S** £110-£120; **D** £138-£150 (incl. bkfst)* **Facilities Spa** STV ⊗ supervised Fishing ⛵ **Gym** Electric motor launches for hire Apr-Oct Xmas New Year Wi-fi **Conf** Class 80 Board 60 Thtr 140 Del from £165 to £210* **Parking** 170 **Notes** LB Civ Wed 130

BRISTOL

The Berkeley Square
★★★ 78% ◉◉ HOTEL

☎ 0117 925 4000 📠 0117 925 2970
15 Berkeley Square, Clifton BS8 1HB
e-mail: berkeley@cliftonhotels.com
web: www.cliftonhotels.com/chg.html
dir: M32 follow Clifton signs. 1st left at lights by Nills Memorial Tower (University) into Berkeley Sq

PETS: Bedrooms unattended **Charges Public areas** except restaurant **Grounds Exercise area** adjacent to park

Set in a pleasant square close to the university, art gallery and Clifton Village, this smart, elegant Georgian hotel has modern, stylishly decorated bedrooms that feature many welcome extras. There is a cosy lounge and stylish restaurant on the ground floor and a smart, contemporary bar in the basement. A small garden is also available at the rear of the hotel.

Rooms 43 (4 GF) **Facilities** Use of local gym & swimming pool **Services** Lift **Parking** 20

BRISTOL

Arnos Manor Hotel
★★★ 74% HOTEL

☎ 0117 971 1461 📠 0117 971 5507
470 Bath Rd, Arno's Vale BS4 3HQ
e-mail: arnos.manor@forestdale.com
web: www.arnosmanorhotel.co.uk
dir: From end of M32 follow signs for Bath. Hotel on right of A4 after 2m. Next to ITV West TV studio

PETS: Bedrooms unattended Charges Public areas except restaurant/bar

Once the home of a wealthy merchant, this historic 18th-century building is now a comfortable hotel and offers spacious, well-appointed bedrooms with plenty of workspace. The lounge was once the chapel and has many original features, while meals are taken in the atmospheric, conservatory-style restaurant.

Rooms 73 (5 fmly) (7 GF) S £74-£99; D £87-£159 (incl. bkfst)* Facilities FTV Xmas New Year Wi-fi Conf Class 50 Board 30 Thtr 150 Services Lift Parking 200 Notes Civ Wed 100

BRISTOL

Clifton Hotel
★★ 75% HOTEL

☎ 0117 973 6882 📠 0117 974 1082
St Pauls Rd, Clifton BS8 1LX
e-mail: clifton@cliftonhotels.com
web: www.cliftonhotels.com/clifton
dir: M32 follow Bristol/Clifton signs, along Park St. Left at lights into St Pauls Rd

PETS: Bedrooms unattended Charges Public areas Exercise area 0.5m

This popular hotel offers very well equipped bedrooms and relaxed, friendly service. There is a welcoming lounge by the reception, and in summer months drinks and meals can be enjoyed on the terrace. Racks Bar and Restaurant offers an interesting selection of modern dishes in informal surroundings. There is some street parking, but for a small charge, secure garage parking is available.

Rooms 59 (2 fmly) (12 GF) (9 smoking) S £37-£77; D £58-£86* Facilities STV Wi-fi Services Lift Parking 12 Notes LB

BRISTOL

Washington
★★★ GUEST HOUSE

☎ 0117 973 3980 🖷 0117 973 4740
11-15 St Pauls Rd, Clifton BS8 1LX
e-mail: washington@cliftonhotels.com
dir: A4018 into city, right at lights opp BBC,
house 200yds on left

PETS: Bedrooms unattended Charges Public
areas except breakfast room Grounds Facilities
food (pre-bookable)

This large terrace house is within walking
distance of the city centre and Clifton Village.
The bedrooms, many refurbished, are well
equipped for business guests. Public areas
include a modern reception lounge and a bright
basement breakfast room. The property has
secure parking and a rear patio garden.

Rooms 46 rms (40 en suite) (4 fmly) (10 GF) (7
smoking) S £39-£69; D £48-£87* Facilities STV
tea/coffee Direct Dial Cen ht Licensed Wi-fi
Reduced rate pass for local health club
Parking 16 Notes Closed 23 Dec-3 Jan

AYLESBURY

Hartwell House Hotel, Restaurant & Spa
★★★★ ⊛⊛⊛ HOTEL

☎ 01296 747444 🖷 01296 747450
Oxford Rd HP17 8NR
e-mail: info@hartwell-house.com
web: www.hartwell-house.com
dir: From S: M40 junct 7, A329 to Thame, A418
towards Aylesbury. After 6m, through Stone, hotel
on left. From N: M40 junct 9 for Bicester. A41 to
Aylesbury, A418 to Oxford for 2m. Hotel on right

PETS: Bedrooms unattended Charges Public
areas Grounds Exercise area Other dogs in
Hartwell Crt suites only;1 large/2 small dogs only

This beautiful, historic house is set in 90 acres
of parkland. The grand public rooms are truly
magnificent, and feature many fine works of
art. The service standards are very high, being
attentive and traditional without stuffiness.
There is an elegant, award-winning restaurant.
Bedrooms are spacious and elegant.

Rooms 46 (16 annexe) (3 fmly) (10 GF)
S £160-£200; D £185-£360 (incl. bkfst)*
Facilities Spa STV ⊗ supervised ⌕ ⌕ Gym
Sauna treatment rooms Steam rooms ♫ Xmas
New Year Wi-fi Services Lift Parking 91 Notes LB
No children 6yrs RS Xmas/New Year Civ Wed 60

11

BUCKINGHAM

Best Western Buckingham Hotel

★★★ 75% HOTEL

☎ 01280 822622 📠 01280 823074
Buckingham Ring Rd MK18 1RY
e-mail: info@thebuckinghamhotel.co.uk
dir: Follow A421 for Buckingham, take ring road S towards Brackley & Bicester. Hotel on left

PETS: Bedrooms unattended **Charges Public areas Grounds Restrictions** small dogs only

A purpose-built hotel, which offers comfortable and spacious rooms with well designed working spaces for business travellers. There are also extensive conference facilities. The open-plan restaurant and bar offer a good range of dishes, and the well-equipped leisure suite is popular with guests.

Rooms 70 (6 fmly) (31 GF) **S** £40-£60; **D** £40-£60
Facilities STV 🏊 supervised Gym Xmas New Year Wi-fi **Conf** Class 60 Board 60 Thtr 200
Parking 200 **Notes** LB Civ Wed 120

HIGH WYCOMBE

Fox Country Inn

★★★ 64% SMALL HOTEL

☎ 01491 639333 📠 01491 639444
Ibstone HP14 3XT
e-mail: info@foxcountryinn.co.uk
dir: M40 junct 5 follow signs to Ibstone, hotel 1.5m on left

PETS: Bedrooms unattended for kennels **Charges Public areas Grounds Exercise area** 100yds **Facilities** food (pre-bookable) food bowl water bowl **Other** prior notice required; bedding & blankets charged

This delightful inn benefits from a new conversion to the small family-run hotel. The totally refurbished bedrooms are very well appointed with many added extras, and are designed with comfort in mind. Public areas are modern, and external decking provides further seating in summer months. There is a wide ranging choice of dishes including a Thai menu.

Rooms 18 (3 fmly) (10 GF) **S** £77-£137;
D £87-£167* **Facilities** FTV Xmas New Year Wi-fi
Conf Class 40 Board 35 Thtr 45 Del from £110 to £195* **Parking** 45 **Notes** LB ⊗ Civ Wed 100

TAPLOW

Cliveden Country House Hotel
★★★★★ @@@ COUNTRY HOUSE HOTEL
☎ 01628 668561 📠 01628 661837
SL6 0JF
e-mail: reservations@clivedenhouse.co.uk
web: www.vonessenhotels.co.uk
dir: M4 junct 7, A4 towards Maidenhead for 1.5m, onto B476 towards Taplow, 2.5m, hotel on left

PETS: **Bedrooms** unattended **Charges Public areas** except restaurants **Grounds Exercise area** woodland walk **Facilities** food (pre-bookable & charged) food bowl water bowl

This wonderful stately home stands at the top of a gravelled boulevard. Visitors are treated as house-guests and staff recapture the tradition of fine hospitality. Bedrooms have individual quality and style, and reception rooms retain a timeless elegance. Exceptional leisure facilities include cruises along Cliveden Reach and massages in the Pavilion. The Terrace Restaurant has two AA Rosettes, and Waldo's has three.

Rooms 39 (8 GF) S £276-£1989.50;
D £276-£1989.50 (incl. bkfst)* **Facilities** Spa
STV FTV 🕒 ⚓ 🏊 🏌 Gym Squash Full range of beauty treatments, 3 vintage boats ♫
Xmas New Year Wi-fi **Services** Lift **Parking** 60
Notes Civ Wed 150

CAMBRIDGE

Hotel du Vin Cambridge
★★★★ 74% @ TOWN HOUSE HOTEL
☎ 01223 227330 📠 01223 227331
15-19 Trumpington St CB2 1QA
e-mail: info.cambridge@hotelduvin.com
web: www.hotelduvin.com
dir: M11 junct 11 Cambridge S, pass Trumpington Park & Ride on left. Hotel 2m on right after double rdbt

PETS: **Bedrooms** unattended **Charges Public areas** except restaurant & bar **Facilities** food bowl water bowl

This beautiful building, which dates back in part to medieval times, has been transformed to enhance its many quirky architectural features. The bedrooms and suites, some with private terraces, have the company's trademark monsoon showers and Egyptian linen. The French-style bistro has an open-style kitchen and the bar is set in the unusual labyrinth of vaulted cellar rooms. There is also a library, specialist wine tasting room and private dining room.

Rooms 41 (3 annexe) (6 GF) **Facilities** STV Xmas New Year Wi-fi **Conf** Class 18 Board 18 Thtr 30 **Services** Lift Air con **Parking** 24

ELY

Castle Lodge
★★★ GUEST HOUSE

☎ 01353 662276 📄 01353 666606
50 New Barns Rd CB7 4PW
e-mail: castlelodgehotel@supanet.com
dir: Off B1382 Prickwillow Rd, NE from town centre

PETS: Bedrooms unattended **Charges Public areas** except restaurant **Grounds Exercise area** field nearby **Facilities** food (pre-bookable) food bowl water bowl

Located within easy walking distance of the cathedral, this extended Victorian house offers well-equipped bedrooms in a variety of sizes. Public areas include a traditionally furnished dining room and a comfortable air-conditioned bar lounge. Service is friendly and helpful.

Rooms 11 rms (6 en suite) (3 fmly) **S** £32.50-£55; **D** £75* **Facilities** TVL tea/coffee Dinner available Direct Dial Cen ht Licensed Wi-fi **Conf** Max 40 Board 40 **Parking** 6

HUNTINGDON

Huntingdon Marriott Hotel
★★★★ 77% HOTEL

☎ 01480 446000 📄 01480 451111
Kingfisher Way, Hinchingbrooke Business Park PE29 6FL
e-mail: mhrs.cbghd.front.office@marriotthotels.com
web: www.huntingdonmarriott.co.uk
dir: on A14, 1m from Huntington centre close to Brampton racecourse

PETS: Bedrooms unattended **Charges Public areas** except food service area **Exercise area** park nearby

With its excellent road links, this modern, purpose-built hotel is a popular venue for conferences and business meetings, and is convenient for Huntingdon, Cambridge and racing at Newmarket. Bedrooms are spacious and offer every modern comfort, including air conditioning. The leisure facilities are also impressive.

Rooms 150 (5 fmly) (45 GF) **Facilities** ⊗ supervised Gym Sauna Steam room ♪ Xmas New Year Wi-fi **Conf** Class 150 Board 100 Thtr 300 **Services** Lift Air con **Parking** 200 **Notes** LB Civ Wed 300

HUNTINGDON

The Old Bridge Hotel
★★★ 83% @@ HOTEL

☎ 01480 424300 🖹 01480 411017
1 High St PE29 3TQ
e-mail: oldbridge@huntsbridge.co.uk
web: www.huntsbridge.com
dir: From A14 or A1 follow Huntingdon signs.
Hotel visible from inner ring road

PETS: **Bedrooms** unattended **Charges Public
areas Grounds Exercise area** adjacent

An imposing 18th-century building situated close
to shops and amenities. This charming hotel
offers superb accommodation in stylish and
individually decorated bedrooms that include
many useful extras. Guests can choose from the
same menu whether dining in the open-plan
terrace, or the more formal restaurant with its
bold colour scheme. There is also an excellent
business centre.

Rooms 24 (2 fmly) (2 GF) **S** £95-£130;
D £130-£195 (incl. bkfst) **Facilities** STV FTV
Fishing Private mooring for boats Xmas New
Year Wi-fi **Conf** Class 50 Board 30 Thtr 60
Del from £190 to £225 **Services** Air con
Parking 50 **Notes** LB Civ Wed 100

BURWARDSLEY

The Pheasant Inn
★★★★★ ⊜ INN

☎ 01829 770434 🖹 01829 771097
Higher Burwardsley CH3 9PF
e-mail: info@thepheasantinn.co.uk
dir: From A41, left to Tattenhall, right at 1st
junct & left at 2nd Higher Burwardsley. At post
office left, signed

PETS: **Bedrooms** unattended **Public areas** at
manager's discretion **Grounds Exercise area**
surrounding countryside **Facilities** water bowl

This delightful 300-year-old inn sits high on
the Peckforton Hills and enjoys spectacular
views over the Cheshire Plain. Well-equipped,
comfortable bedrooms are housed in an adjacent
converted barn. Creative dishes are served either
in the stylish restaurant or in the traditional,
beamed bar. Real fires are lit in the winter
months.

Rooms 2 en suite 10 annexe en suite (2 fmly) (5
GF) **Facilities** tea/coffee Dinner available Cen ht
Wi-fi Fishing **Parking** 80

CHESTER

Dene Hotel
★★ 75% HOTEL

☎ 01244 321165 📠 01244 350277
95 Hoole Rd CH2 3ND
e-mail: info@denehotel.com
web: www.denehotel.com
dir: M53 junct 12 take A56 for 1m towards
Chester. Hotel 1m from M53 next to Alexander
Park

PETS: Bedrooms unattended Public areas except
restaurant Grounds Exercise area 2 mins walk

This friendly hotel is now part of a small privately
owned group and is located close to both the
city centre and M53. The bedrooms are very well
equipped and many are on ground floor level.
Family rooms and interconnecting rooms are also
available. In addition to bar meals, an interesting
choice of dishes is offered in the welcoming
Castra Brasserie, which is also very popular with
locals.

Rooms 52 (8 annexe) (5 fmly) (20 GF)
S £30-£110; D £35-£125* Facilities FTV New
Year Wi-fi Conf Class 12 Board 16 Thtr 30
Del from £75 to £120 Parking 55

CHESTER

Hamilton Court
★★★★ GUEST ACCOMMODATION

☎ 01244 345387 📠 01244 317404
5-7 Hamilton St CH2 3JG
e-mail: hamiltoncourth@aol.com
dir: From town centre, All Saints Church on left,
2nd turn on left

PETS: Bedrooms unattended Charges Public
areas Exercise area 500yds Other dogs
accepted by prior arrangement only

Hamilton Court is a family-run establishment,
only ten minutes walk from the city centre.
All bedrooms are en suite and have useful
facilities. Children are welcome and pets can be
accommodated by arrangement.

Rooms 11 en suite (4 fmly) (1 GF) Facilities FTV
tea/coffee Cen ht Licensed Wi-fi Parking 4
Notes Closed 24 Dec-3 Jan

Best Western Moorside Grange Hotel & Spa

★★★ 72% HOTEL

☎ 01663 764151 📠 01663 762794
Mudhurst Ln, Higher Disley SK12 2AP
e-mail: sales@moorsidegrangehotel.com
web: www.moorsidegrangehotel.com
dir: Exit A6 at Rams Head in Disley, onto Buxton
Old Rd for 1m, right onto Mudhurst Ln, hotel
on left

PETS: **Bedrooms** unattended **Charges Public areas** except restaurants **Grounds Exercise area Facilities** water bowl

Situated on the edge of the Peak District National Park, and with spectacular views of the moors above Higher Disley, this large complex is in an area considered a walkers' paradise. The hotel has excellent conference and function facilities, a well-equipped leisure centre and two tennis courts in the extensive grounds. Suites, and bedrooms with four-poster beds, are available.

Rooms 98 (3 fmly) **Facilities Spa** 🕲 supervised ♨ Gym Squash Xmas New Year Wi-fi **Conf** Class 140 Board 100 Thtr 280 Del from £99 to £145 **Services** Lift **Parking** 250 **Notes** Civ Wed 280

Rostherne Country House

★★★★ GUEST ACCOMMODATION

☎ 01565 832628
Rostherne Ln, Rostherne WA16 6RY
e-mail: info@rosthernehouse.co.uk

PETS: **Bedrooms** unattended **Charges Public areas** lounge only **Exercise area** adjacent **Facilities** water bowl **Restrictions** no dangerous dogs (see page 5) **Resident Pet:** Boo Boo (Irish Setter)

Set in its own spacious gardens in the village of Rostherne, this elegant Victorian house retains much original charm with spacious, well-equipped bedrooms and character lounges with open fires. It is a wonderful relaxing base for exploring the delights of Cheshire and dinner is available by arrangement. Other facilities include an honesty bar and a paddock for guests' horses. Courses in various subjects are also available.

Rooms 4 rms (3 en suite) (1 pri facs) (1 fmly) S fr £49.50; D £75-£95* **Facilities** FTV TVL tea/coffee Dinner available Cen ht Wi-fi Guest arrangement for indoor swimming pool & spa **Conf** Max 20 Thtr 20 **Parking** 12

TARPORLEY

Willington Hall
★★★ 78% COUNTRY HOUSE HOTEL

☎ 01829 752321 ▤ 01829 752596
Willington CW6 0NB
e-mail: enquiries@willingtonhall.co.uk
web: www.willingtonhall.co.uk
dir: 3m NW off unclass road linking A51 & A54, at Clotton exit A51 at Bulls Head. Follow signs

PETS: **Bedrooms** unattended **Charges Public areas Grounds**

Situated in 17 acres of parkland and built in 1829, this attractively furnished country-house hotel offers spacious bedrooms, many with views over open countryside. Service is courteous and friendly, and freshly prepared meals are offered in the dining room or in the adjacent bar and drawing room. A smart function suite confirms the popularity of this hotel as a premier venue for weddings and conferences.

Rooms 10 (4 fmly) **S** £80; **D** £120-£130 (incl. bkfst)* **Facilities** Fishing ⛵ New Year Wi-fi **Conf** Class 80 Board 50 Thtr 160 **Parking** 60 **Notes** LB Closed 25 & 26 Dec Civ Wed 130

WARRINGTON

Paddington House
★★ 74% HOTEL

☎ 01925 816767 ▤ 01925 816651
514 Old Manchester Rd WA1 3TZ
e-mail: hotel@paddingtonhouse.co.uk
web: www.paddingtonhouse.co.uk
dir: 1m from M6 junct 21, off A57, 2m from town centre

PETS: **Bedrooms** unattended **Charges Public areas Grounds Exercise area Facilities** water bowl **Restrictions** no large dogs

This busy, friendly hotel is conveniently situated just over a mile from the M6. Bedrooms are attractively furnished, and include four-poster and ground-floor rooms. Guests can dine in the wood-panelled Padgate Restaurant or in the cosy bar. Conference and function facilities are available.

Rooms 37 (9 fmly) (6 GF) **Facilities** FTV New Year Wi-fi **Conf** Class 100 Board 40 Thtr 180 Del from £70 to £95* **Services** Lift **Parking** 50 **Notes** Civ Wed 150

BODMIN

Trehellas House Hotel & Restaurant
★★★ 74% @ SMALL HOTEL

☎ 01208 72700 📠 01208 73336
Washaway PL30 3AD
e-mail: enquiries@trehellashouse.co.uk
web: www.trehellashouse.co.uk
dir: A389 from Bodmin towards Wadebridge.
Hotel on right 0.5m beyond road to Camelford

PETS: Bedrooms unattended Charges Public
areas Grounds Exercise area Facilities food
bowl water bowl Resident Pets: Bonnie & Clyde
(Chocolate Labradors)

This 18th-century former posting inn retains
many original features and provides comfortable
accommodation. Bedrooms are located in both
the main house and adjacent coach house - all
provide the same high standards. An interesting
choice of cuisine, with an emphasis on locally-
sourced ingredients, is offered in the impressive
slate-floored restaurant.

Rooms 12 (7 annexe) (2 fmly) (5 GF) S £40-£75;
D £50-£160 (incl. bkfst) Facilities FTV ᐟ
Xmas New Year Wi-fi Conf Board 12 Thtr 12
Del from £100 to £150* Parking 32 Notes LB

BODMIN

Westberry
★★ 78% HOTEL

☎ 01208 72772 📠 01208 72212
Rhind St PL31 2EL
e-mail: westberry@btconnect.com
web: www.westberryhotel.net
dir: On ring road off A30 & A38. St Petroc's
Church on right, at mini rdbt turn right. Hotel
on right

PETS: Bedrooms unattended Charges Public
areas Grounds Exercise area 300yds Facilities
food bowl water bowl

This popular hotel is conveniently located for both
Bodmin town centre and the A30. The bedrooms
are attractive and well equipped. A spacious bar
lounge and a billiard room are also provided. The
restaurant serves a variety of dishes, ranging
from bar snacks to a more extensive carte menu.

Rooms 20 (8 annexe) (2 fmly) (6 GF) S £48-£68;
D £58-£78 (incl. bkfst)* Facilities STV Full sized
snooker table Wi-fi Conf Class 80 Board 80
Thtr 100 Del from £78 to £98* Parking 30
Notes LB

BUDE

The Cliff at Bude
★★★★ GUEST HOUSE

☎ 01288 353110 & 356833
📠 01288 353110
Maer Down, Crooklets Beach EX23 8NG
e-mail: cliff-hotel@btconnect.com
web: www.cliffhotel.co.uk
dir: A39 through Bude, left at top of High St, pass Somerfields, 1st right between golf course, over x-rds, premises at end on left

PETS: Bedrooms unattended Charges Public areas except restaurant & lounge Grounds on leads Exercise area adjacent to hotel Resident Pets: Janus & Crystal (Boxers), 13 rabbits

Overlooking the sea from a clifftop location, this friendly and efficient establishment provides spacious, well-equipped bedrooms. The various public areas include a bar and lounge and an impressive range of leisure facilities. Delicious dinners and tasty breakfasts are available in the attractive dining room.

Rooms 15 en suite (15 fmly) (8 GF) S £45.54; D £75.90* Facilities FTV TVL tea/coffee Dinner available Direct Dial Cen ht Licensed ⌖ 🏊 ♨ Gymnasium Pool Table Parking 18 Notes LB Closed Nov-Mar

BRYHER

Hell Bay
★★★ ⊛⊛ HOTEL

☎ 01720 422947 📠 01720 423004
TR23 0PR
e-mail: contactus@hellbay.co.uk
web: www.hellbay.co.uk
dir: Access by helicopter or boat from Penzance, plane from Bristol, Exeter, Newquay, Southampton, Land's End

PETS: Bedrooms unattended Charges Public areas Grounds Exercise area public coastal path adjacent Facilities food bowl water bowl Resident Pet: Suzie (Springer Spaniel)

Located on the smallest of the inhabited islands of the Scilly Isles, this hotel makes a really special destination. The interior is decorated in cool blues and greens creating an extremely restful environment. The contemporary bedrooms are equally stylish and many have garden access and stunning sea views. Eating here is a delight, and naturally, seafood features strongly on the award-winning, daily-changing menus.

Rooms 25 (25 annexe) (3 fmly) (15 GF) S £155-£600; D £310-£600 (incl. bkfst & dinner)* Facilities STV ⤳ ♨ 7 Gym Wi-fi Notes LB Closed Nov-Feb

CONSTANTINE

Trengilly Wartha Inn
★★★ ◉ INN

☎ 01326 340332 📄 01326 340332
Nancenoy TR11 5RP
e-mail: reception@trengilly.co.uk
web: www.trengilly.co.uk
dir: Follow signs to Nancenoy, left towards Gweek until 1st sign for inn, left & left again at next sign, continue to inn

PETS: Bedrooms unattended Charges Public areas except restaurant Grounds Exercise area Facilities food (pre-bookable) food bowl water bowl Resident Pets: Kerris & Tara (mongrels), goats, chickens

Located in a very peaceful wooded valley, just one and a half miles from the village of Constantine, this inn offers cosy, comfortable accommodation with nicely appointed and well equipped bedrooms. An interesting menu is offered in the restaurant together with a well balanced wine list; there is also a wide selection of bar meals available at lunch and dinner.

Rooms 6 en suite 2 annexe en suite (2 fmly) (2 GF) S £50-£65; D £80-£96* Facilities tea/coffee Dinner available Direct Dial Cen ht Wi-fi Boules Conf Max 30 Class 30 Board 30 Parking 60 Notes LB RS 25 Dec No food

CRACKINGTON HAVEN

Bears & Boxes Country Guest House
★★★★ GUEST HOUSE

☎ 01840 230318
Penrose, Dizzard EX23 0NX
e-mail: rwfrh@btinternet.com
web: www.bearsandboxes.com
dir: 1.5m NE of St Gennys in Dizzard

PETS: Bedrooms unattended Public areas Grounds Exercise area 100yds Facilities food (pre-bookable) food bowl water bowl

Dating in part from the mid 17th century, Bears & Boxes is a small, family-run guest house situated 500yds from the coastal path. Guests are welcomed with a tray of tea and home-made cake, and the caring owners are always around to help and advise about the locality. The cosy bedrooms have numerous thoughtful extras, and evening meals, using the very best of local ingredients and cooked with flair, are served by arrangement.

Rooms 3 en suite 1 annexe rms (1 pri facs) (1 fmly) (1 GF) S £28.80-£32; D £57.60-£64* Facilities FTV TVL tea/coffee Dinner available Cen ht Wi-fi Parking 6

FALMOUTH

Green Lawns
★★★ 77% HOTEL

☎ 01326 312734 📄 01326 211427
Western Ter TR11 4QJ
e-mail: info@greenlawnshotel.com
web: www.greenlawnshotel.com
dir: On A39

PETS: Bedrooms unattended **Charges Public areas Exercise area** 0.25m **Facilities** food food bowl water bowl

This attractive property enjoys a convenient location close to the town centre and within easy reach of the sea. Spacious public areas include inviting lounges, an elegant restaurant, conference and meeting facilities and a leisure centre. Bedrooms vary in size and style but all are well equipped and comfortable. The friendly service is particularly noteworthy.

Rooms 39 (8 fmly) (11 GF) (2 smoking)
S £65-£120; **D** £90-£200 (incl. bkfst)*
Facilities FTV 🕙 🏊 Gym Squash Sauna Steam room Spa bath New Year Wi-fi **Conf** Class 80 Board 100 Thtr 200 **Del** from £95 to £120*
Parking 69 **Notes** LB Closed 24-30 Dec Civ Wed 50

FOWEY

Trevanion
★★★★ GUEST ACCOMMODATION

☎ 01726 832602
70 Lostwithiel St PL23 1BQ
e-mail: alisteve@trevanionguesthouse.co.uk
web: www.trevanionguesthouse.co.uk
dir: A3082 into Fowey, down hill, left onto Lostwithiel St, Trevanion on left

PETS: Bedrooms unattended **Public areas** except dining room **Exercise area** directly across road **Facilities** food food bowl water bowl **Other** please telephone for details of additional facilities for dogs **Resident Pet:** Poppy (parrot)

This 16th-century merchant's house provides friendly, comfortable accommodation within easy walking distance of the historic town of Fowey and is convenient for visiting the Eden Project. A hearty farmhouse-style cooked breakfast, using local produce, is served in the attractive dining room and other menu options are available.

Rooms 5 rms (4 en suite) (1 pri facs) (2 fmly) (1 GF) **S** £35-£40; **D** £50-£70* **Facilities** FTV tea/coffee Cen ht Wi-fi **Parking** 5 **Notes** LB 🐾

HELSTON

Gwealdues Hotel

★★ 76% HOTEL

☎ 01326 572808 📠 01326 561388
Falmouth Rd TR13 8JX
e-mail: thegwealdueshotel@hotmail.co.uk
web: www.gwealdueshotel.com
dir: Off rdbt on A394. On town outskirts

PETS: Bedrooms unattended Charges Public
areas except food areas during service
Restrictions dog owners must be aware of small
children staying at hotel Resident Pets: Mr B
(cat), Hunny (rabbit)

A family owned and run hotel that is within easy
access of the coast and the cathedral city of
Truro. The staff are friendly and attentive. The
comfortable bedrooms include family rooms.
There is a well stocked bar and a traditionally
styled restaurant.

Rooms 18 (2 fmly) (1 GF) S £50-£55; D £70-£80
(incl. bkfst)* Facilities FTV Wi-fi Conf Class 80
Board 40 Thtr 120 Parking 50 Notes LB

LISKEARD

Redgate Smithy

★★★★ 🏠 BED AND BREAKFAST

☎ 01579 321578
Redgate, St Cleer PL14 6RU
e-mail: enquiries@redgatesmithy.co.uk
web: www.redgatesmithy.co.uk
dir: 3m NW of Liskeard. Off A30 at Bolventor/
Jamaica Inn onto St Cleer Rd for 7m, B&B just
past x-rds

PETS: Bedrooms unattended Public areas except
at breakfast Grounds Exercise area adjacent
lane Facilities food bowl Restrictions small,
friendly dogs only; no Rottweilers, Staffordshire
Bull Terriers or Rhodesian Ridgebacks Resident
Pet: Sinbad (Cocker Spaniel)

This 200-year-old converted smithy is on the
southern fringe of Bodmin Moor near Golitha
Falls. The friendly accommodation offers smartly
furnished, cottage style bedrooms with many
extra facilities. There are several dining options
nearby, and a wide choice of freshly cooked
breakfasts are served in the conservatory.

Rooms 3 rms (2 en suite) (1 pri facs) S £45; D
£70* Facilities FTV tea/coffee Cen ht Parking 3
Notes LB No Children 12yrs Closed Xmas & New
Year 🐾

LOOE

Trelaske Hotel & Restaurant
★★★ 79% ® HOTEL

☎ 01503 262159 📄 01503 265360
Polperro Rd PL13 2JS
e-mail: info@trelaske.co.uk
dir: B252 signed Looe. Over Looe bridge signed
Polperro. 1.9m, hotel signed on right

PETS: Bedrooms unattended **Charges Public
areas Grounds Exercise area Facilities** food
bowl water bowl **Resident Pet:** Moe (Blue Fronted
Amazon Parrot)

This small hotel offers comfortable
accommodation and professional yet friendly
service and award-winning food. Set in its own
very well tended grounds and only minutes away
from Looe and its attractions.

Rooms 7 (4 annexe) (2 fmly) (2 GF) **S** £65-£70;
D £95-£105 (incl. bkfst) **Facilities** FTV Mountain
bikes for hire Wi-fi **Conf** Class 30 Board 40
Thtr 100 Del from £135 to £140* **Parking** 50

LOOE

Hannafore Point
★★★ 70% HOTEL

☎ 01503 263273 📄 01503 263272
Marine Dr, West Looe PL13 2DG
e-mail: stay@hannaforepointhotel.com
dir: A38, left onto A385 to Looe. Over bridge turn
left. Hotel 0.5m on left

PETS: Bedrooms unattended **Charges Public
areas** except terrace & bar **Exercise area**
adjacent **Facilities** water bowl

With panoramic coastal views of St George's
Island around to Rame Head, this popular hotel
provides a warm welcome. The wonderful view is
certainly a feature of the spacious restaurant and
bar, providing a scenic backdrop for both dinners
and breakfasts. Additional facilities include a
heated indoor pool and gym.

Rooms 37 (5 fmly) **Facilities** STV 🕃 Gym
Spa pool Steam room Sauna 🎵 Xmas New
Year Wi-fi **Conf** Class 80 Board 40 Thtr 120
Del from £75 to £120 **Services** Lift **Parking** 32
Notes Civ Wed 150

LOSTWITHIEL

Lostwithiel Hotel Golf & Country Club

★★★ 67% HOTEL

☎ 01208 873550 📠 01208 873479

Lower Polscoe PL22 0HQ

e-mail: reception@golf-hotel.co.uk

web: www.golf-hotel.co.uk

dir: Off A38 at Dobwalls onto A390. In Lostwithiel turn right & hotel signed

PETS: Bedrooms unattended **Charges Public areas** except restaurant **Grounds**

This rural hotel is based around its own golf club and other leisure activities. The main building offers guests a choice of eating options, including all-day snacks in the popular Sports Bar. The bedroom accommodation, designed to incorporate beamed ceilings, has been developed from old Cornish barns that are set around a courtyard.

Rooms 27 (2 fmly) (15 GF) (2 smoking) **S** £39-£61; **D** £78-£122 (incl. bkfst)* **Facilities** ⓢ ⛳ 18 ♨ Putt green Fishing Gym Undercover floodlit driving range Indoor golf simulator Xmas New Year Wi-fi **Conf** Class 40 Board 40 Thtr 120 Del from £75 to £95* **Parking** 120 **Notes** Civ Wed 120

MAWNAN SMITH

Meudon

★★★ 85% COUNTRY HOUSE HOTEL

☎ 01326 250541 📠 01326 250543

TR11 5HT

e-mail: wecare@meudon.co.uk

web: www.meudon.co.uk

dir: From Truro A39 towards Falmouth at Hillhead (Anchor & Cannons) rdbt, follow signs to Maenporth Beach. Hotel on left 1m after beach

PETS: Bedrooms unattended **Charges Public areas Grounds Exercise area** 8.5-acre gardens & private beach **Resident Pet:** Felix (cat)

This charming late Victorian mansion is a relaxing place to stay, with friendly hospitality and attentive service. It sits in impressive nine-acre gardens that lead down to a private beach. The spacious and comfortable bedrooms are situated in a more modern building. The cuisine features the best of local Cornish produce and is served in the conservatory restaurant.

Rooms 29 (2 fmly) (15 GF) **S** £75-£130; **D** £150-£260 (incl. bkfst & dinner) **Facilities** FTV Fishing Private beach Hair salon Yacht for skippered charter Sub-tropical gardens Xmas Wi-fi **Conf** Class 20 Board 15 Thtr 30 Del from £135 to £155 **Services** Lift **Parking** 52 **Notes** LB Closed Jan

MITCHELL

The Plume of Feathers
★★★★ INN

☎ 01872 510387 & 511122
📠 01872 511124
TR8 5AX
e-mail: enquiries@theplume.info
dir: Just off A30 & A3076, follow signs

PETS: Bedrooms unattended Charges Public
areas Grounds Exercise area Facilities food
bowl water bowl

A very popular inn with origins dating back to
16th century, situated close to Newquay and the
beaches. The restaurant offers a varied menu
which relies heavily on local produce. The stylish
bedrooms are decorated in neutral colours and
have wrought-iron beds with quality linens. The
garden makes an ideal place to enjoy a meal or a
Cornish tea. The staff are very friendly.

Rooms 7 annexe en suite (1 fmly) (5 GF) S
£53.75-£83.75; D £75-£115* Facilities FTV tea/
coffee Dinner available Cen ht Wi-fi Parking 40
Notes LB No coaches

MULLION

Mullion Cove Hotel
★★★ 77% HOTEL

☎ 01326 240328 📠 01326 240998
TR12 7EP
e-mail: enquiries@mullion-cove.co.uk
dir: A3083 towards The Lizard. Through Mullion
towards Mullion Cove. Hotel in approx 1m

PETS: Bedrooms unattended Charges except in
low season Public areas dogs allowed in specific
lounge only Grounds Exercise area

Built at the turn of the last century and set high
above the working harbour of Mullion, this hotel
has spectacular views of the rugged coastline;
seaward facing rooms are always popular. The
stylish restaurant offers some carefully prepared
dishes using local produce; an alternative option
is to eat less formally in the bar. After dinner
guests might like to relax in one of the elegant
lounges.

Rooms 30 (7 fmly) (3 GF) Facilities ⊰ Xmas New
Year Wi-fi Services Lift Parking 60 Notes LB

MULLION

Polurrian

★★★ 77% HOTEL

☎ 01326 240421 📄 01326 240083
TR12 7EN
e-mail: relax@polurrianhotel.com
web: www.polurrianhotel.com
dir: A394 to Helston, follow The Lizard & Mullion signs onto A3083. 5m, right onto B3296 to Mullion. Follow one-way system to T-junct, left signed Mullion Cove. Right in 0.5m

PETS: Bedrooms unattended Charges Public areas Grounds Exercise area adjacent

With spectacular views, this is a well managed and relaxed hotel where guests are assured of a warm welcome from the friendly team of staff. In addition to the formal eating option, the High Point restaurant offers a more casual approach. The popular leisure club has a good range of equipment. Bedrooms vary in size, and the sea-view rooms are always in demand of course.

Rooms 39 (4 fmly) (8 GF) S £61-£87;
D £122-£208 (incl. bkfst & dinner)* Facilities ✈
↘ 🏊 Gym Children's games room & outdoor play area Xmas New Year Wi-fi Child facilities Conf Class 25 Board 26 Thtr 50 Del from £95 to £100* Parking 100 Notes Closed Jan-5 Feb Civ Wed 80

NEWQUAY

Headland

★★★★ 77% ⊛ HOTEL

☎ 01637 872211 📄 01637 872212
Fistral Beach TR7 1EW
e-mail: office@headlandhotel.co.uk
web: www.headlandhotel.co.uk
dir: A30 onto A392 at Indian Queens, follow for Fistral Beach signs, hotel adjacent

PETS: Bedrooms unattended Charges Public areas except restaurant Grounds Exercise area beach 50yds Facilities food water bowl Resident Pet: Twiglet (Airedale Terrier)

This Victorian hotel enjoys a stunning location overlooking the sea on three sides - views can be enjoyed from most of the windows. Bedrooms are comfortable and spacious. The grand public areas include various lounges and in addition to the formal dining room, Sands Brasserie offers a relaxed alternative. Self-catering cottages are available, and guests staying in these can use the hotel facilities.

Rooms 104 (40 fmly) S £80-£135; D £95-£350 (incl. bkfst)* Facilities STV ✈ ↘ ⌥ 9 🏊 Putt green 🏌 Harry Potter playroom New Year Wi-fi Child facilities Conf Class 120 Board 40 Thtr 250 Services Lift Parking 400 Notes LB Closed 24-27 Dec Civ Wed 250

NEWQUAY

Hotel California
★★★ 66% HOTEL

☎ 01637 879292 & 872798 📄 01637 875611
Pentire Crescent TR7 1PU
e-mail: info@hotel-california.co.uk
web: www.hotel-california.co.uk
dir: A392 to Newquay, follow signs for Pentire
Hotels & Guest Houses

PETS: **Bedrooms** unattended **Charges Public
areas Grounds Exercise area Other** dogs are
required to be muzzled

This hotel is tucked away in a delightful location,
close to Fistral Beach and adjacent to the River
Gannel. Many rooms have views across the river
towards the sea, and some have balconies.
There is an impressive range of leisure facilities,
including indoor and outdoor pools, and ten-pin
bowling. Cuisine is enjoyable and menus offer a
range of interesting dishes.

Rooms 70 (27 fmly) (13 GF) **Facilities** FTV 🏷 ⸜
Squash 10 pin bowling alley ♫ Xmas New Year
Conf Class 100 Board 30 Thtr 100 **Services** Lift
Parking 66 **Notes** Closed 3 wks Jan Civ Wed 150

PADSTOW

The Metropole
★★★★ 70% ❀ HOTEL

☎ 01841 532486 📄 01841 532867
Station Rd PL28 8DB
e-mail: info@the-metropole.co.uk
web: www.the-metropole.co.uk
dir: M5/A30 pass Launceston, follow Wadebridge
& N Cornwall signs. Take A39, follow Padstow
signs

PETS: **Bedrooms** unattended **Charges Public
areas** except restaurant & café bar **Grounds**

This long-established hotel first opened its doors
to guests back in 1904 and there is still an air
of the sophistication and elegance of a bygone
age. Bedrooms are soundly appointed and well
equipped; dining options include the informal
Met Café Bar and the main restaurant, with its
enjoyable cuisine and wonderful views over the
Camel estuary.

Rooms 58 (3 fmly) (2 GF) **S** £72-£108;
D £144-£176 (incl. bkfst)* **Facilities** FTV ⸜
Swimming pool open Jul & Aug only Xmas New
Year Wi-fi **Conf** Class 20 Board 20 Thtr 40
Del from £99 to £180* **Services** Lift **Parking** 36
Notes LB

PADSTOW

St Petroc's Hotel and Bistro
★★ 85% ⊛ SMALL HOTEL

☎ 01841 532700   🖷 01841 532942
4 New St PL28 8EA
e-mail: reservations@rickstein.com
dir: A39 onto A389, follow signs to town centre.
Follow one-way system, hotel on right on leaving
town

PETS: Bedrooms unattended Charges Public
areas except restaurant Exercise area beach - 2
mins walk Facilities food bowl water bowl

One of the oldest buildings in town, this
charming establishment is just up the hill
from the picturesque harbour. Style, comfort
and individuality are all great strengths here,
particularly so in the impressively equipped
bedrooms. Breakfast, lunch and dinner all
reflect a serious approach to cuisine, and the
popular restaurant has a relaxed, bistro style.
Comfortable lounges, a reading room and lovely
gardens complete the picture.

Rooms 14 (4 annexe) (3 fmly) (3 GF)
D £132.13-£264.26 (incl. bkfst)* Facilities FTV
Cookery school New Year Wi-fi Conf Board 12
Services Lift Parking 12 Notes Closed 1 May &
25-26 Dec RS 24 Dec eve

PADSTOW

The Seafood Restaurant
★★★★★ ⊛⊛⊛ 🕮 RESTAURANT WITH ROOMS

☎ 01841 532700   🖷 01841 532942
Riverside PL28 8BY
e-mail: reservations@rickstein.com
dir: In town centre

PETS: Bedrooms unattended Charges Public
areas except restaurant Exercise area beach
nearby Facilities food bowl water bowl

Food lovers continue to beat a well-trodden
path to this legendary establishment that has
benefited from considerable recent investment.
Situated on the edge of the harbour, just a
stone's throw from the shops, the Seafood
Restaurant offers stylish and comfortable
bedrooms that boast numerous thoughtful extras;
some have views of the estuary and a couple
have stunning private balconies. Service is
relaxed and friendly, perfect for that break by the
sea; booking is essential for both accommodation
and a table in the restaurant.

Rooms 14 en suite 6 annexe en suite (6 fmly)
(3 GF); D £132.18-£264.26* Facilities STV tea/
coffee Dinner available Direct Dial Cen ht Lift
Cookery School Parking 12 Notes LB Closed
24-26 Dec RS 1 May restaurant closed No
coaches

PADSTOW

Rick Stein's Café
★★★★ BED AND BREAKFAST

☎ 01841 532700 ▤ 01841 532942
10 Middle St PL28 8AP
e-mail: reservations@rickstein.com
dir: A389 into town, one way past church, 3rd right

PETS: Bedrooms unattended Charges Public areas except restaurant Exercise area beach - 2mins walk Facilities food bowl water bowl

Another Rick Stein success story, this lively café by day, restaurant by night, offers good food, quality accommodation, and is just a short walk from the harbour. Three rooms are available, all quite different but sharing high standards of cosseting comfort. Friendly and personable staff complete the picture.

Rooms 3 en suite (1 fmly) Facilities tea/coffee Dinner available Cen ht Licensed Notes LB Closed 1 May BH RS 24-26 Dec

PADSTOW

Little Pentyre
★★ BED AND BREAKFAST

☎ 01841 532246
6 Moyle Rd PL28 8DG
e-mail: jujuLloyd@aol.com
dir: From A389, right onto Dennis Rd, bear right onto Moyle Rd

PETS: Bedrooms unattended Public areas under strict control Grounds Exercise area 50mtrs Facilities food bowl water bowl Resident Pets: Smudge (cat), 3 chickens

Within easy, level walking distance of the town centre, Little Pentyre is situated in a quiet residential area, adjacent to the Camel Estuary and Trail. The comfortable bedrooms are well equipped and guests enjoy a freshly cooked breakfast, featuring eggs from the hens in the rear garden.

Rooms 2 en suite (2 GF) S £30; D £55*
Facilities FTV tea/coffee Cen ht Parking 2
Notes No Children 10yrs 🐾

PENZANCE

Mount View
★★★ INN

☎ 01736 710416 📠 01736 710416
Longrock TR20 8JJ

dir: Off A30 at Marazion/Penzance rdbt, 3rd exit
signed Longrock. On right after pelican crossing

PETS: Bedrooms unattended **Public areas** bar
only **Exercise area** beach & field 50yds **Resident
Pet:** Muppet (Beagle)

This Victorian inn, just a short walk from the
beach and half a mile from the Isles of Scilly
heliport, is a good base for exploring West
Cornwall. Bedrooms are well equipped, including
a hospitality tray, and the bar is a popular with
locals. Breakfast is served in the dining room and
a dinner menu is available.

Rooms 5 rms (3 en suite) (2 fmly) (2 smoking)
Facilities tea/coffee Dinner available Pool Table
Conf Max 20 **Parking** 8 **Notes** RS Sun closed
4.30-7pm

POLPERRO

Penryn House
★★★ GUEST ACCOMMODATION

☎ 01503 272157 📠 01503 273055
The Coombes PL13 2RQ
e-mail: chrispidcock@aol.com
web: www.penrynhouse.co.uk
dir: A387 to Polperro, at mini-rdbt left down hill
into village (ignore restricted access). 200yds
on left

PETS: Bedrooms unattended **Public areas**
except restaurant **Grounds Exercise area** 200yds
Facilities food bowl water bowl **Resident Pet:**
Ella (Great Dane)

Penryn House has a relaxed atmosphere and
offers a warm welcome. Every effort is made
to ensure a memorable stay. Bedrooms are
neatly presented and reflect the character of the
building. After a day exploring, enjoy a drink at
the bar and relax in the comfortable lounge.

Rooms 12 rms (11 en suite) (1 pri facs) (3 fmly)
S £35-£40; D £70-£100* **Facilities** FTV tea/
coffee Licensed Wi-fi **Parking** 13 **Notes** LB

ST IVES

Garrack Hotel & Restaurant

★★★ 77% ◉ HOTEL

☎ 01736 796199 📠 01736 798955
Burthallan Ln, Higher Ayr TR26 3AA
e-mail: aa@garrack.com
dir: Exit A30 for St Ives, then from B3311 follow
brown signs for Tate Gallery, then brown Garrack
signs

PETS: Bedrooms unattended Charges Public
areas Grounds Exercise area country lane & cliff
walks nearby Other prior notice required; dogs
allowed in certain bedrooms only

Enjoying a peaceful, elevated position with
splendid views across the harbour and Porthmeor
Beach, the Garrack sits in its own delightful
grounds and gardens. Bedrooms are comfortable
and many have sea views. Public areas include
a small leisure suite, a choice of lounges and
an attractive restaurant, where locally sourced
ingredients are used in the enjoyable dishes.

Rooms 18 (2 annexe) (2 fmly) Facilities FTV
🏊 Gym New Year Wi-fi Conf Class 10 Board 10
Thtr 20 Parking 30 Notes LB

ST KEVERNE

Gallen-Treath Guest House

★★★ GUEST HOUSE

☎ 01326 280400 📠 01326 280400
Porthallow TR12 6PL
e-mail: gallentreath@btclick.com
dir: 1.5m S of St Keverne in Porthallow

PETS: Bedrooms unattended Charges Public
areas except restaurant/dining room Grounds
Exercise area 2 mins walk to beach, coastal
path & fields Facilities food (pre-bookable) food
bowl water bowl Other all dog facilities by prior
request only; dogs left unattended in bedrooms
at meal times only Resident Pet: J.D.(Bearded
Collie/Lurcher cross)

Gallen-Treath has super views over the
countryside and sea from its elevated position
above Porthallow. Bedrooms are individually
decorated and feature many personal touches.
Guests can relax in the large, comfortable lounge
complete with balcony. Hearty breakfasts and
dinners (by arrangement) are served in the bright
dining room.

Rooms 5 rms (4 en suite) (1 pri facs) (1 fmly)
(1 GF) S £25-£32; D £50-£64* Facilities FTV
TVL tea/coffee Dinner available Cen ht Licensed
Parking 6

SALTASH

Crooked Inn

★★★ GUEST ACCOMMODATION

☎ 01752 848177 📠 01752 843203
Stoketon Cross, Trematon PL12 4RZ
e-mail: info@crooked-inn.co.uk
dir: 1.5m NW of Saltash. A38 W from Saltash,
2nd left to Trematon, sharp right

PETS: Bedrooms unattended ChargesPublic
areas Grounds Exercise area fields Facilities
water bowl Other please phone for further details
of facilities for dogsResident Pets: Laddie (pony),
Dumbo Fancy Rats, Giant African Land Snails,
geese, ducks

The friendly animals that freely roam the
courtyard add to the relaxed country style of
this delightful inn. The spacious bedrooms are
well equipped, and freshly cooked dinners are
available in the bar and conservatory. Breakfast
is served in the cottage-style dining room.

Rooms 18 annexe rms 15 annexe en suite (5
fmly) (7 GF) Facilities tea/coffee Dinner available
Cen ht Licensed ⤷ Conf Max 60 Parking 45
Notes Closed 25 Dec

WATERGATE BAY

The Hotel & Extreme Academy Watergate Bay

★★★ 79% ◉ HOTEL

☎ 01637 860543 📠 01637 860333
TR8 4AA
e-mail: life@watergatebay.co.uk
web: www.watergatebay.co.uk
dir: A30 onto A3059. Follow airport/Watergate
Bay signs

PETS: Bedrooms unattended Charges Public
areas except restaurant, kids' zone & pools
Grounds Exercise area 20yds

With its own private beach (home to the 'Extreme
Academy'), this hotel boasts a truly a spectacular
location. The style is relaxed with a genuine
welcome for all the family. Public areas are
stylish and contemporary. Many bedrooms share
the breathtaking outlook and a number have
balconies. Several dining options are on offer,
including the Beach Hut, Brasserie and Jamie
Oliver's restaurant, Fifteen Cornwall.

Rooms 66 (16 annexe) (36 fmly) (6 GF)
Facilities STV ⊗ ⤷ ⦰ Surfing Table tennis
Billiards Mountain boarding Wave ski-ing Kite
surfing Xmas New Year Wi-fi Child facilities
Conf Class 40 Board 20 Thtr 120 Services Lift
Parking 45 Notes Civ Wed 40

ZENNOR

The Gurnard's Head
★★★ ⊛⊛ INN

☎ 01736 796928 Treen TR26 3DE
e-mail: enquiries@gurnardshead.co.uk
dir: 5m from St Ives on B3306, 4.5m from
Penzance via New Mill

PETS: Bedrooms unattended Public areas except
restaurant Grounds Exercise area adjacent
fields & footpaths Facilities food bowl water bowl

Ideally located for enjoying the beautiful
coastline, this inn offers atmospheric public
areas. The style is relaxed and very popular with
walkers, keen to rest their weary legs. A log fire
in the bar provides a warm welcome on colder
days and on warmer days, outside seating is
available. Lunch and dinner, featuring local
home-cooked food, is available either in the
bar or the adjoining restaurant area. The dinner
menu is not extensive but there are interesting
choices and everything is home made, including
the bread. Breakfast is served around a grand
farmhouse table.

Rooms 7 en suite S £65-£75; D £85-£150*
Facilities tea/coffee Dinner available Wi-fi
Parking 40 Notes Closed 25 Dec & 4 days mid
Jan No coaches

ARMATHWAITE

The Dukes Head Inn
★★★ INN

☎ 016974 72226
Front St CA4 9PB
e-mail: info@dukeshead-hotel.co.uk
web: www.dukeshead-hotel.co.uk
dir: In village centre opp post office

PETS: Bedrooms unattended Charges Public
areas except lounge bar & restaurant Grounds
Exercise area surrounding countryside, public
footpaths Facilities food bowl water bowl Other
day kennels nearby; dog walking & grooming can
be arranged with prior notice

Located in the peaceful village of Armathwaite
close to the River Eden, the Dukes Head offers
comfortable accommodation in a warm friendly
atmosphere. There is a relaxing lounge bar
with open fires and a wide choice of meals are
available either here or in the restaurant.

Rooms 5 rms (3 en suite) (2 pri facs) S fr £42.50;
D fr £62.50* Facilities FTV tea/coffee Dinner
available Cen ht Wi-fi Parking 20 Notes LB
Closed 25 Dec

BASSENTHWAITE

Armathwaite Hall Country House & Spa

★★★★ 80% COUNTRY HOUSE HOTEL

☎ 017687 76551 📠 017687 76220

CA12 4RE

e-mail: reservations@armathwaite-hall.com

web: www.armathwaite-hall.com

dir: M6 junct 40/A66 to Keswick rdbt, A591 signed Carlisle. 8m to Castle Inn junct, left.

PETS: Bedrooms unattended **Charges Public areas Grounds Exercise area** 400-acre estate **Facilities** food (pre-bookable) **Other** dog grooming can be arranged **Resident Pets:** Ben & Millie (Belgium Shepherds), Chrissy (Labrador)

Enjoying fine views over Bassenthwaite Lake, this impressive mansion, dating from the 17th century, is peacefully situated amid 400 acres of deer park. Comfortably furnished bedrooms are complemented by a choice of public rooms featuring splendid wood panelling, and roaring log fires in the cooler months.

Rooms 42 (4 fmly) (8 GF) **Facilities** Spa STV ⚐ supervised ⚒ Putt green Fishing ⚓ Gym Archery Beauty salon Clayshooting Quad & mountain bikes Falconry Xmas New Year Wi-fi **Conf** Class 50 Board 60 Thtr 80 **Services** Lift **Parking** 100 **Notes** LB Civ Wed 80

BORROWDALE

Lodore Falls Hotel

★★★ 83% HOTEL

☎ 017687 77285 📠 017687 77343

CA12 5UX

e-mail: info@lodorefallshotel.co.uk

web: www.lodorefallshotel.co.uk

dir: M6 junct 40 take A66 to Keswick, then B5289 to Borrowdale. Hotel on left

PETS: Bedrooms unattended **Charges Public areas Grounds Exercise area Facilities** food bowl water bowl

This impressive hotel has an enviable location overlooking Derwentwater. The bedrooms, many with lake or fell views, are comfortably equipped; family rooms and suites are also available. The dining room, bar and lounge areas were, at the time of inspection, also undergoing refurbishment to a very high standard. One of the treatments in the hotel's Elemis Spa actually makes use of the Lodore Waterfall!

Rooms 69 (11 fmly) S £75-£209; D £150-£368 (incl. bkfst)* **Facilities** Spa STV FTV ⚐ supervised ⚓ ⚒ Fishing Gym Squash Sauna Xmas New Year Wi-fi **Conf** Class 90 Board 45 Thtr 200 Del from £145 to £185* **Services** Lift **Parking** 93 **Notes** LB Civ Wed 130

BORROWDALE

Borrowdale
★★★ 75% HOTEL

☎ 017687 77224 🖹 017687 77338
CA12 5UY
e-mail: borrowdale@lakedistricthotels.net
dir: 3m from Keswick, on B5289 at S end of Lake
Derwentwater

PETS: Bedrooms unattended **Charges Grounds
Exercise area** adjacent countryside

Situated in the beautiful Borrowdale Valley
overlooking Derwentwater, this traditionally
styled hotel guarantees a friendly welcome.
Extensive public areas include a choice of
lounges, traditional dining room, lounge bar and
popular conservatory which serves more informal
meals. Bedrooms vary in style and size including
two that are suitable for less able guests.

Rooms 36 (3 fmly) (3 GF) **S** £90-£112;
D £180-£224 (incl. bkfst & dinner) **Facilities** STV
FTV Leisure facilities available at nearby sister
hotel Xmas New Year Wi-fi **Conf** Class 30
Board 24 Thtr 80 **Parking** 30 **Notes** LB

BRAITHWAITE

The Royal Oak
★★★★ INN

☎ 017687 78533 🖹 017687 78533
CA12 5SY
e-mail: info@royaloak-braithwaite.co.uk
web: www.royaloak-braithwaite.co.uk
dir: In village centre

PETS: Bedrooms unattended **Charges Public
areas** except in bar/restaurant during food
service **Grounds Facilities** water bowl

The Royal Oak, in the pretty village of
Braithwaite, has delightful views of Skiddaw
and Barrow, and is a good base for tourists and
walkers. Some of the well-equipped bedrooms are
furnished with four-poster beds. Hearty meals
and traditional Cumbrian breakfasts are served
in the restaurant, and there is an atmospheric,
well-stocked bar.

Rooms 10 en suite (1 fmly) **S** £40-£45; **D**
£70-£76* **Facilities** STV tea/coffee Dinner
available Cen ht Wi-fi 🐾 **Parking** 20 **Notes** LB

CARLISLE

Crown

★★★ 80% HOTEL

☎ 01228 561888 📠 01228 561637
Wetheral CA4 8ES
e-mail: info@crownhotelwetheral.co.uk
web: www.crownhotelwetheral.co.uk
dir: M6 junct 42 take B6263 to Wetheral, right at village shop, car park at rear of hotel

PETS: **Bedrooms** unattended **Charges Public areas** except public bar **Grounds Exercise area** 1-2m **Facilities** water bowl

Set in the attractive village of Wetheral and with landscaped gardens to the rear, this hotel is well suited to both business and leisure guests. Rooms vary in size and style and include two apartments in an adjacent house ideal for long stays. A choice of dining options is available, with the popular Waltons Bar an informal alternative to the main restaurant.

Rooms 51 (2 annexe) (10 fmly) (3 GF) **S** £45-£65; **D** £80-£110 (incl. bkfst)* **Facilities** Spa STV 🏊 supervised Gym Squash Children's splash pool Steam room Beauty facilities Sauna Xmas New Year Wi-fi **Conf** Class 90 Board 50 Thtr 175 Del from £130 to £145* **Parking** 80 **Notes** LB Civ Wed 120

CARLISLE

Angus House & Almonds Restaurant

★★★ 🍴 GUEST ACCOMMODATION

☎ 01228 523546 📠 01228 531895
14-16 Scotland Rd CA3 9DG
e-mail: hotel@angus-hotel.co.uk
web: www.angus-hotel.co.uk
dir: 0.5m N of city centre on A7

PETS: **Bedrooms** unattended **Charges Public areas** except restaurant **Restrictions** no Rottweilers or Bull Terriers

Situated just north of the city, this family-run establishment is ideal for business and leisure. A warm welcome is assured and the accommodation is well equipped. Almonds Restaurant provides enjoyable food and home baking, and there is also a lounge and a large meeting room.

Rooms 10 en suite (2 fmly) **S** £52; **D** £74* **Facilities** FTV tea/coffee Dinner available Direct Dial Cen ht Licensed Wi-fi **Conf** Max 25 Thtr 25 Class 16 Board 16 **Notes** LB

COCKERMOUTH

Shepherds Hotel
★★★ 70% HOTEL

☎ 01900 822673 📠 01900 820129
Lakeland Sheep & Wool Centre, Egremont Rd
CA13 0QX
e-mail: reception@shepherdshotel.co.uk
web: www.shepherdshotel.co.uk
dir: At junct of A66 & A5086 S of Cockermouth,
entrance off A5086, 200mtrs off rdbt

PETS: **Bedrooms** unattended **Public areas**
Grounds Exercise area Resident Pets: dogs,
sheep, geese, Jersey cow

This hotel is modern in style and offers
thoughtfully equipped accommodation. The
property also houses the Lakeland Sheep and
Wool Centre, with live sheep shows from Easter
to mid November. A restaurant serving a wide
variety of meals and snacks is open all day.

Rooms 26 (4 fmly) (13 GF) **Facilities** FTV Pool
table Small childs play area Wi-fi **Conf** Class 30
Board 30 Thtr 40 **Services** Lift **Parking** 100
Notes Closed 25-26 Dec & 4-18 Jan

CROSTHWAITE

Damson Dene
★★★ 72% HOTEL

☎ 015395 68676 📠 015395 68227
LA8 8JE
e-mail: info@damsondene.co.uk
web: www.bestlakesbreaks.co.uk
dir: M6 junct 36, A590 signed Barrow-in-Furness,
5m right onto A5074. Hotel on right in 5m

PETS: **Bedrooms** unattended **Public areas** except
restaurant & leisure club **Grounds Exercise area**

A short drive from Lake Windermere, this hotel
enjoys a tranquil and scenic setting. Bedrooms
include a number with four-poster beds and
jacuzzi baths. The spacious restaurant serves a
daily-changing menu, with some of the produce
coming from the hotel's own kitchen garden. Real
fires warm the lounge in the cooler months and
leisure facilities are available.

Rooms 40 (3 annexe) (7 fmly) (9 GF) **S** £69-£89;
D £108-£148 (incl. bkfst) **Facilities** Spa ⏍ Gym
Beauty salon Xmas New Year **Conf** Class 60
Board 40 Thtr 140 **Parking** 45 **Notes** LB
Civ Wed 120

CROSTHWAITE

Crosthwaite House
★★★★ GUEST HOUSE

☎ 015395 68264 📄 015395 68264
LA8 8BP
e-mail: bookings@crosthwaitehouse.co.uk
web: www.crosthwaitehouse.co.uk
dir: A590 onto A5074, 4m right to Crosthwaite,
0.5m turn left

PETS: Bedrooms unattended Charges Public
areas Grounds

Enjoying stunning views across the Lyth Valley,
this friendly Georgian house is a haven of
tranquillity. Bedrooms are spacious and offer a
host of thoughtful extras. The reception rooms
include a comfortable lounge and a pleasant
dining room with polished floorboards and
individual tables.

Rooms 6 en suite S £27.50-£32; D £55-£64*
Facilities FTV TVL tea/coffee Cen ht Parking 10
Notes Closed mid Nov-Jan RS early Nov &
Feb-Mar

GLENRIDDING

The Inn on the Lake
★★★ 81% ⊛ HOTEL

☎ 017684 82444 📄 017684 82303
Lake Ullswater CA11 0PE
e-mail: info@innonthelakeullswater.co.uk
web: www.innonthelakeullswater.com
dir: M6 junct 40, A66 to Keswick. At rdbt
take A592 to Ullswater Lake. Along lake to
Glenridding. Hotel on left on entering village

PETS: Bedrooms unattended Charges Public
areas bar/conservatory only Grounds Exercise
area countryside Other dogs allowed in certain
bedrooms only Resident Pet: Chrissy (Black
Labrador)

In a picturesque lakeside setting, this restored
Victorian hotel is a popular leisure destination as
well as catering for weddings and conferences.
Superb views can be enjoyed from the bedrooms
and from the garden terrace where afternoon
teas are served during warmer months. There is
a popular pub in the grounds, and moorings for
yachts are available to guests. Sailing tuition can
be arranged.

Rooms 47 (6 fmly) (1 GF) Facilities ♨ 9 ♨ Putt
green Fishing ⇘ Gym Sailing 9-hole pitch &
putt Bowls Lake Bathing Xmas New Year Wi-fi
Conf Class 60 Board 40 Thtr 120 Services Lift
Parking 200 Notes LB Civ Wed 100

GRASMERE

Oak Bank
★★ 79% @ HOTEL

☎ 015394 35217 📠 015394 35685
Broadgate LA22 9TA
e-mail: info@lakedistricthotel.co.uk
web: www.lakedistricthotel.co.uk
dir: N'bound: M6 junct 36 onto A591 to
Windermere, Ambleside, then Grasmere. S'bound:
M6 junct 40 onto A66 to Keswick, A591 to
Grasmere

PETS: Bedrooms unattended Charges Public
areas front lounge only Exercise area 100mtrs
Resident Pet: Louby Lou (Yorkshire Terrier)

This privately owned and personally run hotel
provides well-equipped accommodation,
including a bedroom on the ground-floor and a
four-poster room. Public areas include a choice
of comfortable lounges with welcoming log fires
when the weather is cold. There is a pleasant bar
and an attractive restaurant with a conservatory
extension overlooking the garden.

Rooms 14 (1 GF) S £62.50-£105; D £85-£165
(incl. bkfst) Facilities FTV Corporate membership
of leisure facilities at another hotel Xmas New
Year Wi-fi Parking 14 Notes LB Closed 3-28 Jan

IREBY

Overwater Hall
★★★ 82% @@ COUNTRY HOUSE HOTEL

☎ 017687 76566 📠 017687 76921
CA7 1HH
e-mail: welcome@overwaterhall.co.uk
dir: From A591 take turn to Ireby at Castle Inn.
Hotel signed after 2m on right

PETS: Bedrooms unattended Charges Public
areas except restaurant & drawing room Grounds
Exercise area 18-acre gardens Facilities food
bowl water bowl Resident Pets: Oscar & Bafta
(Black Labradors), Carina (cat)

This privately owned country house dates back to
1811 and is set in lovely gardens surrounded by
woodland. The owners have lovingly restored this
Georgian property over the last 16 years paying
great attention to the authenticity of the original
design; guests will receive warm hospitality
and attentive service in a relaxed manner. The
elegant and well appointed bedrooms include the
more spacious Superior Rooms and the Garden
Room; all bedrooms have Wi-fi. Creative dishes
are served in the traditional-style dining room.

Rooms 11 (2 fmly) (1 GF) S £85-£175;
D £170-£270 (incl. bkfst & dinner)*
Facilities FTV Xmas New Year Wi-fi Parking 20
Notes LB Civ Wed 30

KESWICK

Low Nest Farm B&B
★★★★ GUEST ACCOMMODATION

☎ 017687 72378
Castlerigg CA12 4TF
e-mail: info@lownestfarm.co.uk
dir: 2m S of Keswick, off A591 (Windermere road)

PETS: Bedrooms unattended Charges Public
areas Grounds Exercise area 5-acre adjacent
field Facilities food (pre-bookable) food
bowl water bowl Other kennel block available
Resident Pets: Sophie, Billie, Erik, Max & Lucy
(Weimaraners), Pepsi (Poodle), Jasper (parrot), 3
goats, 2 sheep

Low Nest Farm is a small, family-run farm
set in some typically breath-taking Cumbrian
scenery. Bedrooms are very comfortable with
smart ensuites and lovely views. Dog owners are
especially well catered for. There are of course,
any number of walks available in the area, and
Keswick is just two miles away.

Rooms 8 en suite (4 GF) S £33-£45; D £50-£90*
Facilities FTV TVL tea/coffee Cen ht Wi-fi
Parking 10 Notes No Children 16yrs RS Nov-Mar
renovations taking place 🐾

KIRKBY LONSDALE

The Sun Inn
★★★★★ ◉ INN

☎ 015242 71965   📄 015242 72485
6 Market St LA6 2AU
e-mail: email@sun-inn.info
web: www.sun-inn.info
dir: From A65 follow signs to town centre. Inn on
main street

PETS: Bedrooms unattended Charges Public
areas except restaurant Exercise area adjacent

A 17th-century inn situated in a historic
market town, overlooking St Mary's Church. The
atmospheric bar features stone walls, wooden
beams and log fires with real ales available.
Delicious meals are served in the bar and
more formal, modern restaurant. Traditional
and modern styles are blended together in the
beautifully appointed rooms with excellent en
suites.

Rooms 11 en suite (2 fmly) S £65-£130;
D £90-£150* Facilities tea/coffee Dinner
available Cen ht Wi-fi Notes No coaches

LOWESWATER

Grange Country House
★★ 69% SMALL HOTEL

☎ 01946 861211 & 861570
CA13 0SU
e-mail: info@thegrange-loweswater.co.uk
dir: Exit A5086 for Mockerkin, through village. After 2m left for Loweswater Lake. Hotel at bottom of hill on left

PETS: Bedrooms unattended Charges Public areas except dining room Grounds Exercise area across road Facilities food bowl water bowl Resident Pets: Toby (Labrador/Collie cross)

This delightful country hotel is set in extensive grounds in a quiet valley at the north-western end of Loweswater, and continues to prove popular with guests seeking peace and quiet. It has a friendly and relaxed atmosphere, and the cosy public areas include a small bar, a residents' lounge and an attractive dining room. The bedrooms are well equipped and comfortable, and include four-poster rooms.

Rooms 8 (2 fmly) (1 GF) S £50-£60; D £88-£120 (incl. bkfst) Facilities National Trust boats & fishing Xmas Conf Class 25 Board 25 Thtr 25 Parking 22 Notes RS Jan-Feb

PENRITH

George
★★★ 75% HOTEL

☎ 01768 862696 📄 01768 868223
Devonshire St CA11 7SU
e-mail: georgehotel@lakedistricthotels.net
dir: M6 junct 40, 1m to town centre. From A6/A66 to Penrith

PETS: Bedrooms unattended Public areas except restaurant Exercise area 5 min walk Facilities food bowl water bowl

This inviting and popular hotel dates back to a time when 'Bonnie' Prince Charlie made a visit. Extended over the years this town centre hotel offers well equipped bedrooms. The spacious public areas retain a timeless charm and include a choice of lounge areas, popular venues for morning coffees and afternoon teas.

Rooms 35 (4 fmly) Facilities Xmas New Year Wi-fi Conf Class 80 Board 50 Thtr 120 Parking 40 Notes Civ Wed 120

ROSTHWAITE

Royal Oak

★ 75% SMALL HOTEL

☎ 017687 77214 & 77695
CA12 5XB
e-mail: info@royaloakhotel.co.uk
web: www.royaloakhotel.co.uk
dir: 6m S of Keswick on B5289 in centre of Rosthwaite

PETS: Bedrooms unattended Public areas except dining room Grounds Exercise area Facilities food bowl water bowl Resident Pet: Monty (cat)

Set in a village in one of Lakeland's most picturesque valleys, this family-run hotel offers friendly and obliging service. There is a variety of accommodation styles, with particularly impressive rooms being located in a converted barn across the courtyard and backing onto a stream; family rooms are available. The cosy bar is for residents and diners only, and a set home-cooked dinner is served at 7pm.

Rooms 12 (4 annexe) (5 fmly) (4 GF) S £35-£58; D £72-£96 (incl. bkfst)* Parking 15 Notes LB Closed 4-21 Jan & 5-28 Dec

WATERMILLOCK

Rampsbeck Country House

★★★ @@@ HOTEL

☎ 017684 86442 📠 017684 86688
CA11 0LP
e-mail: enquiries@rampsbeck.co.uk
web: www.rampsbeck.co.uk
dir: M6 junct 40, A592 to Ullswater, at T-junct (with lake in front) turn right, hotel 1.5m

PETS: Bedrooms unattended Charges Public areas hall/lounge only Grounds Exercise area meadow adjacent Other dogs allowed in three bedrooms only

This fine country house lies in 18 acres of parkland on the shores of Lake Ullswater, and is furnished with many period and antique pieces. There are three delightful lounges, an elegant restaurant and a traditional bar. Bedrooms come in three grades; the most spacious rooms are spectacular and overlook the lake. Service is attentive and the cuisine a real highlight.

Rooms 19 (1 fmly) (1 GF) S £95-£270; D £140-£290 (incl. bkfst)* Facilities STV FTV Putt green 🏌 Xmas New Year Wi-fi Conf Class 10 Board 15 Thtr 15 Del from £155 to £255* Parking 25 Notes LB Closed 4-27 Jan Civ Wed 65

Holbeck Ghyll Country House

★★★★ @@@ COUNTRY HOUSE HOTEL

☎ 015394 32375 📄 015394 34743

Holbeck Ln LA23 1LU

e-mail: stay@holbeckghyll.com

dir: 3m N of Windermere on A591, right into Holbeck Ln (signed Troutbeck), hotel 0.5m on left

PETS: Bedrooms unattended Charges Public areas front hall only Grounds Exercise area adjacent Facilities food (pre-bookable) food bowl water bowl Other dog grooming available nearby

With a peaceful setting in extensive grounds, this beautifully maintained hotel enjoys breathtaking views over Lake Windermere and the Langdale Fells. Public rooms include luxurious lounges and two elegant dining rooms, where memorable meals are served. Bedrooms are individually styled and many have balconies or patios. Some in an adjacent, more private lodge are less traditional in design. The staff's professionalism and attentiveness is exemplary.

Rooms 33 (19 annexe) (4 fmly) (14 GF) S £175-£325; D £240-£580 (incl. bkfst & dinner) Facilities Spa STV 🍸 Putt green 🏌 Gym Sauna Steam room Treatment rooms Beauty massage Xmas New Year Wi-fi Conf Class 25 Board 20 Thtr 45 Parking 34 Notes LB Civ Wed 65

Miller Howe

★★★ 86% @@ COUNTRY HOUSE HOTEL

☎ 015394 42536 📄 015394 45664

Rayrigg Rd LA23 1EY

e-mail: info@millerhowe.com

dir: M6 junct 36 follow A591 past Windermere village, left at rdbt towards Bowness

PETS: Bedrooms unattended Charges Public areas only at management's discretion Grounds Exercise area 100yds Facilities food bowl water bowl Resident Pets: Betty & Doris (Cocker Spaniels)

This long established hotel of much character enjoys a lakeside setting amidst delightful landscaped gardens. The bright and welcoming day rooms include sumptuous lounges, a conservatory and an opulently decorated restaurant. Imaginative dinners make use of fresh, local produce where possible and there is an extensive, well-balanced wine list. Stylish bedrooms, many with fabulous lake views, include well-equipped cottage rooms and a number with whirlpool baths.

Rooms 15 (3 annexe) (1 GF) S £90-£150; D £180-£300 (incl. bkfst & dinner)* Facilities Xmas New Year Wi-fi Parking 35 Notes LB Civ Wed 75

WINDERMERE

Cedar Manor Hotel & Restaurant
★★ 83% @ HOTEL

☎ 015394 43192 & 45970 📄 015394 45970
Ambleside Rd LA23 1AX
e-mail: info@cedarmanor.co.uk
dir: From A591 follow signs to Windermere. Hotel on left just beyond St Mary's Church at bottom of hill

PETS: Bedrooms unattended Charges
Public areas Grounds Exercise area 0.25m
Restrictions no dog larger than a labrador

Built in 1854 as a country retreat this lovely old house enjoys a peaceful location that is within easy walking distance of the town centre. Bedrooms, some on the ground floor, are attractive and well equipped, with two bedrooms in the adjacent coach house. There is a comfortable lounge bar where guests can relax before enjoying dinner in the well-appointed dining room.

Rooms 11 (2 annexe) (2 fmly) (3 GF) S £63-£75;
D £90-£150 (incl. bkfst)* Facilities FTV New Year
Wi-fi Parking 11 Notes LB Closed 3-21 Jan

BAKEWELL

Rutland Arms
★★★ 70% @ HOTEL

☎ 01629 812812 📄 01629 812309
The Square DE45 1BT
e-mail: enquiries@rutlandbakewell.co.uk
dir: M1 junct 28 to Matlock, A6 to Bakewell. Hotel in town centre

PETS: Bedrooms unattended Charges Public
areas at certain times only Exercise area 100yds
Other dogs allowed in courtyard rooms only;
may only be left unattended in bedrooms for
short periods Restrictions small, well behaved
dogs only

This 19th-century hotel lies at the very centre of Bakewell and offers comfortable accommodation. With friendly and welcoming staff, and a newly relaunched restaurant, The Square offering interesting fine dining in elegant surroundings.

Rooms 35 (17 annexe) (2 fmly) (7 GF) Facilities
New Year Wi-fi Conf Class 60 Board 40 Thtr 100
Parking 25

BUXTON

Barceló Buxton Palace Hotel
★★★★ 72% HOTEL

☎ 01298 22001 📠 01298 72131
Palace Rd SK17 6AG
e-mail: palace@barcelo-hotels.co.uk
web: www.barcelo-hotels.co.uk
dir: M6 junct 20, follow M56/M60 signs to Stockport then A6 to Buxton, hotel adjacent to railway station

PETS: **Bedrooms** unattended **Charges Public areas** except bar & restaurant **Grounds Exercise area** park 600mtrs

This impressive Victorian hotel is located on the hill overlooking the town. Public areas are traditional and elegant in style, and include chandeliers and decorative ceilings. The bedrooms are spacious and equipped with modern facilities, and The Dovedale Restaurant provides modern British cuisine. Good leisure facilities are available.

Rooms 122 (18 fmly) **Facilities** Spa ⊛ supervised Gym Beauty facilities Xmas New Year Wi-fi **Conf** Class 125 Board 80 Thtr 350 Del from £100* **Services** Lift **Parking** 180 **Notes** Civ Wed 100

CROMFORD

Alison House
★★★★ GUEST ACCOMMODATION

☎ 01629 822211 📠 01629 822316
Intake Ln DE4 3RH
e-mail: info@alison-house-hotel.co.uk

PETS: **Bedrooms** unattended **Charges Public areas** except restaurant **Grounds Exercise area** 100yds

This very well furnished and spacious 18th-century house stands in seven acres of grounds just a short walk from the village. Public rooms are comfortable and bedrooms are mostly very spacious.

Rooms 16 en suite (1 fmly) (4 GF) S £49; D £79-£99* **Facilities** tea/coffee Dinner available Direct Dial Cen ht Licensed Wi-fi ⛵ **Conf** Max 40 Thtr 40 Class 40 Board 40 **Parking** 30 **Notes** LB Civ Wed 50

DERBY

Littleover Lodge
★★★ 68% HOTEL

☎ 01332 510161 📠 01332 514010
222 Rykneld Rd, Littleover DE23 4AN
e-mail: enquiries@littleoverlodge.co.uk
web: www.littleoverlodge.co.uk
dir: A38 towards Derby approx 1m on left slip
lane signed Littleover/Mickleover/Findon, take
2nd exit off island marked Littleover 0.25m on
right

PETS: **Bedrooms** unattended **Charges Public
areas Grounds Exercise area Restrictions** no
breed larger than Labrador accepted

Situated in a rural location this friendly hotel
offers modern bedrooms with direct access from
the car park. Two styles of dining are available
- an informal carvery operation which is very
popular locally, and a more formal restaurant
which is open for lunch and dinner each day.
Service is excellent with long serving staff being
particularly friendly.

Rooms 16 (3 fmly) (6 GF) **S** £60-£90; **D** £70-£90
(incl. bkfst)* **Facilities** STV 🎵 Xmas New Year
Wi-fi **Parking** 75 **Notes** LB Civ Wed 100

FENNY BENTLEY

Bentley Brook Inn
★★★ INN

☎ 01335 350278 📠 01335 350422
DE6 1LF
e-mail: all@bentleybrookinn.co.uk
dir: 2m N of Ashbourne at junct of A515 & B5056

PETS: **Bedrooms** unattended **Charges Public
areas** except restaurant **Grounds Exercise area**
inn surrounded by fields

This popular inn is located in the Peak District
National Park, just north of Ashbourne. It is a
charming building with an attractive terrace,
sweeping lawns, and nursery gardens. A well-
appointed family restaurant dominates the
ground floor, where a wide range of dishes is
available all day. The character bar serves beer
from its own micro-brewery. Bedrooms are well
appointed and thoughtfully equipped.

Rooms 11 en suite (1 fmly) (2 GF) **Facilities** TVL
tea/coffee Dinner available Direct Dial Cen ht
Wi-fi **Conf** Max 11 Thtr 11 Class 11 Board 11
Parking 60 **Notes** LB Civ Wed 40

HOPE

Stoney Ridge
★★★★ 🏠 GUEST ACCOMMODATION

☎ 01433 620538
Granby Rd, Bradwell S33 9HU
e-mail: toneyridge@aol.com
web: www.stoneyridge.org.uk
dir: From N end of Bradwell, Gore Ln uphill past
Bowling Green Inn, turn left onto Granby Rd

PETS: **Bedrooms** unattended **Public areas** except
dining room **Grounds Exercise area** 100mtrs
Resident Pets: Paddy (cockatiel), Bruno, Bertie &
Boris (cockerels), 17 hens

This large, split-level bungalow stands in
attractive mature gardens at the highest part of
the village and has extensive views. Hens roam
freely in the landscaped garden, and their fresh
eggs add to the hearty breakfasts. Bedrooms are
attractively furnished and thoughtfully equipped,
and there is a spacious comfortable lounge and a
superb indoor swimming pool.

Rooms 4 rms (3 en suite) (1 pri facs) **S** £45-£55;
D £54-£70* **Facilities** TVL tea/coffee Cen ht Wi-fi
🏊 **Parking** 3 **Notes** LB No Children 10yrs RS
Winter Pool may be closed for maintenance

MATLOCK

Hodgkinsons Hotel & Restaurant
★★ 67% HOTEL

☎ 01629 582170 📠 01629 584891
150 South Pde, Matlock Bath DE4 3NR
e-mail: enquiries@hodgkinsons-hotel.co.uk
dir: On A6 in village centre. On corner of Waterloo
Rd & South Parade

PETS: **Bedrooms** unattended **Charges Public
areas** except restaurant/bar area **Grounds
Facilities** food bowl water bowl **Other** only 1 dog
per room

This fine Georgian building was renovated in
the Victorian era and has many interesting and
unusual features. Bedrooms are equipped with
fine antique furniture and a wealth of thoughtful
extras. The elegant dining room is the setting for
imaginative dinners and a comfortable lounge is
also available.

Rooms 8 (1 fmly) **S** £40-£85; **D** £90-£140 (incl.
bkfst)* **Facilities** Wi-fi **Conf** Class 12 Board 10
Thtr 10 Del from £125 to £145* **Parking** 5
Notes LB Closed 24-26 Dec

SANDIACRE

Holiday Inn Derby/Nottingham

★★★ 75% HOTEL

☎ 0870 400 9062 📠 0115 949 0469
Bostocks Ln NG10 5NJ
e-mail: reservations-derby-nottingham@ihg.com
web: www.holidayinn.co.uk
dir: M1 junct 25 follow signs for Sandiacre, hotel on right

PETS: Bedrooms unattended Charges Public areas Grounds

This hotel is conveniently located by the M1, ideal for exploring Derby and Nottingham. The bedrooms are modern and smart. The newly refurbished restaurant offers a wide range of dishes for breakfast, lunch and dinner. The lounge/bar area is a popular meeting place, with food served all day.

Rooms 92 (31 fmly) (53 GF) (2 smoking)
Facilities STV Xmas New Year Wi-fi Conf Class 32 Board 30 Thtr 75 Del from £89 to £155
Services Air con Parking 200 Notes Civ Wed 50

THORPE (DOVEDALE)

Izaak Walton

★★★ 79% ⍟⍟ HOTEL

☎ 01335 350555 📠 01335 350539
Dovedale DE6 2AY
e-mail: reception@izaakwaltonhotel.com
web: www.izaakwaltonhotel.com
dir: A515 onto B5054, to Thorpe, continue straight over cattle grid & 2 small bridges, 1st right & sharp left

PETS: Bedrooms unattended Charges Public areas except main restaurant & 1st floor Grounds Exercise area adjacent Facilities water bowl

This hotel is peacefully situated, with magnificent views over the valley of Dovedale to Thorpe Cloud. Many of the bedrooms have lovely views, and the executive rooms are particularly spacious. Meals are served in the bar area, with more formal dining in the Haddon Restaurant. Staff are friendly and efficient. Fishing on the River Dove can be arranged.

Rooms 35 (6 fmly) (8 GF) S fr £110; D fr £145 (incl. bkfst)* Facilities Fishing ⍤ Xmas New Year Wi-fi Conf Class 40 Board 50 Thtr 50 Parking 80 Notes Civ Wed 80

ASHBURTON

The Rising Sun

★★★★ ⇔ INN

☎ 01364 652544
Woodland TQ13 7JT
e-mail: admin@therisingsunwoodland.co.uk
dir: A38, exit signed Woodland/Denbury, continue
straight on for 1.5m Rising Sun on left

PETS: Bedrooms unattended Public areas
Grounds Exercise area 50yds

Peacefully situated in scenic south Devon
countryside, this inn is just a short drive from
the A38. A friendly welcome is extended to all
guests; business, leisure and families alike.
Bedrooms are comfortable and well equipped.
Dinner and breakfast feature much local and
organic produce. A good selection of homemade
puddings, West Country cheeses, local wines and
quality real ales are available.

Rooms 5 en suite (2 fmly) (2 GF) Facilities FTV
tea/coffee Dinner available Cen ht Parking 30
Notes No coaches

AXMINSTER

Fairwater Head Hotel

★★★ 75% ⊛ HOTEL

☎ 01297 678349 📠 01297 678459
Hawkchurch EX13 5TX
e-mail: stay@fairwaterheadhotel.co.uk
web: www.fairwaterheadhotel.co.uk
dir: Off B3165 (Crewkerne to Lyme Regis road).
Hotel signed to Hawkchurch

PETS: Bedrooms unattended Charges Public
areas except dining room Grounds Exercise
area countryside Facilities food (pre-bookable)
food bowl water bowl Other outside pen area
Resident Pets: Mocca (Springer/Cocker Spaniel),
Lollipop (Black Labrador)

This elegant Edwardian country house provides
a perfect location for anyone seeking a peaceful
break. Surrounded by extensive gardens and
rolling countryside, relaxation is guaranteed
Bedrooms are located both in the main house
and the garden wing; all provide good levels of
comfort. Public areas have much appeal and
include lounge areas, a bar and an elegant
restaurant. Food is a highlight with excellent
local produce prepared with care and skill.

Rooms 16 (4 annexe) (8 GF) S £75-£100;
D £95-£120 (incl. bkfst)* Facilities Xmas
New Year Wi-fi Conf Class 25 Board 20 Thtr 35
Parking 30 Notes LB Closed 1-30 Jan Civ Wed 50

BISHOPSTEIGNTON

Cockhaven Manor Hotel
★★ 69% HOTEL

☎ 01626 775252   🖷 01626 775572
Cockhaven Rd TQ14 9RF
e-mail: cockhaven@btconnect.com
web: www.cockhavenmanor.com
dir: M5/A380 towards Torquay, then A381
towards Teignmouth. Left at Metro Motors. Hotel
500yds on left

PETS: Bedrooms unattended Charges Public
areas except restaurant, dining room Grounds
Exercise area garden & river walks 0.25m
Facilities food (pre-bookable) food bowl water
bowl Resident Pet: Bitsi (rescue dog)

A friendly, family-run inn that dates back to the
16th century. Bedrooms are well equipped and
many enjoy views across the beautiful Teign
estuary. A choice of dining options is offered, and
traditional and interesting dishes, along with
locally caught fish, prove popular.

Rooms 12 (2 fmly) S £47-£55; D £66-£80 (incl.
bkfst)* Facilities Petanque Wi-fi Conf Class 50
Board 30 Thtr 50 Parking 50 Notes LB
RS 25-26 Dec

CHAGFORD

Gidleigh Park
★★★★ ◉◉◉◉ COUNTRY HOUSE HOTEL

☎ 01647 432367   🖷 01647 432574
TQ13 8HH
e-mail: gidleighpark@gidleigh.co.uk
web: www.gidleigh.com
dir: From Chagford, right at Lloyds Bank into Mill
St. After 150yds fork right, follow lane 2m to end

PETS: Bedrooms unattended Charges Public
areas Grounds Facilities food bowl water bowl
Other suitable bedrooms 75yds from main house,
plus one cottage; 4 kennels (heated), single
kennels (with run)

Set in 45 acres of lovingly tended grounds this
world-renowned hotel retains a timeless charm
and a very endearing, homely atmosphere.
Individually styled bedrooms are sumptuously
furnished; The spacious public areas feature
antique furniture, beautiful flower arrangements
and magnificent artwork. The award-winning
cuisine created by Michael Caines, will make a
stay here a truly memorable experience.

Rooms 24 (3 annexe) (4 fmly) (4 GF)
S £295-£435; D £330-£470 (incl. bkfst)
Facilities STV FTV ♨ Putt green Fishing ⚓ Bowls
Guided walks Sauna & steam room suite Xmas
New Year Wi-fi Conf Board 22 Del from £370 to
£510 Parking 25 Notes Civ Wed 54

COLYFORD

Lower Orchard
★★★★ BED AND BREAKFAST

☎ 01297 553615
Swan Hill Rd EX24 6QQ
e-mail: booking@lowerorchard.com
web: www.lowerorchard.com
dir: On A3052 in Colyford, between Lyme Regis & Sidmouth

PETS: Bedrooms unattended Charges Public areas Grounds Exercise area 200mtrs Resident Pet: Sasha (Tibetan Terrier)

This modern ranch-style family home looks over the Axe Valley. The spacious ground-floor bedrooms are very well equipped. Breakfast is served in the lounge-dining room with patio doors leading to a private sun terrace, well-tended gardens and splash pool. The owners have also created a motoring memories museum and a classic car showroom nearby.

Rooms 2 rms (1 en suite) (1 pri facs) (2 GF) S £45-£55; D £55-£65 Facilities TVL tea/coffee Cen ht ⤳ Parking 3 Notes ☺

DARTMOUTH

The Dart Marina
★★★★ 80% ◉◉ HOTEL

☎ 01803 832580 & 837120 📄 01803 835040
Sandquay Rd TQ6 9PH
e-mail: reservations@dartmarina.com
web: www.dartmarina.com
dir: A3122 from Totnes to Dartmouth. Follow road which becomes College Way, before Higher Ferry. Hotel sharp left in Sandquay Rd

PETS: Bedrooms unattended Charges Public areas except restaurants Exercise area 30yds

Boasting a stunning riverside location with its own marina, this is a truly special place to stay. Bedrooms vary in style but all have wonderful views, and some have private balconies to sit and soak up the atmosphere. Stylish public areas take full advantage of the waterside setting with opportunities to dine alfresco. In addition to the Wildfire Bar & Bistro, the River Restaurant is the venue for accomplished cooking.

Rooms 49 (4 annexe) (4 fmly) (4 GF) S £95-£155; D £130-£195 (incl. bkfst)* Facilities Spa ⓢ Gym Canoeing Sailing Xmas New Year Wi-fi Services Lift Parking 50 Notes LB Civ Wed 40

DARTMOUTH

Royal Castle
★★★ 80% HOTEL

☎ 01803 833033 📄 01803 835445
11 The Quay TQ6 9PS
e-mail: enquiry@royalcastle.co.uk
web: www.royalcastle.co.uk
dir: In centre of town, overlooking Inner Harbour

PETS: **Bedrooms** unattended **Charges Public areas** except restaurant **Exercise area** 800mtrs **Facilities** water bowl **Other** well behaved dogs only **Resident Pets:** Stella (Springer Spaniel)

At the edge of the harbour, this imposing 17th-century former coaching inn is filled with charm and character. Bedrooms are well equipped and comfortable; many have harbour views. A choice of quiet seating areas is offered in addition to both the traditional and contemporary bars. A variety of eating options is available, including the main restaurant which features accomplished cuisine and lovely views.

Rooms 25 (3 fmly) **Facilities** 🎵 Xmas New Year Wi-fi **Conf** Class 30 Board 20 Thtr 50 **Parking** 17 **Notes** Civ Wed 80

DAWLISH

Langstone Cliff Hotel
★★★ 78% HOTEL

☎ 01626 868000 📄 01626 868006
Dawlish Warren EX7 0NA
e-mail: reception@langstone-hotel.co.uk
web: www.langstone-hotel.co.uk
dir: 1.5m NE off A379 Exeter road to Dawlish Warren

PETS: **Bedrooms** unattended **Public areas** except restaurant **Grounds Exercise area** woods

A family owned and run hotel, the Langstone Cliff offers a range of leisure, conference and function facilities. Bedrooms, many with sea views and balconies, are spacious, comfortable and well equipped. There are a number of attractive lounges and a well-stocked bar. Dinner is served, often carvery style, in the restaurant.

Rooms 66 (4 annexe) (52 fmly) (10 GF) **Facilities** STV FTV 🏊 🏌 🛝 Gym Table tennis Golf practice area Hair & beauty salon Ballroom 🎵 Xmas New Year Wi-fi Child facilities **Conf** Class 200 Board 80 Thtr 400 **Services** Lift **Parking** 200 **Notes** Civ Wed 400

EGGESFORD

Fox & Hounds Country Hotel

★★★ 71% ◉ HOTEL

☎ 01769 580345
EX18 7JZ
e-mail: relax@foxandhoundshotel.co.uk
dir: M5 junct 27, A361 towards Tiverton. A396 signed Tiverton/Bickleigh. A3072 to Crediton. A377 towards Barnstaple. 14m pass Eggesford Station, hotel on left

PETS: **Bedrooms** unattended **Charges Public areas** except restaurant **Grounds Facilities** food bowl water bowl

In the beautiful Taw Valley, this extensively developed hotel was originally a coaching inn dating back to the 1800s. Many of the comfortable, elegant bedrooms have lovely countryside views. Impressive cooking utilises excellent local produce and can be enjoyed in either restaurant or the convivial bar. For fishing enthusiasts, the hotel has direct access to the River Taw, and equipment and tuition can be provided if required.

Rooms 15 (4 fmly) (1 GF) S £60-£75; D £80-£130 (incl. bkfst)* **Facilities** FTV Fishing Hair & beauty salon Xmas New Year Wi-fi **Conf** Class 60 Board 60 Thtr 100 Del from £95 to £120* **Parking** 100 **Notes** LB Civ Wed 120

EXETER

Barton Cross Hotel & Restaurant

★★★ 71% ◉ HOTEL

☎ 01392 841245 🖶 01392 841942
Huxham, Stoke Canon EX5 4EJ
e-mail: bartonxhuxham@aol.com
dir: 0.5m off A396 at Stoke Canon, 3m N of Exeter

PETS: **Bedrooms** unattended sign **Charges Public areas Grounds Exercise area Resident Pets:** Alfie (German Shepherd), Purdy (Greyhound)

17th-century charm combined with 21st-century luxury perfectly sums up the appeal of this lovely country hotel. The bedrooms are spacious, tastefully decorated and well maintained. Public areas include the cosy first-floor lounge and the lounge/bar with its warming log fire. The restaurant offers a seasonally changing menu of consistently enjoyable cuisine.

Rooms 9 (2 fmly) (2 GF) (2 smoking) S £80-£90; D £98-£110 (incl. bkfst) **Facilities** STV FTV Xmas New Year Wi-fi **Conf** Class 20 Board 20 Thtr 20 **Parking** 35 **Notes** LB

HONITON

Deer Park Country Hotel

★★★ 72% COUNTRY HOUSE HOTEL

☎ 01404 41266   📠 01404 43958
Weston EX14 3PG
e-mail: admin@deerparkcountryhotel.co.uk
web: www.deerparkcountryhotel.co.uk
dir: M5 junct 28/A373 to Honiton. Right at lights,
left to Heathpark Industrial Estate by BP garage,
hotel signed

PETS: Bedrooms unattended **Charges Public
areas** only in grounds - not in main building
Grounds Exercise area hotel in parkland

Peacefully located in 30 acres of wonderful
countryside, this Georgian squire's mansion
dates back to 1721. There is character here in
abundance with elegant public rooms providing
ample space for guests to relax and unwind.
Bedrooms are split between the main house and
The Mews, with a variation in size and style.
Additional facilities include outdoor swimming
pool, croquet lawn, tennis courts and fishing on
the River Otter.

Rooms 22 (6 annexe) (4 GF) **Facilities** ↖ ♨
Putt green Fishing ⇘ Gym Archery Games
room Shooting Snooker room Xmas New Year
Conf Class 30 Board 28 Thtr 40 **Parking** 50
Notes Civ Wed 50

ILFRACOMBE

Darnley Hotel

★★ 71% HOTEL

☎ 01271 863955
3 Belmont Rd EX34 8DR
e-mail: darnleyhotel@yahoo.co.uk
web: www.darnleyhotel.co.uk
dir: A361 to Barnstaple & Ilfracombe. Left
at Church Hill, 1st left into Belmont Rd. 3rd
entrance on left under walled arch

PETS: Bedrooms unattended **Public areas**
except restaurant **Grounds Exercise area** 400yds
Resident Pet: Pepsi (cat)

Standing in award-winning, mature gardens,
with a wooded path to the High Street and the
beach (about a five minute stroll away), this
former Victorian gentleman's residence offers
friendly, informal service. The individually
furnished and decorated bedrooms vary in size.
Dinners feature honest home-cooking, with 'old
fashioned puddings' always proving popular.

Rooms 10 (2 fmly) (2 GF) S £36-£38; D £53-£79
(incl. bkfst)* **Facilities** FTV Xmas New Year
Parking 10

LIFTON

Arundell Arms
★★★ 81% @@ HOTEL

☎ 01566 784666 📠 01566 784494
PL16 0AA
e-mail: reservations@arundellarms.co.uk
dir: 1m off A30, 3m E of Launceston

PETS: Bedrooms unattended **Charges Public areas** except restaurant **Grounds Exercise area** 0.5m **Facilities** food water bowl **Restrictions** dogs not allowed on river bank

This former coaching inn, boasting a long history, sits in the heart of a quiet Devon village. It is internationally famous for its country pursuits such as winter shooting and angling. The bedrooms offer individual style and comfort. Public areas are full of character and present a relaxed atmosphere, particularly around the open log fire during colder evenings. Award-winning cuisine is a celebration of local produce.

Rooms 21 (4 GF) **S** fr £95; **D** £170-£230 (incl. bkfst)* **Facilities** STV Fishing Skittle alley Game shooting (in winter) Fly fishing school New Year Wi-fi **Conf** Class 30 Board 40 Thtr 100 Del from £137 to £155* **Parking** 70 **Notes** LB Closed 3 days Xmas Civ Wed 80

LYNMOUTH

Tors Hotel
★★★ 72% @ HOTEL

☎ 01598 753236 📠 01598 752544
EX35 6NA
e-mail: info@torshotellynmouth.co.uk
web: www.torslynmouth.co.uk
dir: Adjacent to A39 on Countisbury Hill just before entering Lynmouth from Minehead

PETS: Bedrooms unattended **Charges Public areas** except restaurant, luxury suite & pool area **Grounds Exercise area** surrounding woodland **Facilities** food (pre-bookable) food bowl water bowl

In an elevated position overlooking Lynmouth Bay, this friendly hotel is set in five acres of woodland. The majority of the bedrooms benefit from the superb views, as do the public areas which are generously proportioned and well presented. A fixed-price menu is offered with local, seasonal produce to the fore.

Rooms 31 (6 fmly) **S** £50-£205; **D** £80-£264 (incl. bkfst)* **Facilities** ⚲ Table tennis Pool table Xmas New Year **Conf** Class 40 Board 25 Thtr 60 **Services** Lift **Parking** 40 **Notes** Closed 4-31 Jan RS Oct-Apr Civ Wed 125

LYNMOUTH

Bath Hotel
★★ 69% HOTEL

☎ 01598 752238 📠 01598 753894
Sea Front EX35 6EL
e-mail: info@bathhotellynmouth.co.uk
dir: M5 junct 25, follow A39 to Lynmouth

PETS: Bedrooms unattended **Charges Public areas** except restaurant **Exercise area** 200yds **Facilities** food (pre-bookable) food bowl water bowl

This well-established, friendly hotel is situated near the harbour and offers lovely views from the attractive, sea-facing bedrooms and is an excellent starting point for scenic walks. There are two lounges and a sun lounge. The restaurant menu is extensive and features daily-changing specials that make good use of fresh produce and local fish.

Rooms 22 (9 fmly) **S** £39-£49; **D** £70-£100 (incl. bkfst)* **Parking** 12 **Notes** Closed Dec & Jan

LYNMOUTH

River Lyn View
★★★ GUEST ACCOMMODATION

☎ 01598 75350126
Watersmeet Rd EX35 6EP
e-mail: riverlynview@aol.com
dir: On A39, 200yds past St John's church on right

PETS: Bedrooms unattended **Public areas Facilities** water bowl

A warm welcome awaits at River Lyn View, just a stroll from the picturesque harbour at Lynmouth. Exmoor National Park is a short drive away or you can enjoy a walk along the East Lyn River's tranquil tree-lined banks. Much of the accommodation overlooks the river; all bedrooms are comfortable and include a good range of extras. There is a choice of lounges, and a hearty breakfast is served at individual tables in the open-plan dining area.

Rooms 4 en suite (2 fmly) **S** £30-£40; **D** £52-£60 **Facilities** FTV TVL tea/coffee Cen ht Wi-fi

LYNTON

Lynton Cottage Hotel
★★★ 75% ◉◉ HOTEL

☎ 01598 752342 🖷 01598 754016
Northwalk EX35 6ED
e-mail: mail@lyntoncottage.co.uk
dir: M5 junct 23 to Bridgwater, then A39 to
Minehead & follow signs to Lynton. 1st right after
church & right again

PETS: Bedrooms unattended **Charges Public
areas** except restaurant **Grounds Exercise area**
beach 1.5m **Facilities** water bowl **Resident Pets:**
Mango (Golden Retriever), Chloe & Charlie (cats)

Boasting breathtaking views, this wonderfully
relaxing and friendly hotel stands some 500 feet
above the sea and makes a peaceful hideaway.
Bedrooms are individual in style and size, with
the added bonus of the wonderful views; public
areas have charm and character in equal
measure. Accomplished cuisine is on offer with
dishes created with care and skill.

Rooms 16 (1 fmly) (1 GF) S £48-£78; D £76-£160
(incl. bkfst)* **Facilities** FTV Xmas **Parking** 20
Notes Closed 2 Dec-12 Jan

MORETONHAMPSTEAD

Cookshayes Country Guest House
★★★ GUEST HOUSE

☎ 01647 440374 🖷 01647 440453
33 Court St TQ13 8LG
e-mail: cookshayes@aol.co.uk
web: www.cookshayes.co.uk
dir: A38 onto A382 to Moretonhampstead. Take
B3212 towards Princetown. Cookshayes 400yds
on left

PETS: Bedrooms unattended **Charges Public
areas** except restaurant **Grounds Exercise
area Resident Pets:** Snitchy (Schnauzer cross),
Sammantha (Labrador)

A genuine welcome awaits at this secluded
Victorian house, a perfect base for exploring the
delights of Dartmoor. Bedrooms are comfortably
furnished and well appointed, and one has a
four-poster bed. The smart dining room is the
venue for scrumptious breakfasts and excellent
dinners, where local produce is cooked with skill
and enthusiasm. Additional facilities include
a cosy lounge, which overlooks the attractive
garden.

Rooms 7 rms (5 en suite) (1 fmly) (1 GF) S £25;
D £50-£55* **Facilities** TVL tea/coffee Dinner
available Cen ht Licensed **Conf** Max 16 Class 10
Board 10 **Parking** 10 **Notes** LB No Children 5yrs

OKEHAMPTON

White Hart
★★ 71% HOTEL

☎ 01837 52730 & 54514 📠 01837 53979
Fore St EX20 1HD
e-mail: enquiry@thewhitehart-hotel.com
dir: In town centre, adjacent to lights, car park
at rear of hotel

PETS: Bedrooms unattended Charges Public
areas except restaurant Exercise area 200yds

Dating back to the 17th century and situated
on the edge of the Dartmoor National Park, the
White Hart offers modern facilities. Bedrooms
are well equipped and spacious. Locally sourced,
home-cooked food is on offer in the bars and the
Courtney Restaurant, or guests can choose to
eat in Vines Pizzeria. Wi-fi is available in public
areas.

Rooms 19 (2 fmly) Facilities Xmas
Conf Class 30 Board 40 Thtr 100 Parking 20

PLYMOUTH

Best Western Duke of Cornwall
★★★ 78% ® HOTEL

☎ 01752 275850 & 275855 📠 01752 275854
Millbay Rd PL1 3LG
e-mail: enquiries@thedukeofcornwall.co.uk
web: www.thedukeofcornwall.co.uk
dir: Follow city centre, then Plymouth Pavilions
Conference & Leisure Centre signs. Hotel opposite
Plymouth Pavilions

PETS: Bedrooms unattended Charges Public
areas Exercise area park 50yds Facilities water
bowl

A historic landmark, this city centre hotel is
conveniently located. The spacious public areas
include a popular bar, comfortable lounge and
multi-functional ballroom. Bedrooms, many
with far reaching views, are individually styled
and comfortably appointed. The range of dining
options includes meals in the bar, or guests
might choose the elegant dining room for a more
formal atmosphere.

Rooms 71 (6 fmly) (20 smoking) S £65-£104;
D £78-£120 (incl. bkfst) Facilities STV FTV Xmas
New Year Wi-fi Conf Class 125 Board 84 Thtr 300
Del from £160 to £190* Services Lift Parking 50
Notes LB Civ Wed 300

SALCOMBE

Tides Reach
★★★ 82% ☻ HOTEL

☎ 01548 843466 📄 01548 843954
South Sands TQ8 8LJ
e-mail: enquire@tidesreach.com
web: www.tidesreach.com
dir: Off A38 at Buckfastleigh to Totnes. Then
A381 to Salcombe, follow signs to South Sands

PETS: Bedrooms unattended **Charges Public
areas** except, bar, restaurant & 2 lounges
Grounds Exercise area adjacent **Facilities** food
(pre-bookable) **Other** dogs accepted by prior
arrangement only

Superbly situated at the water's edge, this
personally run, friendly hotel has splendid views
of the estuary and beach. Bedrooms, many with
balconies, are spacious and comfortable. In the
bar and lounge, attentive service can be enjoyed
along with the view, and the Garden Room
restaurant serves appetising and accomplished
cuisine.

Rooms 35 (7 fmly) **S** £77-£150; **D** £128-£310
(incl. bkfst & dinner)* **Facilities Spa** FTV ⓒ
supervised Gym Squash Windsurfing Sailing
Kayaking Scuba diving Hair & beauty treatment
♫ Wi-fi **Services** Lift **Parking** 100 **Notes** LB No
children 8yrs Closed Dec-early Feb

SOURTON

Collaven Manor
★★ 79% COUNTRY HOUSE HOTEL

☎ 01837 861522 📄 01837 861614
EX20 4HH
e-mail: collavenmanor@supanet.com
dir: A30 onto A386 to Tavistock, hotel 2m on right

PETS: Bedrooms unattended **Charges Public
areas Grounds Exercise area** accessed directly
from grounds **Facilities** food bowl water bowl
Other food by prior arrangement **Restrictions**
no Dobermans, Rottweilers or Pit Bulls **Resident
Pets:** Willow, Jas & Jack (cats)

This delightful 15th-century manor house is
quietly located in five acres of well-tended
grounds. The friendly proprietors provide
attentive service and ensure a relaxing
environment. Charming public rooms have old
oak beams and granite fireplaces, and provide a
range of comfortable lounges and a well stocked
bar. In the restaurant, a daily-changing menu
offers interesting dishes.

Rooms 9 (1 fmly) **S** £59-£65; **D** £98-£146 (incl.
bkfst)* **Facilities** FTV 🍴 Bowls **Conf** Class 20
Board 16 Thtr 30 Del from £98 to £125*
Parking 50 **Notes** LB Closed Dec-Jan Civ Wed 50

SOUTH BRENT

Glazebrook House Hotel
★★ 76% ® HOTEL

☎ 01364 73322 📄 01364 72350
TQ10 9JE
e-mail: enquiries@glazebrookhouse.com
web: www.glazebrookhouse.com
dir: Exit A38 at South Brent, follow brown signs
to hotel

PETS: Bedrooms unattended Charges Public
areas except restaurant Grounds Exercise
area 0.5m Restrictions only well behaved dogs
accepted Resident Pets: Bobby (Pointer/Collie
cross), Sly (cat)

Enjoying a tranquil and convenient location next
to the Dartmoor National Park and set within
four acres of gardens, this 18th-century former
gentleman's residence offers a friendly welcome
and comfortable accommodation. Elegant public
areas provide ample space to relax and enjoy the
atmosphere, whilst bedrooms are well appointed
and include a number with four-poster beds. The
dishes on the menus are created from interesting
combinations of fresh, locally-sourced produce.

Rooms 10 S £50-£55; D £80-£125 (incl. bkfst)*
Facilities FTV Xmas New Year Wi-fi Conf Class 60
Board 40 Thtr 80 Del from £82.70 to £90*
Parking 40 Notes LB Closed 2-18 Jan RS 1 wk
Aug Civ Wed 80

THURLESTONE

Thurlestone
★★★★ 81% ® HOTEL

☎ 01548 560382 📄 01548 561069
TQ7 3NN
e-mail: enquiries@thurlestone.co.uk
web: www.thurlestone.co.uk
dir: A38, A384 to Totnes, A381 towards
Kingsbridge, A379 towards Churchstow, onto
B3197 turn into lane signed to Thurlestone

PETS: Bedrooms unattended Charges Public
areas front foyer only Grounds Exercise area
Facilities food (pre-bookable) water bowl

This perennially popular hotel has been in the
same family-ownership since 1896 and continues
to go from strength to strength. A vast range of
facilities is available for all the family. Bedrooms
are equipped to ensure a comfortable stay; many
have wonderful views of the coast. Eating options
include a stylish restaurant with stunning views.

Rooms 64 (23 fmly) S £66-£140; D £132-£372
(incl. bkfst)* Facilities STV ⊕ � supervised ⋆ 9
⛳ Putt green ⋆ Gym Squash Badminton courts
Games room Toddler room Snooker room ♫ Xmas
New Year Wi-fi Child facilities Conf Class 100
Board 40 Thtr 150 Del from £130 to £280*
Services Lift Parking 121 Notes LB Closed 1-2
wks Jan Civ Wed 180

TORQUAY

Barceló Torquay Imperial Hotel
★★★★ 79% HOTEL

☎ 01803 294301 ▤ 01803 298293
Park Hill Rd TQ1 2DG
e-mail: imperialtorquay@barcelo-hotels.co.uk
web: www.barcelo-hotels.co.uk
dir: A380 towards seafront. Turn left to harbour, at clocktower right. Hotel 300yds on right

PETS: Bedrooms unattended **Charges Public areas Grounds Exercise area** 100yds **Facilities** food bowl water bowl **Restrictions** small to medium size dogs only

This hotel has an enviable location with extensive views of the coastline. Traditional in style, the public areas are elegant and offer a choice of dining options including the Regatta Restaurant, with its stunning views over the bay. Bedrooms are spacious, most with private balconies, and the hotel has an extensive range of indoor and outdoor leisure facilities.

Rooms 152 (14 fmly) **Facilities Spa** STV ⊗ ↝ supervised ⊛ **Gym** Squash Beauty salon Hairdresser Steam room ♫ Xmas New Year Wi-fi **Conf Class** 200 **Board** 30 **Thtr** 350 **Del** from £100* **Services Lift Parking** 140 **Notes** Civ Wed 250

TORQUAY

Red House Hotel
★★ 71% HOTEL

☎ 01803 607811 ▤ 0871 5289455
Rousdown Rd, Chelston TQ2 6PB
e-mail: stay@redhouse-hotel.co.uk
web: www.redhouse-hotel.co.uk
dir: Follow signs for seafront & Chelston, turn into Avenue Rd, right at 1st lights. Pass shops & church, next left. Hotel on right

PETS: Bedrooms unattended **Charges Public areas** except restaurant & lounge **Grounds Exercise area** 100yds **Restrictions** small - medium size dogs only **Resident Pet:** Jemima (cat)

Set just a few minutes drive from Torquay town and the seafront, this hotel is in an ideal location to explore the Torbay area. The hotel offers comfortably appointed bedrooms, and facilities include indoor and outdoor swimming pools, plus a gym, sauna, steam room and a treatment room.

Rooms 9 (3 fmly) **Facilities** ⊗ ↝ Gym Sun shower Beauty room Sauna Xmas New Year **Parking** 9 **Notes** LB

TORQUAY

Shelley Court

★★ 68% HOTEL

☎ 01803 295642 🖷 01803 215793
29 Croft Rd TQ2 5UD
e-mail: shelleycourthotel@hotmail.com
dir: From B3199 up Shedden Hill Rd, 1st left into
Croft Rd

PETS: Bedrooms unattended **Charges Public
areas** except dining room **Grounds Exercise
area** adjacent **Resident Pets:** Jack (Parson Jack
Russell), Vera (Jack Russell)

This hotel, popular with groups, is located
in a pleasant, quiet area that overlooks the
town towards Torbay. With a friendly team of
staff, many guests return here time and again.
Entertainment is provided most evenings in the
season. Bedrooms come in a range of sizes and
there is a large and comfortable lounge bar.

Rooms 27 (3 fmly) (6 GF) (incl. bkfst & dinner)
Facilities FTV 🍴 Pool table Indoor skittle alley
🎵 Xmas New Year **Parking** 20 **Notes** LB Closed
4 Jan-10 Feb

TWO BRIDGES

Two Bridges Hotel

★★★ 77% ⊛ HOTEL

☎ 01822 890581 🖷 01822 892306
PL20 6SW
e-mail: enquiries@twobridges.co.uk
web: www.twobridges.co.uk
dir: At junct of B3212 & B3357

PETS: Bedrooms unattended **Public areas** except
restaurant **Grounds Exercise area** Dartmoor
Facilities water bowl

This wonderfully relaxing hotel is set in the heart
of the Dartmoor National Park, in a beautiful
riverside location. Three standards of comfortable
rooms provide every modern convenience, and
include four-poster rooms. There is a choice
of lounges and fine dining is available in the
restaurant, where menus feature local game and
seasonal produce.

Rooms 33 (2 fmly) (6 GF) **S** £70-£95;
D £140-£190 (incl. bkfst) **Facilities** STV Fishing
Xmas New Year Child facilities **Conf** Class 60
Board 40 Thtr 130 Del from £110 to £140
Parking 100 **Notes** LB Civ Wed 130

TWO BRIDGES

Prince Hall

★★ 85% ⚜⚜ COUNTRY HOUSE HOTEL

☎ 01822 890403 📠 01822 890676
PrinceTown PL20 6SA
e-mail: info@princehall.co.uk
dir: On B3357 1m E of Two Bridges road junct

PETS: Bedrooms unattended Public areas except
restaurant Grounds Exercise area adjacent
Facilities food (pre-bookable) water bowl
Resident Pets: Lily (Retriever Collie cross), Poppy
(Retriever)

Charm, peace and relaxed informality pervade at
this small hotel, which has a stunning location
at the heart of Dartmoor. Bedrooms, each named
after a Dartmoor tor, have been equipped with
thoughtful extras. The history of this house
and its location are reflected throughout the
public areas, which are very comfortable. The
accomplished cooking is memorable. Dogs are
welcomed here as warmly as their owners.

Rooms 8 (1 fmly) D £80-£160 (incl. bkfst)*
Facilities FTV Xmas New Year Wi-fi Conf Class 25
Board 20 Del from £120 to £180* Parking 12
Notes LB No children 10yrs Civ Wed 40

WESTWARD HO!

Culloden House

★★★ GUEST HOUSE

☎ 01237 479421
Fosketh Hill EX39 1UL
e-mail: theAA@culloden-house.co.uk
web: www.culloden-house.co.uk
dir: S of town centre. Off B3236 Stanwell Hill onto
Fosketh Hill

PETS: Bedrooms unattended Charges Public
areas except dining room Grounds Exercise area
short walk Other dogs allowed unattended in
bedrooms by arrrangement only

A warm welcome is assured in this family-
friendly Victorian property which stands on
a wooded hillside with sweeping views over
the beach and coast. Guests can relax in the
spacious lounge with its log-burning fire and
enjoy the wonderful sea views.

Rooms 7 en suite (3 fmly) (1 GF) S £40-£50;
D £60-£70* Facilities FTV tea/coffee Cen ht
Parking 4 Notes Closed Xmas & New Year RS
Nov-Feb

YELVERTON

Moorland Links
★★★ 75% HOTEL

☎ 01822 852245 🖹 01822 855004
PL20 6DA
e-mail: moorland.links@forestdale.com
web: www.moorlandlinkshotel.co.uk
dir: A38 from Exeter to Plymouth, then A386
towards Tavistock. 5m onto open moorland, hotel
1m on left

PETS: Bedrooms unattended Charges Public
areas except restaurant Grounds Exercise area
open moorland Facilities food (pre-bookable)
water bowl

Set in nine acres in the Dartmoor National Park,
this hotel offers spectacular views from many
of the rooms across open moorland and the
Tamar Valley. Bedrooms are well equipped and
comfortably furnished, and some rooms have
open balconies. The stylish restaurant looks out
over the oak fringed lawns.

Rooms 44 (4 fmly) (17 GF) S £65-£80;
D £80-£140 (incl. bkfst)* Facilities FTV ⅊ Xmas
New Year Wi-fi Conf Class 60 Board 50 Thtr 170
Parking 120 Notes Civ Wed 80

BLANDFORD FORUM

The Anvil Inn
★★★★ INN

☎ 01258 453431 🖹 01258 480182
Salisbury Rd, Pimperne DT11 8UQ
e-mail: theanvil.inn@btconnect.com
dir: 2m NE of Blandford on A354 in Pimperne

PETS: Bedrooms unattended Charges Public
areas only in bar Grounds Exercise area

Located in a village near Blandford, this 16th-
century thatched inn provides a traditional
country welcome. Bedrooms have been
refurbished to high standards. Dinner is a varied
selection of home-made dishes, plus there is a
tempting variety of hand-pulled ales and wines
by the glass.

Rooms 12 en suite Facilities STV tea/coffee
Dinner available Direct Dial Cen ht Parking 18
Notes LB No coaches

Carrington House

★★★ 77% HOTEL

☎ 01202 369988 🖷 01202 292221
31 Knyveton Rd BH1 3QQ
e-mail: carrington.house@forestdale.com
web: www.carringtonhousehotel.co.uk
dir: A338 at St Paul's rdbt, 200mtrs & left into
Knyveton Rd. Hotel 400mtrs on right

PETS: **Bedrooms** unattended **Charges Public
areas** except restaurant **Facilities** food (pre-
bookable)

This hotel occupies a prominent position on a
tree-lined avenue and a short walk from the
seafront. The bedrooms are comfortable, well
equipped and include many purpose-built
family rooms. There are two dining options,
Mortimers restaurant, and the Kings bar which
serves light meals and snacks. Guests can
relax in the comfortable lounge areas whilst the
leisure complex offers a whole host of activities
including a heated swimming pool.

Rooms 145 (42 fmly) (2 GF) S £60-£80;
D £100-£140 (incl. bkfst)* Facilities FTV ⓧ
Children's play area Xmas New Year Wi-fi
Conf Class 250 Board 110 Thtr 500 Services Lift
Parking 85 Notes Civ Wed 60

Wessex

★★★ 77% HOTEL

☎ 01202 551911 🖷 01202 297354
West Cliff Rd BH2 5EU
e-mail: wessex@forestdale.com
web: www.thewessexhotel.co.uk
dir: Follow M27/A35 or A338 from Dorchester &
A347 N. Hotel on West Cliff side of town

PETS: **Bedrooms** unattended **Charges Public
areas** except restaurant **Grounds Facilities** food
(pre-bookable)

Centrally located and handy for the beach, the
Wessex is a popular, relaxing hotel. Bedrooms
are well equipped and comfortable with a range
of modern amenities. The Lulworth restaurant
provides a range of appetizing dishes. The
excellent leisure facilities boast both indoor and
outdoor pools, sauna, ample function rooms and
an open-plan bar and lounge.

Rooms 109 (32 fmly) (17 GF) S £65-£90;
D £110-£170 (incl. bkfst)* Facilities FTV ⓧ
↖ Gym Table tennis Xmas New Year Wi-fi
Conf Class 150 Board 100 Thtr 400 Services Lift
Parking 160 Notes Civ Wed 200

BOURNEMOUTH

Burley Court
★★★ 66% HOTEL

☎ 01202 552824 & 556704 📠 01202 298514
Bath Rd BH1 2NP
e-mail: info@burleycourthotel.co.uk
dir: Leave A338 at St Paul's rdbt, take 3rd exit at next rdbt into Holdenhurst Rd. 3rd exit at next rdbt into Bath Rd, over crossing, 1st left

PETS: Bedrooms unattended Charges Public areas Exercise area 50mtrs Facilities food (pre-bookable) food bowl water bowl

Located on Bournemouth's West Cliff, this well-established hotel is easily located and convenient for the town and beaches. Bedrooms are pleasantly furnished and decorated in bright colours. A daily-changing menu is served in the spacious dining room.

Rooms 38 (8 fmly) (4 GF) Facilities ⟲ Xmas Conf Class 15 Board 15 Thtr 30 Services Lift Parking 35 Notes Closed 30 Dec-14 Jan RS 15-31 Jan

BOURNEMOUTH

Tower House
★★ 76% HOTEL

☎ 01202 290742 & 299311 📠 01202 553305
West Cliff Gardens BH2 5HP
e-mail: towerhouse.hotel@btconnect.com

PETS: Bedrooms unattended Charges Public areas Grounds

A popular family owned and run hotel on the West Cliff. Owners and their staff are friendly and helpful, rooms are comfortable and well maintained and it has good off-road parking.

Rooms 32 (12 fmly) (3 GF) S £29-£46; D £58-£92 (incl. bkfst)* Facilities FTV Xmas New Year Wi-fi Services Lift Parking 30

BRIDPORT

Bridge House Hotel
★★ 76% HOTEL

☎ 01308 423371 📄 01308 459573
115 East St DT6 3LB
e-mail: info@bridgehousebridport.co.uk
dir: Follow signs to town centre from A35 rdbt, hotel 200mtrs on right

PETS: Bedrooms unattended **Charges Public areas** except restaurant; dogs must be well behaved **Grounds Exercise area** park adjacent

A short stroll from the town centre, this 18th-century Grade II listed property offers well-equipped bedrooms that vary in size. In addition to the main lounge, there is a small bar-lounge and a separate breakfast room. An interesting range of home-cooked meals is provided in the newly created wine bar and brasserie.

Rooms 10 (3 fmly) **S** £65-£89; **D** £89-£134 (incl. bkfst) **Facilities** FTV Complimentary membership to leisure park New Year Wi-fi **Conf** Class 20 Board 15 **Parking** 13 **Notes** LB

BRIDPORT

The Shave Cross Inn
★★★★★ 🏠 INN

☎ 01308 868358 📄 01308 867064
Marshwood Vale DT6 6HW
e-mail: roy.warburton@virgin.net
web: www.theshavecrossinn.co.uk
dir: From B3165 turn at Birdsmoorgate, follow brown signs

PETS: Bedrooms unattended **Charges Public areas** allowed in bar but not restaurant **Grounds Exercise area** walks adjacent **Restrictions** no Pit Bulls, Rottweilers, Dobermans etc **Resident Pets:** Luck, Liddy, Lotty (Great Danes), Libby & Dillon (horses)

This historic inn continues to offer a warm and genuine welcome. The snug bar is dominated by a wonderful fireplace with crackling logs. Bedrooms are located in a separate building. Quality is impressive throughout with wonderful stone floors and oak beams, combined with feature beds and luxurious bathrooms. Food has a distinct Caribbean and International slant.

Rooms 7 en suite (1 fmly) (3 GF) **Facilities** STV FTV tea/coffee Dinner available Direct Dial Cen ht Wi-fi Pool Table **Parking** 29 **Notes** No Children RS Mon (ex BH) Closed for lunch & dinner No coaches

CHRISTCHURCH

Christchurch Harbour Hotel
★★★★ 82% ◉◉ HOTEL

☎ 01202 483434 📄 01202 479004
95 Mudeford BH23 3NT
e-mail: christchurch@harbourhotels.co.uk
web: www.christchurch-harbour-hotel.co.uk
dir: A35 to Christchurch, A337 to Highcliffe.
Right at rdbt, hotel 1.5m on left

PETS: **Bedrooms** unattended **Charges Public
areas** except restaurant **Grounds Exercise area**
beach

Delightfully situated on Mudeford Quay close
to sandy beaches and conveniently located for
Bournemouth Airport and the BIC. After a multi-
million pound refurbishment, the hotel boasts
now an impressive spa and leisure facility. The
bedrooms are particularly well appointed and
stylishly finished; many have excellent views
and some have balconies. Guests can eat in the
Harbour Restaurant, or the waterside Rhodes
South - the latest enterprise of Gary Rhodes.

Rooms 64 (7 fmly) (14 GF) **D** £110-£270 (incl.
bkfst)* **Facilities** Spa FTV 🕲 Gym Steam room
Sauna Exercise classes Hydrotherapy pool 🎵
Xmas New Year Wi-fi **Conf** Class 20 Board 24
Thtr 70 Del from £155 to £255* **Services** Lift
Parking 55 **Notes** Civ Wed 80

CHRISTCHURCH

Captain's Club Hotel and Spa
★★★★ 80% ◉◉ HOTEL

☎ 01202 475111 📄 01202 490111
Wick Ferry, Wick Ln BH23 1HU
e-mail: enquiries@captainsclubhotel.com
web: www.captainsclubhotel.com
dir: B3073 to Christchurch. On Fountain rdbt take
5th exit (Sopers Ln) 2nd left (St Margarets Ave)
1st right onto Wick Ln

PETS: **Bedrooms** unattended **Charges Public
areas** outside terrace area only **Grounds
Exercise area** 2 min walk **Restrictions** small -
medium size dogs only

Situated in the heart of the town on the banks of
the River Stour at Christchurch Quay, and only
ten minutes from Bournemouth. All bedrooms,
including the suites and apartments have views
overlooking the river. Guests can relax in the
hydrotherapy pool, enjoy a spa treatment or enjoy
the cuisine in Tides Restaurant.

Rooms 29 (12 fmly) **S** £125-£169; **D** £149-£199
(incl. bkfst)* **Facilities** Spa FTV Hydrotherapy pool Sauna 🎵 Xmas New Year Wi-fi
Conf Class 72 Board 64 Thtr 140 Del from £165
to £195* **Services** Lift Air con **Parking** 41
Notes LB Civ Wed 80

LOWER ANSTY

The Fox Inn
★★★★ INN

☎ 01258 880328 📠 01258 881440
DT2 7PN
e-mail: fox@anstyfoxinn.co.uk
web: www.anstyfoxinn.co.uk
dir: Off A354 at Millbourne St Andrew, follow brown signs to Ansty

PETS: Bedrooms unattended Charges Public areas bar only Grounds Exercise area public footpath 200yds Facilities food bowl water bowl Resident Pet: Reggie (Labrador)

This popular inn has a long and interesting history including strong links to the Hall and Woodhouse brewery. Surrounded by beautiful Dorset countryside, this is a great base for exploring the area. Bedrooms are smartly appointed and offer generous levels of comfort. The interesting menu focuses on excellent local produce, with a choice of dining options including the oak-panelled dining room. An extensive garden and patio area is also available.

Rooms 11 en suite (7 fmly) S £45-£100; D £55-£105 Facilities TVL tea/coffee Dinner available Cen ht ✤ Conf Max 60 Thtr 60 Class 40 Board 45 Parking 30 Notes LB

POOLE

Hotel du Vin Poole
★★★★ 78% ❀ HOTEL

☎ 01202 758570 📠 01202 758571
Thames St BH15 1JN
e-mail: info.poole@hotelduvin.com
web: www.hotelduvin.com
dir: A31 to Poole, follow channel ferry signs. Left at Poole bridge onto Poole Quay, 1st left into Thames St. Hotel opposite St James Church

PETS: Bedrooms unattended Charges Public areas except Bistro (restaurant) Exercise area 0.25m

Offering a fresh approach to the well established company style, this property boasts some delightful rooms packed with comfort and all the expected Hotel du Vin features. Situated near the harbour the hotel offers nautically-themed bedrooms and suites that have plasma TVs, DVD players and bathrooms with power showers. The public rooms have been transformed into light and open spaces, and as with the other hotels in this group the bar and restaurant form centre stage.

Rooms 38 (4 GF) D £170-£400 (incl. bkfst)* Facilities STV Xmas New Year Wi-fi Conf Class 20 Board 20 Thtr 35 Del from £170 to £210* Services Air con Notes LB Civ Wed 40

POOLE

Salterns Harbourside Hotel
★★★ 71% HOTEL

☎ 01202 707321 📠 01202 707488
38 Salterns Way, Lilliput BH14 8JR
e-mail: reception@salterns-hotel.co.uk
web: www.salterns-hotel.co.uk
dir: In Poole follow B3369 Sandbanks road. 1m at Lilliput shops turn into Salterns Way by Barclays Bank

PETS: Bedrooms unattended Charges Public areas except restaurant Exercise area 0.5m

Located next to the marina with superb views across to Brownsea Island, this modernised hotel used to be the headquarters for the flying boats in WWII and was later a yacht club. Bedrooms are spacious and some have private balconies, whilst the busy bar and restaurant both share harbour views.

Rooms 20 (4 fmly) S £75-£125; D £85-£135 (incl. bkfst)* Facilities Wi-fi Conf Class 50 Board 30 Thtr 100 Del from £115 to £130* Parking 40 Notes Civ Wed 120

SHAFTESBURY

Best Western Royal Chase Hotel
★★★ 71% ⚛ HOTEL

☎ 01747 853355 📠 01747 851969
Royal Chase Roundabout SP7 8DB
e-mail: royalchasehotel@btinternet.com
web: www.theroyalchasehotel.co.uk
dir: A303 to A350 signed Blandford Forum. Avoid town centre, follow road to 3rd rdbt

PETS: Bedrooms unattended Charges Public areas except bar & restaurant Grounds

Equally suitable for both leisure and business guests, this well-known local landmark is situated close to the famous Gold Hill. Both Standard and Crown bedrooms offer good levels of comfort and quality. In addition to the fixed-price menu in the Byzant Restaurant, guests have the option of eating more informally in the convivial bar.

Rooms 33 (13 fmly) (6 GF) S £54-£160; D £54-£160* Facilities ⓣ Turkish steam room Wi-fi Conf Class 90 Board 50 Thtr 180 Del from £105 to £117.50* Parking 100 Notes LB Civ Wed 76

SWANAGE

The Pines
★★★ 77% HOTEL

☎ 01929 425211 📠 01929 422075

Burlington Rd BH19 1LT
e-mail: reservations@pineshotel.co.uk
web: www.pineshotel.co.uk
dir: A351 to seafront, left then 2nd right. Hotel at end of road

PETS: Bedrooms unattended **Public areas Grounds Exercise area**

Enjoying a peaceful location with spectacular views over the cliffs and sea, The Pines is a pleasant place to stay. Many of the comfortable bedrooms have sea views. Guests can take tea in the lounge, enjoy appetising bar snacks in the attractive bar, and interesting and accomplished cuisine in the restaurant.

Rooms 41 (26 fmly) (6 GF) **S** £59-£105; **D** £118-£162 (incl. bkfst)* **Facilities** ♫ Xmas New Year Wi-fi **Conf** Class 80 Board 80 Thtr 80 Del from £94.20* **Services** Lift **Parking** 60 **Notes** LB

WEST BEXINGTON

The Manor Hotel
★★ 74% HOTEL

☎ 01308 897616 📠 01308 897704

Beach Rd DT2 9DF
e-mail: themanorhotel@btconnect.com
dir: B3157 to Burton Bradstock, continue to The Bull public house in Swire. Immediately right to West Bexington

PETS: Bedrooms unattended **Charges Public areas** except restaurant **Grounds Exercise area** 5 mins to beach & countryside

Surrounded by scenic splendour and just a short stroll from the magnificent sweep of Chesil Beach, the atmosphere is relaxed and welcoming with snug lounges and crackling wood fires. Bedrooms are individual in style, many with wonderful sea views and the sound of waves in the background. With an abundance of excellent local produce, dining here, in either the convivial Cellar Bar, or the elegant dining room is recommended.

Rooms 13 (2 fmly) **Facilities** Xmas New Year **Conf** Class 40 Board 40 Thtr 40 **Parking** 80 **Notes** Civ Wed 65

WEST LULWORTH

Cromwell House

★★ 75% HOTEL

☎ 01929 400253 & 400332 📄 01929 400566
Lulworth Cove BH20 5RJ
e-mail: catriona@lulworthcove.co.uk
web: www.lulworthcove.co.uk
dir: 200yds beyond end of West Lulworth, left
onto high slip road, hotel 100yds on left opposite
beach car park

PETS: Bedrooms unattended Charges Public
areas except dining room Grounds Exercise area
adjacent Facilities water bowl Resident Pets:
Jaldi (Springer Spaniel), Douglas (Bearded Collie
cross), Lily (cat)

Built in 1881 by the Mayor of Weymouth,
specifically as a guest house, this family-run
hotel now provides visitors with an ideal base for
touring the area and for exploring the beaches
and coast. The house enjoys spectacular views
across the sea and countryside. Bedrooms, many
with sea views, are comfortable and some have
been specifically designed for family use.

Rooms 18 (1 annexe) (3 fmly) (2 GF) S £40-£60;
D £80-£102 (incl. bkfst)* Facilities ↖ Access
to Dorset coastal footpath & Jurassic Coast Wi-fi
Parking 17 Notes LB Closed 22 Dec-3 Jan

DARLINGTON

Headlam Hall

★★★ 85% ◉ HOTEL

☎ 01325 730238 📄 01325 730790
Headlam, Gainford DL2 3HA
e-mail: admin@headlamhall.co.uk
web: www.headlamhall.co.uk
dir: 2m N of A67 between Piercebridge & Gainford

PETS: Bedrooms unattended Charges Public
areas Grounds Exercise area 50yds Facilities
water bowl Other dogs allowed in certain
bedrooms only; dogs not to be fed in bedrooms
Restrictions small & medium size dogs only;
no Rottweilers, Dobermans, Alsatians or similar
breeds

This impressive Jacobean hall lies in farmland
and has its own 9-hole golf course. The main
house retains many historical features, including
flagstone floors and a pillared hall. Bedrooms
are well proportioned and traditionally styled; a
converted coach house contains the more modern
rooms. The hotel is popular as a wedding venue
and there is a stunning spa complex.

Rooms 40 (22 annexe) (4 fmly) (10 GF)
S £90-£115; D £115-£190 (incl. bkfst)*
Facilities Spa STV ⊕ ⅃ 9 ⛳ Putt green Fishing
⛹ Gym New Year Wi-fi Conf Class 40 Board 40
Thtr 120 Del from £135* Services Lift Parking 80
Notes LB Closed 24-26 Dec Civ Wed 150

GREAT CHESTERFORD

The Crown House
★★★ 74% ☺ HOTEL

☎ 01799 530515 📠 01799 530683
CB10 1NY
e-mail: reservations@crownhousehotel.com
web: www.crownhousehotel.com
dir: From N exit M11 at junct 9, from S junct 10, follow signs for Saffron Walden & then Great Chesterford (B1383)

PETS: Bedrooms unattended Charges Public areas lounge only Grounds

This Georgian coaching inn, situated in a peaceful village close to the M11, has been sympathetically restored and retains much original character. The bedrooms are well equipped and individually decorated; some rooms have delightful four-poster beds. Public rooms include an attractive lounge bar, an elegant oak-panelled restaurant and an airy conservatory.

Rooms 22 (14 annexe) (2 fmly) (5 GF) Facilities New Year Wi-fi Conf Class 14 Board 12 Thtr 30 Del from £110 to £130 Parking 30 Notes Closed 27-30 Dec Civ Wed 50

BIBURY

Swan Hotel
★★★ 82% ☺ HOTEL

☎ 01285 740695 📠 01285 740473
GL7 5NW
e-mail: info@swanhotel.co.uk
web: www.cotswold-inns-hotels.co.uk
dir: 9m S of Burford A40 onto B4425. 6m N of Cirencester A4179 onto B4425

PETS: Bedrooms unattended Charges Public areas except eating areas

This hotel, built in the 17th century as a coaching inn, is set in peaceful and picturesque surroundings. It provides well-equipped and smartly presented accommodation, including four luxury cottage suites set just outside the main hotel. The elegant public areas are comfortable and have feature fireplaces. There is a choice of dining options to suit all tastes.

Rooms 22 (4 annexe) (1 fmly) Facilities Fishing Xmas New Year Wi-fi Conf Class 50 Board 32 Thtr 80 Services Lift Parking 22 Notes Civ Wed 110

BOURTON-ON-THE-WATER

Chester House Hotel
★★ 79% HOTEL

☎ 01451 820286 📠 01451 820471
Victoria St GL54 2BU
e-mail: info@chesterhousehotel.com
dir: On A429 between Northleach &
Stow-on-the-Wold

PETS: Bedrooms unattended **Charges Public areas** except dining areas **Grounds Exercise area** 300mtrs **Resident Pets:** Poppy (Patterdale Terrier)

This hotel occupies a secluded but central location in this delightful Cotswold village. Rooms, some at ground floor level, are situated in the main house and adjoining coach house. The public areas are stylish, light and airy. Breakfast is taken in the main building whereas dinner is served in the attractive restaurant just a few yards away.

Rooms 22 (10 annexe) (8 fmly) (8 GF)
D £85-£120 (incl. bkfst)* **Facilities** Beauty therapist New Year Wi-fi **Parking** 18
Notes Closed 7 Jan-1 Feb

CHELTENHAM

Hotel du Vin Cheltenham
★★★★ 80% ◉ HOTEL

☎ 01242 588450 📠 01242 588455
Parabola Rd GL50 3AQ
e-mail: info@cheltenham.hotelduvin.com
web: www.hotelduvin.com
dir: M5 junct 11, follow signs for city centre. At rdbt opposite Morgan Estate Agents take 2nd left, 200mtrs to Parabola Rd

PETS: Bedrooms unattended **Charges Public areas** except bistro **Exercise area** 10 mins walk **Facilities** food bowl water bowl

This hotel, in the Montpellier area of the town, has spacious public areas that are packed with stylish features. The pewter-topped bar has comfortable seating and the spacious restaurant has all the characteristic Hotel du Vin trademark design in evidence; alfresco dining is possible on the extensive terrace area. Bedrooms are very comfortable, with Egyptian linen, deep baths and power showers. The spa is the ideal place to relax and unwind. Although parking is limited, it is a definite bonus. Service is friendly and attentive.

Rooms 49 (2 fmly) (5 GF) **Facilities** Spa STV Wi-fi **Conf** Class 12 Board 12 Thtr 20 **Services** Lift Air con **Parking** 26 **Notes** LB

CHELTENHAM

Charlton Kings Hotel

★★★ 74% SMALL HOTEL

☎ 01242 231061 📠 01242 241900

London Rd, Charlton Kings GL52 6UU

e-mail: enquiries@charltonkingshotel.co.uk

dir: Enter Cheltenham from Oxford on A40, 1st on left

PETS: Bedrooms unattended **Public areas** except restaurant **Grounds Exercise area** 100yds **Resident Pet:** Charlie (Collie cross)

Personally run by the resident proprietors, the relatively small size of this hotel enables a good deal of individual guest care and attention. Bedrooms are very well decorated and furnished and include some welcome extras. Breakfast and dinner, served in the comfortable conservatory-style restaurant, offer a good selection of carefully prepared ingredients. There's a pleasant garden and rear car park.

Rooms 13 (4 GF) **S** £65-£85; **D** £95-£115 (incl. bkfst)* **Facilities** STV Wi-fi **Parking** 15 **Notes** LB

CHELTENHAM

Hope Orchard

★★★★ GUEST ACCOMMODATION

☎ 01452 855556 📠 01452 530037

Gloucester Rd, Staverton GL51 0TF

e-mail: info@hopeorchard.com

web: www.hopeorchard.com

dir: A40 onto B4063 at Arlecourt rdbt, Hope Orchard 1.25m on right

PETS: Bedrooms unattended **Charges Public areas Grounds Exercise area Facilities** food bowl water bowl **Other** local kennel can provide day sitting service **Resident Pets:** Toby (Staffordshire Bull Terrier), Jessie, Jasper & Louis (cats)

Situated midway between Gloucester and Cheltenham, Hope Orchard is a good base for exploring the area. The comfortable bedrooms are next to the main house, and all are on the ground floor and have their own separate entrances. There is a large garden, and ample off-road parking is available.

Rooms 8 en suite (8 GF) **Facilities** FTV tea/coffee Direct Dial Cen ht Wi-fi **Parking** 10

CHELTENHAM

White Lodge
★★★★ GUEST ACCOMMODATION

☎ 01242 242347 📄 01242 242347
Hatherley Ln GL51 6SH
e-mail: pamela@whitelodgebandb.wanadoo.co.uk
dir: M5 junct 11, A40 to Cheltenham, 1st rdbt 4th exit Hatherley Ln, White Lodge 1st on right

PETS: Bedrooms unattended Charges Public areas except dining room Grounds Exercise area

Built around 1900, this well cared for, smart and friendly establishment is convenient for access to the M5. Bedrooms, of varied size, offer quality and many extra facilities, including fridges and Wi-fi. The very comfortable dining room, where breakfast is served around a grand table, looks out across the pleasant backdrop of White Lodge's extensive gardens.

Rooms 4 en suite (1 GF) S £42-£45; D £60-£65 Facilities FTV tea/coffee Cen ht Wi-fi Parking 6 Notes ⊛

CHIPPING CAMPDEN

Three Ways House
★★★ 81% ⊛ HOTEL

☎ 01386 438429 📄 01386 438118
Mickleton GL55 6SB
e-mail: reception@puddingclub.com
web: www.puddingclub.com
dir: In Mickleton centre, on B4632 (Stratford-upon-Avon to Broadway road)

PETS: Bedrooms unattended Public areas Grounds Exercise area 100mtrs Facilities water bowl

Built in 1870, this charming hotel has welcomed guests for over 100 years and is home to the world famous Pudding Club, formed in 1985 to promote traditional English puddings. Individuality is a hallmark here, as reflected in a number of the bedrooms that have been styled around to a pudding theme. Public areas are stylish and include the air-conditioned restaurant, lounges and meeting rooms.

Rooms 48 (7 fmly) (14 GF) S £80-£95; D £139-£220 (incl. bkfst) Facilities ♫ Xmas New Year Wi-fi Conf Class 40 Board 35 Thtr 100 Del from £145 to £155 Services Lift Parking 37 Notes LB Civ Wed 100

CHIPPING CAMPDEN

Noel Arms

★★★ 75% HOTEL

☎ 01386 840317 📠 01386 841136
High St GL55 6AT
e-mail: reception@noelarmshotel.com
web: www.noelarmshotel.com
dir: Off A44 onto B4081 to Chipping Campden,
1st right down hill into town. Hotel on right
opposite Market Hall

PETS: Bedrooms unattended Charges Public
areas except restaurant Exercise area car park
Restrictions small - medium size dogs preferred

This historic 14th-century hotel has a wealth of
character and charm, and retains some of its
original features. Bedrooms are very individual
in style, but all have high levels of comfort and
interesting interior design. Such distinctiveness
is also evident throughout the public areas,
which include the popular bar, conservatory
lounge and attractive restaurant.

Rooms 26 (1 fmly) (6 GF) Facilities Xmas
New Year Wi-fi Conf Class 40 Board 40 Thtr 80
Parking 26 Notes Civ Wed 100

CIRENCESTER

Best Western Stratton House

★★★ 77% HOTEL

☎ 01285 651761 📠 01285 640024
Gloucester Rd GL7 2LE
e-mail: stratton.house@forestdale.com
web: www.strattonhousehotel.co.uk
dir: M4 junct 15, A419 to Cirencester. Hotel on
left on A417 or M5 junct 11 to Cheltenham onto
B4070 to A417. Hotel on right

PETS: Bedrooms unattended Charges Public
areas except restaurant

This attractive 17th-century manor house is
quietly situated about half a mile from the
town centre. Bedrooms are well presented, and
spacious, stylish premier rooms are available.
The comfortable drawing rooms and restaurant
have views over well-tended gardens - the
perfect place to enjoy pre-dinner drinks on a
summer evening.

Rooms 39 (9 GF) S £66-£105; D £91-£145 (incl.
bkfst)* Facilities FTV Xmas New Year Wi-fi
Conf Class 50 Board 30 Thtr 150 Parking 100
Notes Civ Wed 100

CIRENCESTER

The Crown of Crucis
★★★ 74% HOTEL

☎ 01285 851806 📠 01285 851735
Ampney Crucis GL7 5RS
e-mail: reception@thecrownofcrucis.co.uk
web: www.thecrownofcrucis.co.uk
dir: A417 to Fairford, hotel 2.5m on left

PETS: Bedrooms unattended Charges Public
areas in bar only Grounds Exercise area over
bridge nearby

This delightful hotel consists of two buildings;
one a 16th-century coaching inn, which now
houses the bar and restaurant, and a more
modern bedroom block which surrounds a
courtyard. Rooms are attractively appointed and
offer modern facilities; the restaurant serves a
range of imaginative dishes.

Rooms 25 (2 fmly) (13 GF) (4 smoking)
S £60-£72.50; D £80-£99 (incl. bkfst)*
Facilities FTV Wi-fi Conf Class 40 Board 25
Thtr 80 Del from £120 to £140* Parking 82
Notes RS 25-26 Dec & 1 Jan Civ Wed 90

CIRENCESTER

Fleece Hotel
★★★ 73% HOTEL

☎ 01285 658507 📠 01285 651017
Market Place GL7 2NZ
e-mail: relax@fleecehotel.co.uk
web: www.fleecehotel.co.uk
dir: A417/A419 Burford road junct, follow
signs for town centre. Right at lights into 'The
Waterloo', car park 250yds on left

PETS: Bedrooms unattended Charges Public
areas except restaurant Exercise area 200yds

This old, town centre coaching inn, which dates
back to the Tudor period, retains many original
features such as flagstone-floors and oak
beams. Well-equipped bedrooms vary in size and
shape, but all offer good levels of comfort and
have plenty of character. The bar lounge is a
popular venue for morning coffee, and the stylish
restaurant offers a range of dishes in an informal
and convivial atmosphere.

Rooms 28 (3 fmly) (4 GF) S £59-£88; D £79-£114
(incl. bkfst)* Facilities Xmas New Year Wi-fi
Parking 10

CLEARWELL

Tudor Farmhouse Hotel & Restaurant

★★★ 75% ⊛⊛ HOTEL

☎ 01594 833046 📠 01594 837093
High St GL16 8JS
e-mail: info@tudorfarmhousehotel.co.uk
web: www.tudorfarmhousehotel.co.uk
dir: Off A4136 onto B4228, through Coleford, turn right into Clearwell, hotel on right just before War Memorial Cross

PETS: Bedrooms unattended Charges Public areas Grounds Exercise area Resident Pets: Wallace & Gromet (cats)

Dating from the 13th century, this idyllic former farmhouse retains a host of original features including exposed stonework, oak beams, wall panelling and wonderful inglenook fireplaces. Bedrooms have great individuality and style and are located either within the main house or in converted buildings in the grounds. Creative menus offer quality cuisine, served in the intimate, candlelit restaurant.

Rooms 20 (15 annexe) (3 fmly) (8 GF) S £60-£65; D £90-£170 (incl. bkfst) Facilities STV FTV New Year Wi-fi Conf Class 20 Board 12 Thtr 30 Del from £90 to £92.50 Parking 30 Notes LB Closed 24-27 Dec

CLEARWELL

Wyndham Arms

★★★ 64% HOTEL

☎ 01594 833666 📠 01594 836450
GL16 8JT
e-mail: nigel@thewyndhamhotel.co.uk
dir: Off B4228, in village centre on B4231

PETS: Bedrooms unattended Charges Public areas except at food service Grounds Exercise area field at top of car park Resident Pets: Ruby & Poppy (Irish Red Setters)

The history of this charming village inn can be traced back over 600 years. It has exposed stone-walls, original beams and an impressive inglenook fireplace in the friendly bar. Most bedrooms are in a modern extension, whilst the other rooms, in the main house, are more traditional in style. A range of dishes is offered in the bar or restaurant.

Rooms 18 (12 annexe) (3 fmly) (6 GF) S £55-£65; D £80-£115 (incl. bkfst)* Facilities Xmas Wi-fi Conf Class 30 Board 22 Thtr 56 Parking 52 Notes LB Civ Wed 80

COLEFORD

Speech House
★★★ 66% HOTEL

☎ 01594 822607 📄 01594 823658
GL16 7EL
e-mail: info@thespeechhouse.co.uk
dir: M48 junct 2 to Chepstow, A48 to Blakeney, turn left signed Parkend, right, hotel on right

PETS: Bedrooms unattended Charges Public areas except dining room Grounds Exercise area adjacent

This hotel, dating from the 17th century, is located in the heart of the Forest of Dean, and has plenty of history and character. Bedrooms vary considerably in terms of space, from the larger rooms in the main building to a range of smaller rooms in the adjacent courtyard. The eating options, Verderer's Court and the Freeminer's Restaurant, provide a good selection of carefully prepared ingredients.

Rooms 37 (22 annexe) (3 fmly) (18 GF)
S £65-£80; D £98-£125 (incl. bkfst)* Facilities Xmas New Year Wi-fi Conf Class 20 Board 20 Thtr 40 Del from £130* Parking 65 Notes LB Civ Wed

CORSE LAWN

Corse Lawn House
★★★ ◉◉ HOTEL

☎ 01452 780771 📄 01452 780840
GL19 4LZ
e-mail: enquiries@corselawn.com
web: www.corselawn.com
dir: On B4211 5m SW of Tewkesbury

PETS: Bedrooms unattended Public areas except restaurant Grounds Exercise area 100yds Facilities food (pre-bookable) Resident Pets: Sugar & Spice (Black Labradors), Donna & Gigi (horses)

This gracious Grade II listed Queen Anne house has been home to the Hine family for 31 years. Aided by an enthusiastic and committed team, the family continues to preside over all aspects of the hotel, creating a wonderfully relaxed environment. Bedrooms offer a reassuring mix of comfort and quality. The impressive cuisine is based on excellent produce, much of it locally sourced.

Rooms 19 (2 fmly) (5 GF) S £95-£100;
D £150-£170 (incl. bkfst)* Facilities STV 🐾 🏊 🎾 Badminton Table tennis New Year Wi-fi Conf Class 30 Board 25 Thtr 50 Parking 62 Notes LB Closed 24-26 Dec Civ Wed 70

FAIRFORD

Bull Hotel

★★ 68% HOTEL

☎ 01285 712535 & 712217 📠 01285 713782
The Market Place GL7 4AA
e-mail: info@thebullhotelfairford.co.uk
dir: On A417 in market square adjacent to post office

PETS: **Bedrooms** unattended **Charges Public areas** except restaurant **Grounds Exercise area** 100yds **Facilities** food bowl water bowl **Resident Pet:** Foxy '5' (Pomeranian)

Located in a picturesque Cotswold market town, this family-run inn dates back to the 15th century and still retains much period character and charm. A wide range of meals can be enjoyed in the popular bar or alternatively in the bistro restaurant. Bedrooms are individual in style, and a number overlook the square.

Rooms 26 (4 annexe) (4 fmly) (2 GF) S £55-£70; D £81-£100 (incl. bkfst) **Facilities** FTV Fishing Cycle hire Horse riding New Year Wi-fi **Conf** Class 40 Board 40 Thtr 60 **Parking** 10 **Notes** LB

LAVERTON

Leasow House

★★★★ GUEST ACCOMMODATION

☎ 01386 584526 📠 01386 584596
Laverton Meadows WR12 7NA
e-mail: leasow@hotmail.com
web: www.leasow.co.uk
dir: 2m SW of Broadway. Off B4632 towards Wormington, 500yds on right

PETS: **Bedrooms** unattended **Charges** donation to Guide Dogs or Dogs Trust **Public areas Grounds Exercise area**

Located in the countryside to the south-west of Broadway, this 16th-century former farmhouse has been restored to provide high standards of comfort. Bedrooms have a wealth of extras and the attractive dining room is the setting for comprehensive breakfasts. There is also an elegant library lounge and a warm welcome is assured.

Rooms 5 en suite 2 annexe en suite (2 fmly) (1 GF) **Facilities** tea/coffee Direct Dial Cen ht **Parking** 10 **Notes** No Children 8yrs Closed Xmas & New Year

LOWER SLAUGHTER

Washbourne Court Hotel
★★★ 88% ®® HOTEL
☎ 01451 822143 📠 01451 821045
GL54 2HS
e-mail: info@washbournecourt.co.uk
web: www.vonessenhotels.co.uk
dir: Exit A429 at `The Slaughters' sign, between
Stow-on-the-Wold & Bourton-on-the-Water. Hotel
in village centre

PETS: Bedrooms unattended Charges Public
areas except restaurant Grounds Exercise area
50mtrs Facilities food (pre-bookable) food bowl
water bowl Other dog basket available; dog
pamper packs

Beamed ceilings, log fires and flagstone floors
are some of the attractive features of this
part 17th-century hotel, set in four acres of
immaculate grounds beside the River Eye.
The hotel has undergone a stylish, elegant
contemporary refurbishment and boasts stunning
bedrooms with up-to-the-minute technology
and marble bathrooms. Dining, whether in the
restaurant or bar is memorable and utilises fine
local produce.

Rooms 30 (9 GF) S £135-£225; D £135-£350
(incl. bkfst)* Facilities FTV Xmas New Year Wi-fi
Conf Class 40 Board 30 Thtr 70 Del from £170 to
£260* Parking 40 Notes LB Civ Wed 60

MICHAEL WOOD MOTORWAY SERVICE AREA
(M5)

Days Inn Michaelwood
BUDGET HOTEL
☎ 01454 261513 📠 01454 269150
Michaelwood Service Area, Lower Wick
GL11 6DD
e-mail: michaelwood.hotel@welcomebreak.co.uk
web: www.welcomebreak.co.uk
dir: M5 N'bound between junct 13 & 14

PETS: Bedrooms unattended Charges Public
areas Grounds Restrictions no dangerous breeds
(see page 5)

This modern building offers accommodation in
smart, spacious and well-equipped bedrooms,
suitable for families and business travellers,
and all with en suite bathrooms. Continental
breakfast is available and other refreshments
may be taken at the nearby family restaurant.

Rooms 38 (34 fmly) S £29-£49; D £39-£69*
Conf Board 10

STOW-ON-THE-WOLD

Old Stocks

★★ 72% SMALL HOTEL

☎ 01451 830666 📠 01451 870014
The Square GL54 1AF
e-mail: aa@oldstockshotel.co.uk
web: www.oldstockshotel.co.uk
dir: Exit A429 to town centre. Hotel facing village green

PETS: **Bedrooms** unattended **Charges Public areas** except restaurant **Grounds Exercise area** 500yds **Other** patio garden bedrooms most suitable **Restrictions** well behaved dogs only

Overlooking the old market square, this Grade II listed, mellow Cotswold-stone building is a comfortable and friendly base from which to explore this picturesque area. There's lots of character throughout, and the bedrooms offer individuality and charm. Facilities include a guest lounge, restaurant and bar, whilst outside, the patio is a popular summer venue for refreshing drinks and good food.

Rooms 18 (3 annexe) (5 fmly) (4 GF) S £35-£55; D £70-£130 (incl. bkfst) **Facilities** New Year Wi-fi **Parking** 12 **Notes** LB

STROUD

The Bear of Rodborough

★★★ 77% HOTEL

☎ 01453 878522 📠 01453 872523
Rodborough Common GL5 5DE
e-mail: info@bearofrodborough.info
web: www.cotswold-inns-hotels.co.uk
dir: M5 junct 13, A419 to Stroud. Follow signs to Rodborough. Up hill, left at top at T-junct. Hotel on right.

PETS: **Bedrooms** unattended **Charges Public areas** except restaurant **Grounds Facilities** water bowl

This popular 17th-century coaching inn is situated high above Stroud within acres of National Trust parkland. Character abounds in the lounges and cocktail bar, and in the Box Tree Restaurant where the cuisine utilises fresh local produce. Bedrooms offer equal measures of comfort and style with plenty of extra touches. There is also a traditional and well-patronised public bar.

Rooms 46 (2 fmly) **Facilities** STV Putt green 🐕 Xmas New Year Wi-fi **Conf** Class 35 Board 30 Thtr 60 **Parking** 70 **Notes** Civ Wed 70

TETBURY

Hare & Hounds Hotel
★★★ 78% HOTEL

☎ 01666 880233 & 881000 📠 01666 880241
Westonbirt GL8 8QL
e-mail: enquiries@hareandhoundshotel.com
web: www.cotswold-inns-hotels.co.uk
dir: 2.5m SW of Tetbury on A433

PETS: **Bedrooms** unattended **Charges Public areas** except restaurant **Grounds Exercise area Facilities** water bowl

This popular hotel, set in extensive grounds, is situated close to Westonbirt Arboretum and has remained under the same ownership for over 50 years. Bedrooms are individual in style; those in the main house are more traditional and the stylish cottage rooms are contemporary in design. Public rooms include the informal bar and light, airy lounges - one with a log fire in colder months. Guests can eat either in the bar or the attractive restaurant.

Rooms 45 (21 annexe) (8 fmly) (13 GF)
Facilities FTV ⌣ Putt green ⮽ Xmas New Year Wi-fi **Conf** Class 80 Board 40 Thtr 120 **Parking** 85 **Notes** Civ Wed 200

ALTRINCHAM

Best Western Cresta Court Hotel
★★★ 77% HOTEL

☎ 0161 927 7272 & 927 2601
📠 0161 929 6548
Church St WA14 4DP
e-mail: rooms@cresta-court.co.uk
web: www.cresta-court.co.uk

PETS: **Bedrooms** unattended **Charges Public areas** except bar & restaurant **Grounds Exercise area**

This modern hotel enjoys a prime location on the A56, close to the station, town centre shops and other amenities. Bedrooms vary in style from spacious four-posters to smaller, traditionally furnished rooms. Public areas include a choice of bars and extensive function and conference facilities.

Rooms 140 (9 fmly) **Facilities** FTV Wi-fi
Conf Class 200 Board 150 Thtr 350
Del from £120 to £145 **Services** Lift **Parking** 200
Notes Civ Wed 300

BOLTON

Broomfield House
★★★ GUEST HOUSE

☎ 01204 61570   📠 01204 65093233
35 Wigan Rd, Deane BL3 5PX
e-mail: chris@broomfield.force9.net
dir: M61 junct 5, A58 to 1st lights, straight onto
A676, premises on right

PETS: Bedrooms unattended Charges Public
areas Exercise area across road

A friendly relaxed atmosphere prevails at
Broomfield House, close to the motorway and
west of the town centre. There is a comfy lounge
and separate bar area. Hearty breakfasts are
served in the dining room.

Rooms 20 en suite (2 fmly) (2 GF) (9 smoking)
S £42; D £55 Facilities TVL tea/coffee Cen ht
Licensed Wi-fi Parking 12

MANCHESTER

Novotel Manchester Centre
★★★ 77% HOTEL

☎ 0161 235 2200   📠 0161 235 2210
21 Dickinson St M1 4LX
e-mail: H3145@accor.com
web: www.novotel.com
dir: From Oxford Street, into Portland Street, left
into Dickinson Street. Hotel on right

PETS: Bedrooms unattended Charges Public
areas Exercise area outside front door -
courtyard

This smart, modern property enjoys a central
location convenient for theatres, shops, China
Town, and Manchester's business district.
Spacious bedrooms are thoughtfully equipped
and brightly decorated. Open-plan, contemporary
public areas include an all-day restaurant and
a stylish bar. Extensive conference and meeting
facilities are available.

Rooms 164 (15 fmly) (10 smoking) S £65-£125;
D £65-£125* Facilities STV FTV Gym Steam
room Sauna Aromatherapy Wi-fi Conf Class 50
Board 36 Thtr 90 Del from £115 to £165*
Services Lift Air con Notes LB

WORSLEY

Novotel Manchester West
★★★ 72% HOTEL

☎ 0161 799 3535 📄 0161 703 8207
Worsley Brow M28 2YA
e-mail: H0907@accor.com
web: www.novotel.com
dir: Adjacent to M60 junct 13

PETS: Bedrooms unattended Charges Public
areas Grounds Exercise area 100yds

Well placed for access to the Peak and the Lake
District, as well as the City of Manchester,
this modern hotel successfully caters for both
families and business guests. The spacious
bedrooms have sofa beds and a large work area;
the hotel boasts an outdoor swimming pool,
children's play area, and secure parking.

Rooms 119 (10 fmly) (41 GF) S £59-£109;
D £59-£109* Facilities STV ↘ Gym
Wi-fi Conf Class 140 Board 25 Thtr 200
Del from £119 to £140* Services Lift Parking 95
Notes Civ Wed 140

ALTON

Alton Grange Hotel
★★★ 77% ◉◉ HOTEL

☎ 01420 86565 📄 01420 541346
London Rd GU34 4EG
e-mail: info@altongrange.co.uk
web: www.altongrange.co.uk
dir: From A31 right at rdbt signed Alton/
Holybourne/Bordon B3004. Hotel 300yds on left

PETS: Bedrooms unattended Charges Public
areas bar only Grounds Exercise area 100yds
Resident Pets: Caramel, Barley, Smartie, Treacle,
Honey, Saffron (cats)

A friendly family owned hotel, conveniently
located on the outskirts of this market town and
set in two acres of lovingly tended gardens. The
individually styled bedrooms, including three
suites, are all thoughtfully equipped. Diners
can choose between the more formal Truffles
Restaurant or relaxed Muffins Brasserie. The
attractive public areas include a function suite.

Rooms 30 (4 annexe) (4 fmly) (7 GF) S £75-£99;
D £90-£120 (incl. bkfst)* Facilities Hot air
ballooning Wi-fi Conf Class 30 Board 40 Thtr 80
Parking 48 Notes No children 3yrs Closed 24
Dec-4 Jan Civ Wed 100

ANDOVER

Esseborne Manor
★★★ 79% ® HOTEL

☎ 01264 736444 📄 01264 736725
Hurstbourne Tarrant SP11 0ER
e-mail: info@esseborne-manor.co.uk
web: www.esseborne-manor.co.uk
dir: Halfway between Andover & Newbury on
A343, just 1m N of Hurstbourne Tarrant

PETS: Bedrooms unattended Charges Public
areas Grounds Exercise area Facilities food
bowl water bowl

Set in two acres of well-tended gardens, this
attractive manor house is surrounded by the
open countryside of the North Wessex Downs.
Bedrooms are delightfully individual and are
split between the main house, an adjoining
courtyard and separate garden cottage. There's a
wonderfully relaxed atmosphere throughout, and
public rooms combine elegance with comfort.

Rooms 19 (8 annexe) (2 fmly) (6 GF) S £90-£130;
D £125-£180 (incl. bkfst)* Facilities STV FTV
🐕 🐾 Wi-fi Conf Class 40 Board 30 Thtr 60
Del from £140 to £150 Parking 50 Notes LB
Civ Wed 100

BEAULIEU

The Master Builders at Bucklers Hard
★★★ 79% ® HOTEL

☎ 01590 616253 📄 01590 616297
Buckler's Hard SO42 7XB
e-mail: enquiries@themasterbuilders.co.uk
web: www.themasterbuilders.co.uk
dir: M27 junct 2, follow Beaulieu signs. At T-junct
left onto B3056, 1st left to Buckler's Hard. Hotel
2m on left before village

PETS: Bedrooms unattended Charges Public
areas except restaurant & lounge Grounds

A tranquil historic riverside setting creates the
backdrop for this newly refurbished property.
The main house bedrooms are full of historical
features and of individual design, and in addition
there are some bedrooms in the newer wing.
Public areas include a popular bar and guest
lounge, whilst grounds are an ideal location for
alfresco dining in the summer months. Award-
winning cuisine is served in the stylish dining
room.

Rooms 25 (17 annexe) (4 fmly) (8 GF)
S £100-£140; D £140-£180 (incl. bkfst)*
Facilities FTV Xmas New Year Wi-fi Conf Class 30
Board 20 Thtr 40 Del from £148.50 to £178.50*
Parking 40 Notes LB

BEAULIEU

Beaulieu Hotel
★★★ 74% ® HOTEL

☎ 023 8029 3344 📄 023 8029 2729
Beaulieu Rd SO42 7YQ
e-mail: beaulieu@newforesthotels.co.uk
web: www.newforesthotels.co.uk
dir: M27 junct 1/A337 towards Lyndhurst. Left
at lights, through Lyndhurst, right onto B3056,
continue for 3m

PETS: **Bedrooms** unattended **Charges Public
areas** except food areas **Grounds Exercise area**
adjacent

Conveniently located in the heart of the New
Forest and close to Beaulieu Road railway
station, this popular, small hotel provides an
ideal base for exploring this lovely area. Facilities
include an indoor swimming pool, an outdoor
children's play area and an adjoining pub. A daily
changing menu is offered in the restaurant.

Rooms 28 (7 annexe) (6 fmly) (4 GF)
D £120-£160 (incl. bkfst)* **Facilities** ⊙ Steam
room Xmas **Conf** Class 100 Board 160 Thtr 290
Del from £110 to £120* **Services** Lift **Parking** 60
Notes LB Civ Wed 205

BROCKENHURST

Balmer Lawn
★★★★ 75% ® HOTEL

☎ 01590 623116 📄 01590 623864
Lyndhurst Rd SO42 7ZB
e-mail: info@balmerlawnhotel.com
dir: Just off A337 from Brockenhurst towards
Lymington

PETS: **Bedrooms** unattended **Charges Public
areas** except restaurant **Grounds Exercise
area** direct access to New Forest National
Park **Facilities** water bowl **Other** dog training
available

Situated in the heart of the New Forest, this
peacefully located hotel provides comfortable
public rooms and a wide range of bedrooms. A
selection of carefully prepared and enjoyable
dishes is offered in the spacious restaurant. The
extensive function and leisure facilities make
this popular with both families and conference
delegates.

Rooms 54 (10 fmly) **Facilities** FTV ⊙ ⊰ ♨
Gym Squash Indoor leisure suite ♫ Xmas New
Year Wi-fi **Conf** Class 76 Board 48 Thtr 150
Services Lift **Parking** 100 **Notes** LB Civ Wed 120

Forest Park Hotel

★★★ 73% HOTEL

☎ 01590 622844 📠 01590 623948
Rhinefield Rd SO42 7ZG
e-mail: forest.park@forestdale.com
web: www.forestparkhotel.co.uk
dir: A337 to Brockenhurst turn into Meerut Rd,
follow road through Waters Green. Right at
T-junct into Rhinefield Rd

PETS: **Bedrooms** unattended **Charges Public
areas** except restaurant **Grounds Exercise area**
across road **Facilities** food (pre-bookable)

Situated in the heart of the New Forest, this
former vicarage and war field hospital is now a
hotel which offers a warm and friendly welcome
to all its guests. The hotel offers a heated pool,
riding, a log cabin sauna and tennis courts. The
bedrooms and public areas are comfortable and
stylish.

Rooms 38 (2 fmly) (7 GF) **S** £69-£89; **D** £89-£140
(incl. bkfst)* **Facilities** FTV ⤳ ⤵ Horse
riding stables Sauna Xmas New Year Wi-fi
Conf Class 20 Board 30 Thtr 50 **Parking** 80
Notes Civ Wed 50

Watersplash Hotel

★★ 63% HOTEL

☎ 01590 622344
The Rise SO42 7ZP
e-mail: bookings@watersplash.co.uk
web: www.watersplash.co.uk
dir: M3 junct 13/M27 junct 1/A337 S through
Lyndhurst & Brockenhurst. The Rise on left, hotel
on left

PETS: **Bedrooms** unattended **Charges Public
areas Grounds**

This popular, welcoming hotel that dates from
Victorian times, has been in the same family for
over 40 years. Bedrooms have co-ordinated decor
and good facilities. The restaurant overlooks
the neatly tended garden and there is also a
comfortably furnished lounge, separate bar and
an outdoor pool.

Rooms 23 (6 fmly) (3 GF) **Facilities** ⤳ Xmas
New Year **Conf** Class 20 Board 20 Thtr 80
Del from £95 to £135* **Parking** 29

BURLEY

Burley Manor

★★★ 75% HOTEL

☎ 01425 403522 📠 01425 403227
Ringwood Rd BH24 4BS
e-mail: burley.manor@forestdale.com
web: www.theburleymanorhotel.co.uk
dir: Exit A31 at Burley sign, hotel 3m on left

PETS: Bedrooms unattended Charges Public
areas except restaurant

Set in extensive grounds, this 18th-century
mansion house enjoys a relaxed ambience and
a peaceful setting. Half of the well-equipped,
comfortable bedrooms, including several with
four-posters, are located in the main house.
The remainder, many with balconies, are in the
adjacent converted stable block overlooking the
outdoor pool. Cosy public rooms benefit from log
fires in winter.

Rooms 38 (17 annexe) (2 fmly) (17 GF)
S £73-£129; D £83-£169 (incl. bkfst)*
Facilities FTV ⚲ Horse riding stables Xmas
New Year Wi-fi Conf Class 24 Board 40 Thtr 70
Parking 60 Notes Civ Wed 70

BURLEY

Moorhill House Hotel

★★★ 71% ® COUNTRY HOUSE HOTEL

☎ 01425 403285 📠 01425 403715
BH24 4AH
e-mail: moorhill@newforesthotels.co.uk
web: www.newforesthotels.co.uk
dir: M27, A31, follow signs to Burley, through
village, up hill, right opposite school & cricket
grounds

PETS: Bedrooms unattended Charges Public
areas except restaurant & bar Grounds Exercise
area nearby Facilities water bowl

Situated deep in the heart of the New Forest
and formerly a grand gentleman's residence,
this charming hotel offers a relaxed and friendly
environment. Bedrooms, of varying sizes, are
smartly decorated. A range of facilities is
provided and guests can relax by walking around
the extensive grounds. Both dinner and breakfast
offer a choice of interesting and freshly prepared
dishes.

Rooms 31 (13 fmly) (3 GF) Facilities ⚲ Putt
green 🏊 Gym Badminton (Apr-Sep) Xmas New
Year Wi-fi Conf Class 60 Board 65 Thtr 120
Parking 50 Notes LB Civ Wed 80

CADNAM

Bartley Lodge Hotel
★★★ 75% ⊛ HOTEL

☎ 023 8081 2248 🖹 023 8081 2075
Lyndhurst Rd SO40 2NR
e-mail: bartley@newforesthotels.co.uk
web: www.newforesthotels.co.uk
dir: M27 junct 1 at 1st rdbt 1st exit, at 2nd rdbt
3rd exit onto A337. Hotel sign on left

PETS: Bedrooms unattended Charges Public
areas except restaurant & bar Grounds

This 18th-century former hunting lodge is very
quietly situated, yet is just minutes from the
M27. Bedrooms vary in size but all are well
equipped. There is a selection of small lounge
areas, a cosy bar and an indoor pool, together
with a small fitness suite. The Crystal dining
room offers a tempting choice of well prepared
dishes.

Rooms 31 (12 fmly) (2 GF) S £60-£68;
D £120-£160 (incl. bkfst)* Facilities ⊙ Gym
Xmas New Year Wi-fi Conf Class 60 Board 60
Thtr 120 Del from £110 to £120* Parking 60
Notes LB Civ Wed 80

FAREHAM

Travelrest - Solent Gateway
★★★ GUEST ACCOMMODATION

☎ 01329 232175 🖹 01329 23219622 The
Avenue PO14 1NS
 e-mail: solentreservations@travelrest.co.uk
web: www.travelrest.co.uk
dir: 0.5m from town centre on A27. 0.25m from
railway station

PETS: Bedrooms unattended Charges Public
areas Grounds Exercise area 1m Other dogs
allowed in 2 bedrooms only

Situated just west of the town centre, this
well-presented accommodation is convenient
for the ferry terminals and naval heritage sites.
The comfortable bedrooms are spacious and
well equipped, and one has a four-poster bed.
Breakfast is served in the cosy conservatory-
dining room and conference rooms are available.

Rooms 19 en suite (3 fmly) (6 GF) S £50-£75;
D £50-£75 (room only)* Facilities FTV tea/
coffee Dinner available Direct Dial Cen ht Wi-fi
Parking 27

HARTLEY WINTNEY

The Elvetham Hotel

★★★ 79% HOTEL

☎ 01252 844871 📄 01252 844161
RG27 8AR
e-mail: enq@theelvetham.co.uk
web: www.theelvetham.co.uk
dir: M3 junct 4A W, junct 5 E (or M4 junct 11, A33, B3011). Hotel signed from A323 between Hartley Wintney & Fleet

PETS: Bedrooms unattended Charges Public areas Grounds Exercise area Facilities water bowl Resident pets: Harvey (Golden Retriever), Chess (Golden Labrador)

A spectacular 19th-century mansion set in 35 acres of grounds with an arboretum. All bedrooms are individually styled and many have views of the manicured gardens. A popular venue for weddings and conferences, the hotel lends itself to team building events and outdoor pursuits.

Rooms 70 (29 annexe) (7 GF) S £60-£110; D £95-£135* Facilities STV 🏊 Putt green ⛳ Gym Badminton Boules Volleyball New Year Wi-fi Conf Class 80 Board 48 Thtr 110 Parking 200 Notes Closed 24-27 Civ Wed 200

LYNDHURST

Best Western Forest Lodge

★★★ 79% ⑧⑧ HOTEL

☎ 023 8028 3677 📄 023 8028 2940
Pikes Hill, Romsey Rd SO43 7AS
e-mail: forest@newforesthotels.co.uk
web: www.newforesthotels.co.uk
dir: M27 junct 1, A337 towards Lyndhurst. In village, with police station & courts on right, take 1st right into Pikes Hill

PETS: Bedrooms unattended Charges Public areas except restaurant & bar Grounds Exercise area Facilities water bowl

Situated on the edge of Lyndhurst, this hotel is set well back from the main road. The smart, contemporary bedrooms include four-poster rooms and family rooms; children are very welcome here and parents will find that the hotel offers many child-friendly facilities. The eating options are the Forest Restaurant and the fine-dining Glasshouse Restaurant. There is an indoor swimming pool and Nordic sauna.

Rooms 28 (7 fmly) (6 GF) D £120-£160 (incl. bkfst)* Facilities FTV ⑦ Xmas New Year Wi-fi Conf Class 70 Board 60 Thtr 120 Del from £110 to £120* Parking 50 Notes LB Civ Wed 60

LYNDHURST

Lyndhurst Park
★★★ 73% HOTEL

☎ 023 8028 3923 📄 023 8028 3019
High St SO43 7NL
e-mail: lyndhurst.park@forestdale.com
web: www.lyndhurstparkhotel.co.uk
dir: M27 junct 1-3 to A35 to Lyndhurst. Hotel at bottom of High St

PETS: Bedrooms unattended Charges Public areas except restaurant

Although it is just by the High Street, this hotel is afforded seclusion and tranquillity from the town due to its five acres of mature grounds. The comfortable bedrooms include home-from-home touches. The bar offers a stylish setting for a snack whilst the oak-panelled Tudor restaurant provides a more formal dining venue.

Rooms 59 (3 fmly) S £69-£94; D £90-£149 (incl. bkfst)* Facilities FTV ↖ ⌚ Sauna Xmas New Year Wi-fi Conf Class 120 Board 85 Thtr 300 Services Lift Parking 100 Notes Civ Wed 120

LYNDHURST

Knightwood Lodge
★★ 67% SMALL HOTEL

☎ 023 8028 2502 📄 023 8028 3730
Southampton Rd SO43 7BU
e-mail: jackie4r@aol.com
web: www.knightwoodlodge.co.uk
dir: M27 junct 1, A337 to Lyndhurst. Left at lights in village onto A35 towards Southampton. Hotel 0.25m on left

PETS: Bedrooms unattended Charges Public areas except restaurant & bar Exercise area New Forest adjacent Facilities food bowl water bowl Resident Pet: Henry (Golden Retriever)

This friendly, family-run hotel is situated on the outskirts of Lyndhurst. Comfortable bedrooms are modern in style and well equipped with many useful extras. The hotel offers an excellent range of facilities including a swimming pool, a jacuzzi and a small gym area. Two separate cottages are available for families or larger groups, and dogs are also welcome to accompany their owners in these units.

Rooms 18 (4 annexe) (2 fmly) (3 GF) S £35-£50; D £70-£100 (incl. bkfst)* Facilities FTV ⌚ Gym Steam room Sauna Spa bath Parking 15 Notes LB

MILFORD ON SEA

Westover Hall Hotel
★★★ 88% ◉◉ COUNTRY HOUSE HOTEL

☎ 01590 643044 📠 01590 644490
Park Ln SO41 0PT
e-mail: info@westoverhallhotel.com
dir: M3 & M27 W, A337 to Lymington, follow
Milford on Sea/B3058 signs. Hotel towards cliff

PETS: Bedrooms unattended Charges Public
areas except restaurants & bar Grounds
Exercise area beach 100mtrs Resident Pet:
Lancelot (Manx cat)

Just a few moments' walk from the beach
and boasting uninterrupted views across
Christchurch Bay to the Isle of Wight in the
distance, this late-Victorian mansion offers
a relaxed, informal and friendly atmosphere
together with efficient standards of hospitality
and service. Bedrooms do vary in size and
aspect, but all have been decorated with flair and
style. Architectural delights include a galleried
entrance hall. The cuisine is prepared with much
care and attention to detail.

Rooms 15 (3 annexe) (2 fmly) (2 GF) S fr £145;
D fr £290 (incl. bkfst & dinner) Facilities Xmas
New Year Wi-fi Conf Class 14 Board 18 Thtr 35
Del from £195 to £220 Parking 50 Notes LB
Civ Wed 50

PETERSFIELD

Langrish House
★★★ 75% ◉◉ HOTEL

☎ 01730 266941 📠 01730 260543
Langrish GU32 1RN
e-mail: frontdesk@langrishhouse.co.uk
web: www.langrishhouse.co.uk
dir: A3 onto A272 towards Winchester. Hotel
signed, 2.5m on left

PETS: Bedrooms unattended Charges Public
areas except restaurant Grounds Exercise
area surrounding area Other pet pack for dogs
(welcome letter, blanket, poop scoop, biscuits &
towel) Resident Pets: Tonga (Black Labrador),
cat, chickens, ducks, guineafowl

Langrish House has been in the same family for
7 generations, and is located in an extremely
peaceful area just a few minutes drive from
Petersfield. Bedrooms are comfortable and well
equipped with stunning views across the gardens
Guests can eat in the intimate Frederick's
Restaurant or in the Old Vaults which have an
interesting history dating back to 1644. Various
themed events take place throughout the year.

Rooms 13 (1 fmly) (3 GF) S £80-£100;
D £116-£170 (incl. bkfst)* Facilities 🐾 Xmas
New Year Wi-fi Conf Class 18 Board 25 Thtr 60
Parking 80 Notes LB Closed 2 weeks in Jan
Civ Wed 60

SOUTHAMPTON

Southampton Park Hotel
★★★ 71% HOTEL

☎ 023 8034 3343   🖷 023 8033 2538
Cumberland Place SO15 2WY
e-mail: southampton.park@forestdale.com
web: www.southamptonparkhotel.com
dir: At north end of Inner Ring Road, opposite
Watts Park & Civic Centre

PETS: **Bedrooms** unattended **Charges Public
areas** except restaurant **Exercise area Facilities**
food (pre-bookable) food bowl

This modern hotel, in the heart of the city,
provides well-equipped, smartly appointed and
comfortable bedrooms. It boasts a well equipped
spa with all modern facilities and a beauty
salon for those who wish to pamper themselves.
The public areas are spacious and include the
popular MJ's Brasserie. Parking is available in a
multi-storey behind the hotel.

Rooms 72 (10 fmly) S £55-£85; D £80-£140
(incl. bkfst)* **Facilities** Spa FTV ⬡ supervised
Gym New Year Wi-fi **Conf** Class 60 Board 50
Thtr 150 **Services** Lift **Notes** Closed 25 & 26
Dec nights

SWAY

Sway Manor Restaurant & Hotel
★★★ 75% HOTEL

☎ 01590 682754   🖷 01590 682955
Station Rd SO41 6BA
e-mail: info@swaymanor.com
web: www.swaymanor.com
dir: Exit B3055 (Brockenhurst/New Milton road)
into village centre

PETS: **Bedrooms** unattended **Charges Public
areas** except restaurant **Grounds Exercise area**
0.5m **Resident Pets:** Bobby (Chocolate Labrador),
Bernard (Golden Labrador)

Built at the turn of the 20th century, this
attractive mansion is set in its own grounds,
and conveniently located in the village centre.
Bedrooms are well appointed and generously
equipped; most have views over the gardens
and pool. The bar and conservatory restaurant,
both with views over the gardens, are popular
with locals.

Rooms 15 (3 fmly) S £63.50-£69.50;
D £127-£139 (incl. bkfst)* **Facilities** ⌇ ♫
Xmas New Year Wi-fi **Conf** Class 20 Board 15
Del from £86.50 to £92.50* **Services** Lift
Parking 40 **Notes** LB Civ Wed 80

ROSS-ON-WYE

Wilton Court Hotel
★★★ 81% ☺☺ HOTEL

☎ 01989 562569 📠 01989 768460
Wilton Ln HR9 6AQ
e-mail: info@wiltoncourthotel.com
web: www.wiltoncourthotel.com
dir: M50 junct 4, A40 towards Monmouth at 3rd
rdbt left signed Ross-on-Wye. 1st right

PETS: **Bedrooms** unattended **Charges Public
areas** except restaurant **Grounds Exercise area
Restrictions** very large dogs not accepted

Dating back to the 16th century, this hotel
has great charm and a wealth of character.
Standing beside the River Wye and just a short
walk from the town centre, there is a genuinely
relaxed, friendly and unhurried atmosphere
here. Bedrooms are tastefully furnished and well
equipped; public areas include a comfortable
lounge, traditional bar and pleasant restaurant
with a conservatory extension overlooking the
garden. High standards of food, using fresh
locally-sourced ingredients, are offered.

Rooms 10 (1 fmly) **S** £80-£135; **D** £105-£155
(incl. bkfst)* **Facilities** FTV Fishing 🛶 Boule
Xmas New Year Wi-fi **Conf** Class 25 Board 25
Thtr 40 Del from £120 to £145* **Parking** 24
Notes LB Civ Wed 50

ROSS-ON-WYE

Pengethley Manor
★★★ 77% HOTEL

☎ 01989 730211 📠 01989 730238
Pengethley Park HR9 6LL
e-mail: reservations@pengethleymanor.co.uk
web: www.pengethleymanor.co.uk
dir: 4m N on A49 (Hereford road), from
Ross-on-Wye

PETS: **Bedrooms** unattended **Charges Public
areas** except restaurant & bar **Grounds Exercise
area Facilities** food bowl water bowl

This fine Georgian mansion is set in extensive
grounds with glorious views and two successful
vineyards that produce over 1,000 bottles a year.
The bedrooms are tastefully appointed and come
in a wide variety of styles; all are well equipped.
The elegant public rooms are furnished in a style
that is in keeping with the house's character.
Dinner provides a range of enjoyable options and
is served in the spacious restaurant.

Rooms 25 (14 annexe) (3 fmly) (4 GF)
Facilities 🏹 ♨ 9 🛶 Golf improvement course
Xmas New Year Wi-fi **Conf** Class 25 Board 28
Thtr 70 **Parking** 70 **Notes** LB Civ Wed 90

ROSS-ON-WYE

Glewstone Court

★★★ 73% ◉ COUNTRY HOUSE HOTEL

☎ 01989 770367 📠 01989 770282
Glewstone HR9 6AW
e-mail: glewstone@aol.com
web: www.glewstonecourt.com
dir: From Ross-on-Wye take A40/A49 Monmouth/
Hereford, over Wilton Bridge to rdbt, left onto A40
to Monmouth, after 1m turn right for Glewstone

PETS: Bedrooms unattended Charges Public
areas except restaurant Grounds Exercise
area 50mtrs Facilities food (pre-bookable)
food bowl water bowl Resident Pets: Buster &
Brecon (Golden Retrievers), Barney (Long Haired
Miniature Dachshund), Toots & Tilly (cats)

This charming hotel enjoys an elevated position
with views over Ross-on-Wye, and is set in well-
tended gardens. Informal service is delivered
with great enthusiasm by Bill Reeve-Tucker,
whilst the kitchen is the domain of Christine
Reeve-Tucker who offers an extensive menu of
well executed dishes. Bedrooms come in a variety
of sizes and are tastefully furnished and well
equipped.

Rooms 8 (2 fmly) S £80-£95; D £120-£140 (incl.
bkfst) Facilities ᛃ New Year Wi-fi Conf Board 12
Thtr 18 Del from £120 to £170* Parking 25
Notes LB Closed 25-27 Dec Civ Wed 65

ROSS-ON-WYE

Chasedale Hotel

★★ 72% SMALL HOTEL

☎ 01989 562423 & 565801 📠 01989 567900
Walford Rd HR9 5PQ
e-mail: chasedale@supanet.com
web: www.chasedale.co.uk
dir: From town centre, S on B4234, hotel 0.5m
on left

PETS: Bedrooms unattended Public areas except
restaurant Grounds Exercise area 300mtrs
Facilities food bowl water bowl Resident Pets:
Marmite (Chocolate Labrador), Cassis (Black
Labrador)

This large, mid-Victorian property is situated on
the south-west outskirts of the town. Privately
owned and personally run, it provides spacious,
well-proportioned public areas and extensive
grounds. The accommodation is well equipped
and includes ground floor and family rooms,
whilst the restaurant offers a wide selection of
wholesome food.

Rooms 10 (2 fmly) (1 GF) S £42-£45; D £84-£90
(incl. bkfst) Facilities Xmas Wi-fi Conf Class 30
Board 25 Thtr 40 Parking 14 Notes LB

ROSS-ON-WYE

King's Head Hotel
★★ 72% HOTEL

☎ 01989 763174 📠 01989 769578
8 High St HR9 5HL
e-mail: enquiries@kingshead.co.uk
web: www.kingshead.co.uk
dir: In town centre, turn right past Royal Hotel

PETS: Bedrooms unattended Public areas bar
only Grounds Exercise area 200yds Facilities
food (pre-bookable) food bowl water bowl

This establishment dates back to the 14th
century and has a wealth of charm and
character. Bedrooms are well equipped and
include both four-poster and family rooms. The
restaurant doubles as a coffee shop during the
day and is a popular venue with locals. There is
also a very pleasant bar and comfortable lounge.

Rooms 15 (1 fmly) (2 smoking) S £45-£53.50;
D £90-£100 (incl. bkfst)* Facilities Wi-fi
Parking 13 Notes LB

ROSS-ON-WYE

Lumleys
★★★★ BED AND BREAKFAST

☎ 01600 890040 📠 0870 706 2378
Kern Bridge, Bishopswood HR9 5QT
e-mail: helen@lumleys.force9.co.uk
web: www.thelumleys.co.uk
dir: Off A40 onto B4229 at Goodrich, over Kern
Bridge, right at Inn On The Wye, 400yds opp
picnic ground

PETS: Bedrooms unattended Public areas
except dining room Grounds Exercise area 20yds
Resident Pets: Megan (Golden Cocker Spaniel)

This pleasant and friendly guest house overlooks
the River Wye, and has been a hostelry since
Victorian times. It offers the character of a
bygone era combined with modern comforts and
facilities. Bedrooms are individually and carefully
furnished and one has a four-poster bed and its
own patio. Comfortable public areas include a
choice of sitting rooms.

Rooms 3 en suite; D £60-£70* Facilities STV FTV
TVL tea/coffee Dinner available Direct Dial Cen ht
Wi-fi Parking 15 Notes 🚭

SYMONDS YAT (EAST)

The Royal Lodge
★★★ GUEST ACCOMMODATION

☎ 01600 890238 📠 01600 891425
HR9 6JL
e-mail: info@royalhotel-symondsyat.com
web: www.royallodgesymondsyat.co.uk
dir: Midway between Ross & Monmouth. Turn off at signs for Goodrich/B4229 to Symonds Yat East

PETS: Bedrooms unattended **Charges Public areas** except restaurant **Grounds Exercise area** 5mtrs

The Royal Lodge is under new ownership and stands at the top end of the village overlooking the River Wye. Bedrooms are spacious and comfortable and there is a cosy lounge with an open fireplace, along with a television. The bedrooms do not have TVs, as the Lodge operates a quiet policy. Meals are offered in the welcoming restaurant which provides carefully prepared fresh and local ingredients. Staff are pleasant and friendly.

Rooms 20 en suite (5 fmly) **Facilities** TVL tea/coffee Dinner available Direct Dial Cen ht Licensed Wi-fi **Conf** Max 70 Thtr 70 Class 20 Board 30 **Parking** 150

BISHOP'S STORTFORD

Down Hall Country House Hotel
★★★★ 76% ⍟⍟ HOTEL

☎ 01279 731441 📠 01279 730416
Hatfield Heath CM22 7AS
e-mail: reservations@downhall.co.uk
web: www.downhall.co.uk
dir: A1060, at Hatfield Heath keep left. Turn right into lane opposite Hunters Meet restaurant & left at end, follow sign

PETS: Bedrooms unattended **Charges Public areas Grounds Exercise area Facilities** food food bowl water bowl **Other** welcome pack on arrival **Resident Pets:** deer & peacocks

Imposing country-house hotel set amidst 100 acres of mature grounds in a peaceful location just a short drive from Stansted Airport. Bedrooms are generally quite spacious; each one is pleasantly decorated, tastefully furnished and equipped with modern facilities. Public rooms include a choice of restaurants, a cocktail bar, two lounges and leisure facilities.

Rooms 99 (20 GF) (10 smoking) S £74-£125; D £109-£155* **Facilities** ⍟ ⍟ ⍟ Giant chess Whirlpool Sauna Snooker room Gym equipment Xmas New Year Wi-fi **Conf** Class 140 Board 68 Thtr 200 **Services** Lift **Parking** 150 **Notes** LB Civ Wed 120

SOUTH MIMMS SERVICE AREA (M25)

Days Inn South Mimms
BUDGET HOTEL

☎ 01707 665440 📠 01707 660189
Bignells Corner EN6 3QQ
e-mail: south.mimms@welcomebreak.co.uk
web: www.welcomebreak.co.uk
dir: M25 junct 23, at rdbt follow signs

PETS: Bedrooms unattended Charges Public
areas Grounds

This modern building offers accommodation in
smart, spacious and well-equipped bedrooms,
suitable for families and business travellers,
and all with en suite bathrooms. Continental
breakfast is available and other refreshments
may be taken at the nearby family restaurant.

Rooms 74 (55 fmly) S £29-£49; D £39-£69*
Conf Board 10 Del from £79 to £109*

STEVENAGE

Ibis Stevenage Centre
BUDGET HOTEL

☎ 01438 779955 📠 01438 741880
Danestrete SG1 1EJ
e-mail: H2794@accor.com
web: www.ibishotel.com
dir: In town centre adjacent to Tesco & Westgate
multi storey car park

PETS: Bedrooms unattended Charges Public
areas

Modern, budget hotel offering comfortable
accommodation in bright and practical
bedrooms. Breakfast is self-service and dinner is
available in the restaurant.

Rooms 98 (10 smoking)

Roebuck Hotel

★★★ 74% HOTEL

☎ 01920 409955 🖹 01920 468016
Baldock St SG12 9DR
e-mail: roebuck@forestdale.com
web: www.theroebuckhotel.co.uk
dir: A10 onto B1001, left at rdbt, 1st left behind
fire station

PETS: Bedrooms unattended Charges Public
areas except restaurant Facilities food (pre-
bookable) food bowl water bowl

The Roebuck is a comfortable and friendly hotel
situated close to the old market town of Ware,
it is also within easy reach of Stansted Airport,
Cambridge and Hertford. The hotel has spacious
bedrooms, a comfortable lounge, bar and
conservatory restaurant. There is also a range of
air-conditioned meeting rooms.

Rooms 47 (1 fmly) (16 GF) S £57-£77;
D £77-£119 (incl. bkfst)* Facilities FTV Wi-fi
Conf Class 75 Board 60 Thtr 200 Services Lift
Parking 64 Notes Civ Wed 80

BIDDENDEN

Heron Cottage

★★★★ GUEST ACCOMMODATION

☎ 01580 291358 🖹 01580 291358
TN27 8HH
e-mail: susanwort@hotmail.com
web: www.heroncottage.info
dir: 1m NW of Biddenden. A262 W from
Biddenden, 1st right, 0.25m across sharp left
bend through stone pillars, left onto unmade road

PETS: Bedrooms unattended Public areas except
dining room Grounds Other dogs may only be
left unattended for short periods Restrictions no
dangerous dogs (see page 5)

Expect a warm welcome at this picturesque,
extended cottage, set in immaculate, mature
gardens in peaceful Kent countryside. The
bedrooms are thoughtfully equipped and have
co-ordinated soft furnishings. Breakfast is served
in the smart dining room, and the cosy sitting
room has an open fireplace.

Rooms 7 rms (6 en suite) (2 fmly) (1 GF) S
£50-£65; D £55-£75 Facilities TVL tea/coffee
Dinner available Cen ht 🎣 Fishing Conf Max 20
Board 20 Parking 8 Notes Closed Dec-Feb 🐾

CANTERBURY

Cathedral Gate
★★★ GUEST ACCOMMODATION

☎ 01227 464381 📠 01227 46280036
Burgate CT1 2HA
e-mail: cgate@cgate.demon.co.uk
dir: In city centre. Next to main gateway into cathedral precincts

PETS: **Bedrooms** unattended **Public areas** except restaurant **Exercise area** Westgate Gardens 0.5m, Blean Woods 3m **Other** guests must bring dog's own bedding if required

Dating from 1438, this house has an enviable central location next to the cathedral. Old beams and winding corridors are part of the character of the property. Bedrooms are traditionally furnished, equipped to modern standards and many have cathedral views. Luggage can be unloaded at reception before parking in a nearby car park.

Rooms 13 rms (2 en suite) 12 annexe rms 10 annexe en suite (5 fmly) S £32.5-£105; D £62-£105 **Facilities** tea/coffee Dinner available Direct Dial Cen ht Licensed Wi-fi **Notes** LB

CHATHAM

Bridgewood Manor
★★★★ 72% HOTEL

☎ 01634 201333 📠 01634 201330
Bridgewood Roundabout, Walderslade Woods
ME5 9AX
e-mail: bridgewoodmanor@qhotels.co.uk
web: www.qhotels.co.uk
dir: Adjacent to Bridgewood rdbt on A229.

PETS: **Bedrooms** unattended **Charges Public areas** except bar, leisure areas & restaurant **Exercise area** woods adjacent

A modern, purpose-built hotel situated on the outskirts of Rochester. Bedrooms are pleasantly decorated, comfortably furnished and equipped with many thoughtful touches. The hotel has an excellent range of leisure and conference facilities. Guests can dine in the informal Terrace Bistro or experience fine dining in the more formal Squires restaurant, where the service is both attentive and friendly.

Rooms 100 (12 fmly) (26 GF) S £65-£105; D £65-£125 (incl. bkfst)* **Facilities** Spa STV 🏊 supervised 🏋 Gym Beauty treatments Xmas New Year Wi-fi **Conf** Class 110 Board 80 Thtr 200 Del from £99 to £145* **Services** Lift **Parking** 170 **Notes** LB Civ Wed 130

DEAL

Sutherland House
★★★★★ GUEST ACCOMMODATION

☎ 01304 362853 📠 01304 381146
186 London Rd CT14 9PT
e-mail: info@sutherlandhouse.fsnet.co.uk
dir: 0.5m W of town centre/seafront on A258

PETS: Bedrooms unattended Charges Public
areas with consideration for other guests'
comfort Grounds Exercise area Facilities water
bowl Restrictions small dogs only

This stylish accommodation demonstrates
impeccable taste with its charming, well-
equipped bedrooms and a comfortable lounge.
A fully stocked bar, books, free Wi-fi, Freeview
TV and radio are some of the many amenities
offered. The elegant dining room is the venue
for a hearty breakfast and dinner is available by
prior arrangement.

Rooms 4 en suite (1 GF) S £57-£65; D £67-£75*
Facilities FTV tea/coffee Dinner available Direct
Dial Cen ht Licensed Wi-fi Conf Max 12 Thtr
12 Class 12 Board 12 Parking 7 Notes LB No
Children 5yrs

FOLKESTONE

Langhorne Garden
★★★ GUEST ACCOMMODATION

☎ 01303 257233 📠 01303 2427600
12 Langhorne Gardens CT20 2EA
e-mail: info@langhorne.co.uk
web: www.langhorne.co.uk
dir: Exit M20 junct 13, follow The Leas signs, 2m

PETS: Bedrooms unattended Public areas except
restaurant Exercise area

Once a Victorian villa, Langhorne Garden is close
to the seafront, shops and restaurants. Bright
spacious bedrooms are traditionally decorated
with plenty of original charm. Public rooms
include a choice of comfortable lounges and a
bar, a spacious dining room and a popular local
bar in the basement with billiards, darts and
table football.

Rooms 29 en suite (8 fmly) Facilities STV FTV
tea/coffee Dinner available Direct Dial Cen ht
Lift Licensed Wi-fi Pool Table Conf Thtr 40 Class
20 Board 20 Notes Closed Xmas RS Jan-Etr no
evening meal

HYTHE

Mercure Hythe Imperial
★★★★ 74% HOTEL

☎ 01303 267441 📄 01303 264610
Princes Pde CT21 6AE
e-mail: h6862@accor.com
web: www.mercure-uk.com
dir: M20, junct 11 onto A261. In Hythe follow
Folkestone signs. Right into Twiss Rd to hotel

PETS: Bedrooms unattended Charges Public
areas except restaurant, bar & lounge Grounds
Exercise area 1m Facilities water bowl

This imposing seafront hotel is enhanced by
impressive grounds including a 13-hole golf
course, tennis court and extensive gardens.
Bedrooms are varied in style but all offer modern
facilities, and many enjoy stunning sea views.
The elegant restaurant, bar and lounges are
traditional in style and retain many original
features. The leisure club includes a gym, a
squash court, an indoor pool, and the spa offers
a range of luxury treatments.

Rooms 100 (6 fmly) (6 GF) S £75-£145;
D £75-£145 Facilities Spa STV ⑨ ♨ 13 ♨
Putt green Gym Squash Xmas New Year Wi-fi
Conf Class 120 Board 80 Thtr 220 Del from £115
to £185* Services Lift Parking 207 Notes LB
Civ Wed 120

KINGSGATE

The Fayreness Hotel
★★★ 79% HOTEL

☎ 01843 868641 & 861103 📄 01843 608750
Marine Dr CT10 3LG
e-mail: info@fayreness.co.uk
web: www.fayreness.co.uk
dir: A28, B2051 which becomes B2052. Pass Holy
Trinity Church on right & '19th Hole' pub. Next
left, down Kingsgate Ave, hotel at end on left

PETS: Bedrooms unattended Charges Public
areas except restaurant & conservatory Grounds
Exercise area clifftop & beach adjacent
Facilities food bowl water bowl

Situated on the cliff top overlooking the English
Channel, just a few steps from a sandy beach
and adjacent to the North Foreland Golf Club. The
spacious bedrooms are tastefully furnished with
many thoughtful touches including free Wi-fi;
some rooms have stunning sea views. Public
rooms include a large open-plan lounge/bar, a
function room, dining room and conservatory
restaurant.

Rooms 29 (3 fmly) (5 GF) (4 smoking)
S £57.50-£157; D £73.50-£167 (incl. bkfst)*
Facilities STV New Year Wi-fi Conf Class 28
Board 36 Thtr 50 Del from £80 to £150*
Parking 70 Notes LB Civ Wed 80

MAIDSTONE

The Black Horse Inn
★★★★ INN

☎ 01622 737185 & 630830
📠 01622 739170
Pilgrims Way, Thurnham ME14 3LD
e-mail: info@wellieboot.net
web: www.wellieboot.net/home_blackhorse.htm
dir: M20 junct 7, N onto A249. Right into Detling,
opp pub onto Pilgrims Way for 1m

PETS: Bedrooms unattended Charges Public
areas in bar area only Grounds Exercise area
North Downs Way adjacent Restrictions no Pit
Bull Terriers Resident Pets: Sam (Pointer cross),
Boston (Staffordshire Terrier)

This charming inn dates from the 17th century,
and the public areas have a wealth of oak
beams, exposed brickwork and open fireplaces.
The stylish bedrooms are in a series of cosy
cabins behind the premises; each one is
attractively furnished and thoughtfully equipped.

Rooms 30 annexe en suite (8 fmly) (30 GF)
S £60-£70; D £70-£95* Facilities FTV tea/
coffee Dinner available Cen ht Wi-fi Parking 40
Notes LB No coaches Civ Wed 40

SITTINGBOURNE

Hempstead House Country Hotel
★★★ 86% ❀ HOTEL

☎ 01795 428020 📠 01795 436362
London Rd, Bapchild ME9 9PP
e-mail: info@hempsteadhouse.co.uk
web: www.hempsteadhouse.co.uk
dir: 1.5m from town centre on A2 towards
Canterbury

PETS: Bedrooms unattended Public areas except
restaurant (ex assist dogs) Grounds Exercise
area adjoining Facilities food (pre-bookable)
food bowl water bowl Resident Pets: 2 Toy
Poodles, 1 Yorkshire Terrier, 1 Labrador

Expect a warm welcome at this charming
detached Victorian property, situated amidst
four acres of mature landscaped gardens.
Bedrooms are attractively decorated with lovely
co-ordinated fabrics, tastefully furnished and
equipped with many thoughtful touches. Public
rooms feature a choice of elegant lounges as well
as a superb conservatory dining room. In summer
guests can eat on the terraces. A spa and fitness
suite, AquaManda, is now open.

Rooms 34 (7 fmly) (1 GF) Facilities Spa STV
FTV 🏊 ⇒ Gym Fitness studio Steam room
Sauna Hydrotherapy pool Xmas New Year Wi-fi
Conf Class 150 Board 100 Thtr 150 Services Lift
Parking 100 Notes Civ Wed 150

SITTINGBOURNE

The Beaumont

★★★★ GUEST ACCOMMODATION

☎ 01795 472536 🖷 01795 42592174
London Rd ME10 1NS
e-mail: info@thebeaumont.co.uk
web: www.thebeaumont.co.uk
dir: From M2 or M20 take A249 N. Exit at A2, 1m
on left towards Sittingbourne

PETS: Bedrooms unattended Public areas
Grounds Exercise area 5 mins walk Facilities
water bowl Restrictions no large dogs accepted
Resident Pet: Scooby (Cocker Spaniel)

This Georgian farmhouse is a charming family-
run property that offers the best hospitality and
service. Comfortable bedrooms and bathrooms
are well equipped for business and leisure
guests. Breakfast in the bright, spacious
conservatory makes good use of local produce
and homemade preserves. Off-road parking is
available.

Rooms 9 rms (6 en suite) (3 pri facs) (3 GF)
S £40-£70; D £70-£80 Facilities STV TVL tea/
coffee Direct Dial Cen ht Wi-fi Conf Max 12 Thtr
12 Class 12 Board 12 Parking 9 Notes Closed
24 Dec-1 Jan

TUNBRIDGE WELLS (ROYAL)

Hotel du Vin Tunbridge Wells

★★★★ 75% ◉ TOWN HOUSE HOTEL

☎ 01892 526455 🖷 01892 512044
Crescent Rd TN1 2LY
e-mail: reception.tunbridgewells@
hotelduvin.com
web: www.hotelduvin.com
dir: Follow town centre to main junct of Mount
Pleasant Road & Crescent Road/Church Road.
Hotel 150yds on right just past Phillips House

PETS: Bedrooms unattended Public areas
Grounds Exercise area 200yds Facilities food
(pre-bookable) food bowl water bowl

This impressive Grade II listed building dates
from 1762, and as a princess, Queen Victoria
often stayed here. The spacious bedrooms are
available in a range of sizes, beautifully and
individually appointed, and equipped with a
host of thoughtful extras. Public rooms include a
bistro-style restaurant, two elegant lounges and
a small bar.

Rooms 34 D £125-£230* Facilities STV Boules
court in garden Wi-fi Conf Class 30 Board 25
Thtr 40 Del from £165 to £205* Services Lift
Parking 30 Notes LB Civ Wed 84

BLACKPOOL

Barceló Blackpool Imperial Hotel
★★★★ 73% HOTEL

☎ 01253 623971 ▤ 01253 751784
North Promenade FY1 2HB
e-mail: imperialblackpool@barcelo-hotels.co.uk
web: www.barcelo-hotels.co.uk
dir: M55 junct 2, take A583 North Shore, follow
signs to North Promenade. Hotel on seafront,
north of tower

PETS: Bedrooms unattended Charges Public
areas only in lobby area Grounds Exercise area
beach adjacent Other dogs allowed in standard
bedrooms only

Enjoying a prime seafront location, this grand
Victorian hotel offers smartly appointed, well-
equipped bedrooms and spacious, elegant public
areas. Facilities include a smart leisure club,
a comfortable lounge, the No.10 bar and an
attractive split-level restaurant that overlooks
the seafront. Conferences and functions are
extremely well catered for.

Rooms 180 (16 fmly) Facilities Spa STV ⊛
supervised supervised Gym Xmas New Year
Wi-fi Conf Class 280 Board 70 Thtr 600
Del from £100* Services Lift Parking 150
Notes Civ Wed 200

GISBURN

Stirk House Hotel
★★★ 71% HOTEL

☎ 01200 445581 ▤ 01200 445581
BB7 4LJ
e-mail: reservations@stirkhouse.co.uk
dir: W of village, on A59. Hotel 0.5m on left

PETS: Bedrooms unattended Charges Public
areas except restaurant Grounds Facilities food
bowl water bowl

This delightful historic hotel enjoys a peaceful
location in its own grounds, amid rolling
countryside. Extensive public areas include
excellent conference and banqueting facilities,
a leisure centre and an elegant restaurant. The
stylish bedrooms and suites vary in size and
style but all are comfortable and well equipped.
Hospitality is warm and friendly, and service
attentive.

Rooms 30 (10 annexe) (2 fmly) (12 GF)
S £55-£98; D £110-£150 (incl. bkfst)*
Facilities STV ⊛ supervised ⤷ Gym
Aromatherapy Personal training Kick boxing Xmas
New Year Wi-fi Conf Class 150 Board 45 Thtr 200
Parking 400 Notes LB Civ Wed 200

LANCASTER

Best Western Royal Kings Arms

★★★ 70% HOTEL

☎ 01524 32451 📄 01524 841698
Market St LA1 1HP
e-mail: reservations.lancaster@ohiml.com
web: www.oxfordhotelsandinns.com
dir: M6 junct 33, follow A6 to city centre, turn
1st left, after Market Hotel. Hotel at lights before
Lancaster Castle

PETS: Bedrooms unattended Charges Public
areas Exercise area 0.5m

A distinctive period building located in the
town centre, close to the castle. Bedrooms are
comfortable and suitable for both business and
leisure guests. Public areas include a small
lounge on the ground floor and The Castle Bar
and Brasserie Restaurant on the first floor. The
hotel also has a private car park.

Rooms 55 (14 fmly) Facilities Xmas
Conf Class 60 Board 40 Thtr 100 Services Lift
Parking 26 Notes Civ Wed 100

MORECAMBE

Beach Mount

★★★ GUEST ACCOMMODATION

☎ 01524 420753
395 Marine Road East LA4 5AN
e-mail: beachmounthotel@aol.com
dir: M6 junct 34/35, follow signs to Morecambe.
Beach Mount 0.5m from town centre on E
Promenade

PETS: Bedrooms unattended Public areas except
restaurant

This spacious property overlooks the bay and
features a range of room styles that includes a
family room and a junior suite. Guests have use
of a comfortable lounge with fully licensed bar,
and breakfasts are served in a pleasant separate
dining room.

Rooms 10 en suite (1 GF) (10 smoking) S
£28-£46.5; D £51-£58* Facilities FTV tea/coffee
Cen ht Licensed Notes LB Closed Nov-Mar

WHITEWELL

The Inn at Whitewell
★★★★★ ◎ INN

☎ 01200 448222 📠 01200 448298
Forest of Bowland, Clitheroe BB7 3AT
e-mail: reception@innatwhitewell.com
dir: M6 junct 31a, B6243 to Longridge. Left at mini-rdbt. After 3 rdbts leave Longridge. Approx 3m, sharp left bend (with white railings), then right. Approx 1m left, right at T-junct. Next left, 3m to Whitewell

PETS: **Bedrooms** unattended **Public areas** except restaurant **Grounds Exercise area** 50yds

This long-established culinary destination is hidden away in quintessential Lancashire countryside just 20 minutes from the M6. The fine dining restaurant is complemented by two historic and cosy bars with roaring fires, real ales and polished service. Bedrooms are richly furnished with antiques and eye-catching bijouterie, while many of the bathrooms have Victorian brass showers.

Rooms 19 en suite 4 annexe en suite (1 fmly) (1 GF) S £77-£165; D £105-£203* **Facilities** STV FTV tea/coffee Dinner available Direct Dial Cen ht Wi-fi Fishing **Conf** Max 45 Thtr 45 Board 35 **Parking** 60 **Notes** No coaches Civ Wed 80

BELTON

The Queen's Head
★★★★ ◎◎ 🍴 RESTAURANT WITH ROOMS

☎ 01530 222359 📠 01530 2246802
Long St LE12 9TP
e-mail: enquiries@thequeenshead.org
web: www.thequeenshead.org
dir: From Loughborough turn left onto B5324, 3m into Belton

PETS: **Bedrooms** unattended **Charges Public areas Grounds Facilities** food bowl water bowl

This well furnished establishment is found in the village centre and has public rooms with a modern feel. The individually designed bedrooms feature crisp white linen, fluffy duvets and pillows, 19-inch LCD TVs with Freeview and DVD players. The restaurant has earned a well deserved reputation for its award-winning cuisine; the menus are based on the freshest, locally sourced produce quality.

Rooms 6 en suite (2 fmly) S £65; D £80-£100 **Facilities** FTV TVL tea/coffee Dinner available Cen ht Wi-fi **Conf** Max 40 Thtr 40 Class 18 Board 30 **Parking** 20 **Notes** Civ Wed 50

EAST MIDLANDS AIRPORT

Donington Manor Hotel
★★★ 78% ® HOTEL

☎ 01332 810253 📄 01332 850330
High St, Castle Donington DE74 2PP
e-mail: enquiries@doningtonmanorhotel.co.uk
dir: 1m into village on B5430, left at lights

PETS: **Bedrooms** unattended **Charges Public
areas** except restaurant & bar **Grounds Exercise
area** 1m

Near the village centre, this refined Georgian
building offers high standards of hospitality
and a professional service. Many of the original
architectural features have been preserved; the
elegant dining room is particularly appealing.
Bedrooms are individually designed, and the
newer suites are especially comfortable and well
equipped.

Rooms 33 (6 annexe) (8 fmly) (4 GF) S £59-£104;
D £69-£114 (incl. bkfst)* **Facilities** STV
New Year Wi-fi **Conf** Class 60 Board 40
Thtr 120 Del from £120 to £135* **Parking** 40
Notes RS 24-30 Dec Civ Wed 100

HINCKLEY

Sketchley Grange Hotel
★★★★ 81% ®® HOTEL

☎ 01455 251133 📄 01455 631384
Sketchley Ln, Burbage LE10 3HU
e-mail: info@sketchleygrange.co.uk
web: www.sketchleygrange.co.uk
dir: SE of town, off A5/M69 junct 1, take B4109
to Hinckley. Left at 2nd rdbt. 1st right onto
Sketchley Lane

PETS: **Bedrooms** unattended **Charges Public
areas** except restaurant & lounge **Grounds
Exercise area Restrictions** small dogs only

Close to motorway connections, this hotel is
peacefully set in its own grounds, and enjoys
open country views. Extensive leisure facilities
include a stylish health and leisure spa with
a crèche. Modern meeting facilities, a choice
of bars, and two dining options, together with
comfortable bedrooms furnished with many
extras, make this a special hotel.

Rooms 52 (9 fmly) (1 GF) **Spa** ⊛

LEICESTER FOREST MOTORWAY SERVICE AREA (M1)

Days Inn Leicester Forest East
BUDGET HOTEL

☎ 0116 239 0534 📄 0116 239 0546
Leicester Forest East, Junction 21 M1 LE3 3GB
e-mail: leicester.hotel@welcomebreak.co.uk
web: www.welcomebreak.co.uk
dir: On M1 northbound between junct 21 & 21A

PETS: Bedrooms unattended Public areas Grounds

This modern building offers accommodation in smart, spacious and well-equipped bedrooms, suitable for families and business travellers, and all with en suite bathrooms. Continental breakfast is available, and other refreshments may be taken at the nearby family restaurant.

Rooms 92 (71 fmly) S £29-£59; D £39-£79*
Conf Board 10 Del from £69 to £99*

MARKET HARBOROUGH

Best Western Three Swans
★★★ 78% HOTEL

☎ 01858 466644 📄 01858 433101
21 High St LE16 7NJ
e-mail: sales@threeswans.co.uk
web: www.bw-threeswanshotel.co.uk
dir: M1 junct 20 take A304 to Market Harborough. Through town centre on A6 from Leicester, hotel on right

PETS: Bedrooms unattended Charges Public areas Exercise area 0.75m Facilities water bowl

Public areas in this former coaching inn include an elegant fine dining restaurant and cocktail bar, a smart foyer lounge and popular public bar areas. Bedroom styles and sizes vary, but are very well appointed and equipped. Those in the wing are particularly impressive, offering high quality and spacious accommodation.

Rooms 61 (48 annexe) (8 fmly) (20 GF) S £71.50-£88.50; D £88-£110 (incl. bkfst) Facilities STV Xmas New Year Wi-fi Conf Class 90 Board 50 Thtr 250 Del from £135 to £150 Services Lift Parking 100 Notes LB Civ Wed 140

LOUTH

Best Western Kenwick Park
★★★ 79% HOTEL

☎ 01507 608806   📠 01507 608027
Kenwick Park Estate LN11 8NR
e-mail: enquiries@kenwick-park.co.uk
web: www.kenwick-park.co.uk
dir: A16 from Grimsby, then A157 Mablethorpe/
Manby Rd. Hotel 400mtrs down hill on right

PETS: **Bedrooms** unattended **Charges Public
areas Grounds Facilities** water bowl **Other**
please phone for information on further facilities
for dogs

This elegant Georgian house is situated on
the 320-acre Kenwick Park estate, overlooking
its own golf course. Bedrooms are spacious,
comfortable and provide modern facilities. Public
areas include a restaurant and a conservatory
bar that overlook the grounds. There is also an
extensive leisure centre and state-of-the-art
conference and banqueting facilities.

Rooms 34 (5 annexe) (10 fmly) **Facilities** Spa
🔄 supervised ⅃ 18 ⅊ Putt green Gym Squash
Health & beauty centre Xmas New Year Wi-fi
Conf Class 40 Board 90 Thtr 250 **Parking** 100
Notes Civ Wed 200

MARTON (VILLAGE)

Black Swan Guest House
★★★★ GUEST ACCOMMODATION

☎ 01427 718878
21 High St DN21 5AH
e-mail: info@blackswanguesthouse.co.uk
web: www.blackswanguesthouse.co.uk
dir: On A156 in village centre at junct A1500

PETS: **Bedrooms** unattended **Charges Public
areas Grounds Exercise area** 300yds

Centrally located in the village, this 18th-
century former coaching inn retains many
original features, and offers good hospitality
and homely bedrooms with modern facilities.
Tasty breakfasts are served in the cosy dining
room and a comfortable lounge with Wi-fi access
is available. Transport to nearby pubs and
restaurants can be provided.

Rooms 6 en suite 4 annexe en suite (3 fmly) (4
GF) **S** £45; **D** £68 **Facilities** FTV TVL tea/coffee
Cen ht Licensed Wi-fi **Parking** 10 **Notes** LB

113

SKEGNESS

Best Western Vine Hotel

★★★ 70% HOTEL

☎ 01754 763018 & 610611 📠 01754 769845
Vine Rd, Seacroft PE25 3DB
e-mail: info@thevinehotel.com
dir: A52 to Skegness, S towards Gibraltar Point, turn right on to Drummond Rd, 0.5m turn right into Vine Rd

PETS: Bedrooms unattended **Charges Public areas Grounds Exercise area** surrounding area

Reputedly the second oldest building in Skegness, this traditional style hotel offers two character bars that serve excellent local beers. Freshly prepared dishes are served in both the bar and the restaurant; service is both friendly and helpful. The smartly decorated bedrooms are well equipped and comfortably appointed.

Rooms 25 (3 fmly) **Facilities** FTV Xmas New Year Wi-fi **Conf** Class 25 Board 30 Thtr 100 **Parking** 50 **Notes** Civ Wed 100

WOODHALL SPA

Petwood Hotel

★★★ 74% HOTEL

☎ 01526 352411 📠 01526 353473
Stixwould Rd LN10 6QG
e-mail: reception@petwood.co.uk
web: www.petwood.co.uk
dir: From Sleaford take A153 (signed Skegness). At Tattershall turn left on B1192. Hotel is signed from village

PETS: Bedrooms unattended **Charges Public areas** certain areas only **Exercise area**

This lovely Edwardian house, set in 30 acres of gardens and woodlands, is adjacent to Woodhall Golf Course. Built in 1905, the house was used by 617 Squadron, the famous Dambusters, as an officers' mess during World War II. Bedrooms and public areas are spacious and comfortable, and retain many original features. Weddings and conferences are well catered for in modern facilities.

Rooms 53 (3 GF) **S** fr £95; **D** fr £145 (incl. bkfst)* **Facilities** Putt green 🐾 🎵 Xmas New Year Wi-fi **Conf** Class 100 Board 50 Thtr 250 Del from £110 to £125* **Services** Lift **Parking** 140 **Notes** LB Civ Wed 200

WOOLSTHORPE

The Chequers Inn
★★★★ ® INN

☎ 01476 870701   🖷 01476 870085
Main St NG32 1LU
e-mail: justinnabar@yahoo.co.uk
dir: In village opp Post Office

PETS: Bedrooms unattended **Charges Public areas** except restaurant **Grounds Exercise area** open countryside adjacent **Resident Pets:** Hector & Ruby (English Springer Spaniels)

A 17th-century coaching inn set in the lee of Belvoir Castle next to the village cricket pitch and having its own pétanque pitch. Exposed beams, open fireplaces and original stone and brickwork, with 24 wines by the glass, a gastro menu, and real ales. Comfortable bedrooms are in the former stable block.

Rooms 4 annexe en suite (1 fmly) (3 GF)
Facilities TVL tea/coffee Dinner available
Cen ht **Conf** Max 80 Thtr 80 Class 50 Board 25
Parking 40

NW1 REGENT'S PARK

Ibis London Euston St Pancras
BUDGET HOTEL

☎ 020 7388 7777   🖷 020 7388 0001

3 Cardington St NW1 2LW
e-mail: H0921@accor-hotels.com
web: www.ibishotel.com
dir: From Euston Rd or station, right to Melton St leading to Cardington St

PETS: Bedrooms unattended **Charges Public areas Exercise area** Regents Park **Facilities** food bowl water bowl

Modern, budget hotel offering comfortable accommodation in bright and practical bedrooms. Breakfast is self-service and dinner is available in the restaurant.

Rooms 380 **S** £75-£130; **D** £75-£130*
Conf Class 40 Board 40 Thtr 100

115

NW7 LONDON GATEWAY MOTORWAY SERVICE AREA (M1)

Days Hotel London North
★★★ 67% HOTEL

☎ 020 8906 7000 📠 020 8906 7011
Welcome Break Service Area NW7 3HU
e-mail: lgw.hotel@welcomebreak.co.uk
web: www.welcomebreak.co.uk
dir: On M1 between junct 2/4 northbound & southbound

PETS: Bedrooms unattended Charges Public areas except restaurant & bar area

This modern building offers accommodation in smart, spacious and well-equipped bedrooms, suitable for families and business travellers, and all with en suite bathrooms. Continental breakfast is available and other refreshments may be taken at the nearby family restaurant.

Rooms 200 (190 fmly) (80 GF) S £29-£59; D £39-£79* Facilities FTV Wi-fi Conf Class 30 Board 50 Thtr 70 Del from £75 to £125* Services Lift Air con Parking 160 Notes LB Civ Wed 80

SW3 CHELSEA, BROMPTON

Egerton House
★★★★★ 84% TOWN HOUSE HOTEL
☎ 020 7589 2412 📠 020 7584 6540

17 Egerton Ter, Knightsbridge SW3 2BX
e-mail: bookeg@rchmail.com
web: www.egertonhousehotel.com
dir: Just off Brompton Rd, between Harrods and Victoria & Albert Museum, opposite Brompton Oratory

PETS: Bedrooms unattended Charges Public areas except restaurant Exercise area Hyde Park (10 mins walk) Facilities food (pre-bookable) food bowl water bowl Other 24 hours' notice required for all pet provisions

This delightful town house enjoys a prestigious Knightsbridge location, a short walk from Harrods and close to the Victoria & Albert Museum. Air-conditioned bedrooms and public rooms are appointed to the highest standards, with luxurious furnishings and quality antique pieces; an exceptional range of facilities include iPods, safes, mini bars and flat-screen TVs. Staff offer the highest levels of personalised, attentive service.

Rooms 28 (5 fmly) (2GF) (1 smoking) S £255-£275 D £255-£495* Facilities STV Xmas New Year Wi-fi Conf Class 12 Board 10 Thtr 14 Services Lift Air con

SW19 WIMBLEDON

Cannizaro House

★★★★ 79% ⚙⚙ COUNTRY HOUSE HOTEL

☎ 020 8879 1464 📄 020 8879 7338
West Side, Wimbledon Common SW19 4UE
e-mail: info@cannizarohouse.com
dir: From A3 follow A219 signed Wimbledon into
Parkside, right onto Cannizaro Rd, sharp right
onto Westside Common

PETS: Bedrooms unattended Charges Public
areas Grounds Exercise area 100yds Facilities
food bowl water bowl Restrictions small to
medium size dogs only

This unique, elegant 18th-century house has a
long tradition of hosting the rich and famous of
London society. A few miles from the city centre,
the landscaped grounds provide a peaceful
escape and a country-house ambience; fine
art, murals and stunning fireplaces feature
throughout. Spacious bedrooms are individually
furnished and equipped to a high standard. The
award-winning restaurant menus proudly herald
locally sourced, organic ingredients.

Rooms 46 (10 fmly) (5 GF) S £99-£395;
D £99-£395 (incl. bkfst)* Facilities STV ⛳ Xmas
New Year Wi-fi Conf Class 50 Board 40 Thtr 120
Del from £199 to £350* Services Lift Parking 95
Notes LB Civ Wed 100

SOUTHPORT

Cambridge House

★★ 81% HOTEL

☎ 01704 538372 📄 01704 547183
4 Cambridge Rd PR9 9NG
e-mail: info@cambridgehouse.co.uk
dir: A565 N from town centre, over 2 rdbts

PETS: Bedrooms unattended Charges Public
areas except restaurant Grounds Exercise area
100yds Facilities food water bowl Resident
Pets: Samson (Newfoundland cross), Tomas (cat)

This delightful house is in a peaceful location
close to Hesketh Park, a short drive from
Lord Street. The spacious, individually styled
bedrooms, including a luxurious honeymoon
suite, are furnished to a very high standard.
Stylish public areas include a lounge, a cosy bar
and a dining room. Service is attentive.

Rooms 16 (2 fmly) (2 GF) S £55-£70; D £78-£118
(incl. bkfst) Facilities Wi-fi Conf Class 30
Thtr 30 Parking 20 Notes LB

SOUTHPORT

Bay Tree House B & B

★★★★ ⌂ GUEST ACCOMMODATION

☎ 01704 510555 📠 0870 753 6318
No1 Irving St, Marine Gate PR9 0HD
e-mail: baytreehouseuk@aol.com
web: www.baytreehousesouthport.co.uk
dir: Off Leicester St

PETS: Bedrooms unattended **Charges Public
areas Exercise area** 100mtrs

A warm welcome is assured at this immaculately
maintained house, located a short walk from
promenade and central attractions. Bedrooms are
equipped with a wealth of thoughtful extras, and
delicious imaginative breakfasts are served in an
attractive dining room overlooking the pretty front
patio garden.

Rooms 6 en suite **S** £45-£70; **D** £70-£110
Facilities FTV tea/coffee Dinner available Direct
Dial Cen ht Licensed Wi-fi **Parking** 2 **Notes** LB
Closed 14 Dec-1 Feb

BARTON BENDISH

Spread Eagle Inn

★★★★ ◉ INN

☎ 01366 347995 📠 0871 9005576
Church Rd PE33 9GF
e-mail: info@spreadeaglenorfolk.co.uk
web: www.spreadeaglenorfolk.co.uk
dir: A1122 turn off at sign for Barton Bendish,
1m turn left onto Church Rd

PETS: Bedrooms unattended **Charges Public
areas** except restaurant **Grounds Exercise area**
footpath 500yds **Resident Pets:** Amber (Shih
Tzu), Topaz & Cloud (cats)

Set in the delightfully quiet village of Barton
Bendish, this traditional village inn offers
tastefully appointed public areas with many
original features. There is a good selection of
real ales and enjoyable,imaginative cuisine.The
newly converted bedrooms, situated in the stable
block, are stylish, comfortable and particularly
well equipped.

Rooms 5 annexe en suite (1 fmly) (5 GF); **D**
£70-£200* **Facilities** FTV tea/coffee Dinner
available Cen ht Wi-fi **Parking** 30 **Notes** LB RS
Mon-Wed closed lunchtimes No coaches

BURNHAM MARKET

Hoste Arms
★★★ 87% ◉◉ HOTEL

☎ 01328 738777   🖷 01328 730103
The Green PE31 8HD
e-mail: reception@hostearms.co.uk
web: www.hostearms.co.uk
dir: Signed on B1155, 5m W of
Wells-next-the-Sea

PETS: **Bedrooms** unattended **Charges Public
areas** bar & lounge only **Grounds Exercise area**
green opposite **Facilities** food (pre-bookable)
food bowl water bowl

A stylish, privately-owned inn situated in the
heart of a bustling village close to the north
Norfolk coast. The extensive public rooms
feature a range of dining areas that include a
conservatory with plush furniture, a sunny patio
and a traditional pub. The tastefully furnished
and thoughtfully equipped bedrooms are
generally very spacious and offer a high degree
of comfort.

Rooms 35 (7 GF) **S** £104-£190; **D** £128-£225
(incl. bkfst)* **Facilities** STV Xmas New Year
Wi-fi **Conf** Board 16 Thtr 25 **Services** Air con
Parking 45

CROMER

The Cliftonville
★★★ 74% HOTEL

☎ 01263 512543   🖷 01263 515700
NR27 9AS
e-mail: reservations@cliftonvillehotel.co.uk
web: www.cliftonvillehotel.co.uk
dir: From A149 (coast road), 500yds from town
centre, N'bound on clifftop by sunken gardens

PETS: **Bedrooms** unattended **Charges Public
areas** except restaurants **Exercise area** 50mtrs
Facilities food food bowl water bowl

An imposing Edwardian hotel situated on the
main coast road with stunning views of the sea.
Public rooms feature a magnificent staircase,
minstrels' gallery, coffee shop, lounge bar, a
further residents' lounge, Boltons Bistro and an
additional restaurant. The pleasantly decorated
bedrooms are generally quite spacious and have
lovely sea views.

Rooms 30 (5 fmly) **S** £55-£72; **D** £110-£144
(incl. bkfst)* **Facilities** Xmas New Year Wi-fi
Conf Class 100 Board 60 Thtr 150 Del from £90
to £150* **Services** Lift **Parking** 21 **Notes** LB

CROMER

Glendale
★★★ GUEST HOUSE

☎ 01263 513278
33 Macdonald Rd NR27 9AP
e-mail: glendalecromer@aol.com
dir: A149 (coast road) from Cromer centre, 4th left

PETS: Bedrooms unattended Public areas except breakfast room Grounds Exercise area 200mtrs Other dogs may only be left unattended during breakfast Resident Pets: Daisy & Megan (Jack Russells), Jess (Collie/Springer Spaniel)

Victorian property situated in a peaceful side road adjacent to the seafront and just a short walk from the town centre. Bedrooms are pleasantly decorated, well maintained and equipped with a good range of useful extras. Breakfast is served at individual tables in the smart dining room.

Rooms 5 rms (1 en suite) S £23-£32; D £46-£64 Facilities tea/coffee Parking 2 Notes LB Closed 20 Oct-1 Apr

DOWNHAM MARKET

Crosskeys Riverside House
★★★ BED AND BREAKFAST

☎ 01366 387777 📄 01366 387777
Bridge St, Hilgay PE38 0LD
e-mail: crosskeyshouse@aol.com
web: www.crosskeys.info
dir: 2m S of Downham Market. Off A10 into Hilgay, Crosskeys on bridge

PETS: Bedrooms unattended Charges Public areas Grounds Exercise area 500yds Resident Pets: 2 Shih Tzus, 3 horses

Situated in the small village of Hilgay on the banks of the River Wissey, this former coaching inn offers comfortable accommodation that includes a number of four-poster bedrooms; many rooms have river views. Public rooms include a dining room with oak beams and inglenook fireplace, plus a small, rustic residents' bar.

Rooms 4 en suite (1 fmly) (2 GF) S £30-£55; D £55* Facilities tea/coffee Cen ht Fishing Rowing boat for guests use Parking 10

HUNSTANTON

Caley Hall

★★★ 82% HOTEL

☎ 01485 533486 📠 01485 533348
Old Hunstanton Rd PE36 6HH
e-mail: mail@caleyhallhotel.co.uk
web: www.caleyhallhotel.co.uk
dir: 1m from Hunstanton, on A149

PETS: **Bedrooms** unattended **Charges Public areas** except restaurant & lounge **Grounds Exercise area** 150mtrs **Facilities** food bowl water bowl **Resident Pets:** Basil (Cocker Spaniel), Sox (cat)

Situated within easy walking distance of the seafront. The tastefully decorated bedrooms are in a series of converted outbuildings; each is smartly furnished and thoughtfully equipped. Public rooms feature a large open-plan lounge/bar with plush leather seating, and a restaurant offering an interesting choice of dishes.

Rooms 40 (20 fmly) (30 GF) **S** £50-£200; **D** £70-£200 (incl. bkfst)* **Facilities** STV Wi-fi Child facilities **Parking** 50 **Notes** LB Closed 18 Dec-20 Jan

NORTH WALSHAM

Beechwood Hotel

★★★ ⑳⑳ HOTEL

☎ 01692 403231 📠 01692 407284
Cromer Rd NR28 0HD
e-mail: info@beechwood-hotel.co.uk
web: www.beechwood-hotel.co.uk
dir: B1150 from Norwich. At North Walsham left at 1st lights, then right at next

PETS: **Bedrooms** unattended **Charges Public areas** except restaurant **Grounds Exercise area** park 400yds **Resident Pets:** Emily & Harry (Airedale Terriers)

Expect a warm welcome at this elegant 18th-century house, situated just a short walk from the town centre. The individually styled bedrooms are tastefully furnished with well-chosen antique pieces, attractive co-ordinated soft fabrics and many thoughtful touches. The spacious public areas include a lounge bar with plush furnishings, a further lounge and a smartly appointed restaurant.

Rooms 17 (4 GF) **S** fr £75; **D** £90-£160 (incl. bkfst) **Facilities** FTV ⤳ New Year Wi-fi **Conf** Class 20 Board 20 Thtr 20 **Del** from £130 **Parking** 20 **Notes** LB No children 10yrs

121

NORWICH

Sprowston Manor, A Marriott Hotel & Country Club

★★★★ 81% ⊛⊛ HOTEL

☎ 01603 410871 📄 01603 423911
Sprowston Park, Wroxham Rd, Sprowston
NR7 8RP
e-mail: mhrs.nwigs.frontdesk
@marriotthotels.com
web: www.marriottsprowstonmanor.co.uk
dir: From A11/A47, 2m NE on A115 (Wroxham road). Follow signs to Sprowston Park

PETS: Bedrooms unattended Charges Public areas except restaurants Grounds Facilities food bowl water bowl

Surrounded by parkland, this imposing property is set in attractively landscaped grounds, a short drive from the city centre. Bedrooms are spacious and feature a variety of decorative styles. The hotel also has extensive conference, banqueting and leisure facilities. Other public rooms include the elegant Manor Restaurant.

Rooms 94 (3 fmly) (5 GF) (8 smoking)
S £120-£145; D £130-£155 (incl. bkfst)*
Facilities Spa FTV 🕓 supervised ♨ 18 Putt green Gym Xmas New Year Wi-fi Conf Class 50 Board 50 Thtr 500 Del from £140 to £195 Services Lift Parking 150 Notes LB Civ Wed 300

NORWICH

Stower Grange

★★ 85% ⊛ HOTEL

☎ 01603 860210 📄 01603 860464
School Rd, Drayton NR8 6EF
e-mail: enquiries@stowergrange.co.uk
web: www.stowergrange.co.uk
dir: Norwich ring road N to Asda supermarket. Take A1067 (Fakenham road) at Drayton, right at lights into School Rd. Hotel 150yds on right

PETS: Bedrooms unattended Public areas except restaurant Grounds Exercise area Facilities food (pre-bookable) Resident Pet: Saffy (Staffordshire Bull Terrier)

Expect a warm welcome at this 17th-century, ivy-clad property situated in a peaceful residential area close to the city centre and airport. The individually decorated bedrooms are generally quite spacious; each one is tastefully furnished and equipped with many thoughtful touches. Public rooms include a smart open-plan lounge bar and an elegant restaurant.

Rooms 11 (1 fmly) S fr £75; D £95-£150 (incl. bkfst)* Facilities ♨ New Year Wi-fi Conf Class 45 Board 30 Thtr 100 Del from £135* Parking 40 Notes Civ Wed 100

OXBOROUGH

Bedingfeld Arms
★★★ INN

☎ 01366 328300PE33 9PS
e-mail: sam.clark@tiscali.co.uk
web: www.bedingfeldarms.com

PETS: Bedrooms unattended Charges Public areas except restaurants Grounds Exercise area adjacent Facilities water bowl

This establishment provides five annexe rooms in a newly refurbished stable block adjacent to the Bedingfeld Arms. The rooms are spacious, smartly presented with en suite facilities. This is a family run, traditional English pub offering friendly hospitality and home-made pub food including a selection of specials plus a range of locally produced ales.

Rooms 5 annexe en suite (1 fmly) (5 GF) S fr £35; D fr £55* Facilities TVL tea/coffee Dinner available Cen ht Parking 5

REEPHAM

Old Brewery House
★★ 72% HOTEL

☎ 01603 870881 📠 01603 870969
Market Place NR10 4JJ
e-mail: reservations.oldbreweryhouse@ohiml.com
web: www.oxfordhotelsandinns.com
dir: A1067, right at Bawdeswell onto B1145 into Reepham, hotel on left in Market Place

PETS: Bedrooms unattended Public areas except bar & restaurant areas Grounds Exercise area woods 1m Facilities water bowl Other prior notice required

This Grade II listed Georgian building is situated in the heart of this bustling town centre. Public areas include a cosy lounge, a bar, a conservatory and a smart restaurant. Bedrooms come in a variety of styles; each one is pleasantly decorated and equipped with a good range of facilities.

Rooms 23 (2 fmly) (7 GF) Facilities ⚡ Gym Squash Xmas Conf Class 80 Board 30 Thtr 200 Parking 40 Notes LB Civ Wed 45

TITCHWELL

Titchwell Manor

★★★ 86% ◉◉ HOTEL

☎ 01485 210221 📠 01485 210104
PE31 8BB
e-mail: margaret@titchwellmanor.com
web: www.titchwellmanor.com
dir: On A149 (coast road) between Brancaster & Thornham

PETS: **Bedrooms** unattended **Charges Public areas** except conservatory restaurant **Grounds Exercise area** 1m **Facilities** food bowl water bowl

Friendly family-run hotel ideally placed for touring the north Norfolk coastline. The tastefully appointed bedrooms are very comfortable; some in the adjacent annexe offer ground floor access. Smart public rooms include a lounge area, relaxed informal bar and a delightful conservatory restaurant, overlooking the walled garden. Imaginative menus feature quality local produce and fresh fish.

Rooms 26 (18 annexe) (4 fmly) (16 GF)
D £110-£250 (incl. bkfst) **Facilities** Xmas New Year **Conf** Class 25 Board 25 Thtr 25 **Parking** 50 **Notes** LB Civ Wed 80

DAVENTRY

Barceló Daventry Hotel

★★★★ 72% HOTEL

☎ 01327 307000 📠 01327 706313
Sedgemoor Way NN11 0SG
e-mail: daventry@barcelo-hotels.co.uk
web: www.barcelo-hotels.co.uk
dir: M1 junct 16/A45 to Daventry, at 1st rdbt turn right to Kilsby/M1(N). Hotel on right in 1m

PETS: **Bedrooms** unattended **Charges Public areas Grounds Exercise area** parks nearby

This modern, striking hotel overlooking Drayton Water boasts spacious public areas that include a good range of banqueting, meeting and leisure facilities. It is a popular venue for conferences. Bedrooms are suitable for both business and leisure guests.

Rooms 155 (17 fmly) **Facilities** STV ⓢ supervised Gym Steam room Health & beauty salon Xmas New Year Wi-fi **Conf** Class 200 Board 100 Thtr 600 Del from £99* **Services** Lift **Parking** 350 **Notes** Civ Wed 280

HELLIDON

Hellidon Lakes Golf & Spa Hotel

★★★★ 70% HOTEL

☎ 01327 262550   📠 01327 262559
NN11 6GG
e-mail: hellidonlakes@qhotels.co.uk
web: www.qhotels.co.uk
dir: Off A361 between Daventry & Banbury

PETS: Bedrooms unattended Charges Public
areas Grounds Exercise area Facilities food
(pre-bookable) food bowl water bowl Other dogs
are required to be muzzled & on leads in public
areas

220 acres of beautiful countryside (with 27
holes of golf and 12 lakes) combine to form a
spectacular backdrop to this impressive hotel.
Bedroom vary -ultra smart, modern rooms
through to original wing rooms with superb
views. An extensive range of facilities includes a
swimming pool, gym and ten-pin bowling. Golfers
of all levels can try some of the world's most
challenging courses on the indoor golf simulator.

Rooms 110 (5 fmly) S £109-£145; D £130-£151
(incl. bkfst)* Facilities Spa STV 🕓 ♨ 27 ♨ Putt
green Fishing 🦢 Gym Beauty therapist Indoor
smart golf 10-pin bowling Steam room Coarse
fishing lake Xmas New Year Wi-fi Conf Class 150
Board 80 Thtr 300 Services Lift Parking 200
Notes LB Civ Wed 220

BAMBURGH

Victoria Hotel

★★ 80% HOTEL

☎ 01668 214431   📠 01668 214404
Front St NE69 7BP
e-mail: enquiries@thevictoriahotelbamburgh.
co.uk
web: www.thevictoriahotelbamburgh.co.uk
dir: Off A1, N of Alnwick onto B1342, near Belford
& follow signs to Bamburgh. Hotel in town centre

PETS: Bedrooms unattended Charges Public
areas except restaurant

Overlooking the village green, this hotel offers
an interesting blend of traditional and modern.
Public areas include the new Jackie Milburn
sports bar with outdoor seating, the traditional
lounge bar serving bar snacks, and the brasserie
offering a more contemporary dinner menu.
Bedrooms come in a variety of styles and sizes
including the new superior rooms that have
castle views.

Rooms 36 (2 fmly) (2 GF) S £40-£70; D £80-£200
(incl. bkfst)* Facilities FTV Xmas New Year Wi-fi
Conf Class 30 Board 20 Thtr 50 Del from £80
to £120 Parking 18 Notes LB Closed 3-8 Jan
Civ Wed 50

CORNHILL-ON-TWEED

Tillmouth Park Country House

★★★ 86% ® COUNTRY HOUSE HOTEL

☎ 01890 882255 🖹 01890 882540
TD12 4UU
e-mail: reception@tillmouthpark.f9.co.uk
web: www.tillmouthpark.co.uk
dir: Off A1(M) at East Ord rdbt at Berwick-upon-Tweed. Take A698 to Cornhill and Coldstream. Hotel 9m on left

PETS: Bedrooms unattended Public areas bar only Grounds Exercise area Facilities water bowl Resident Pets: Carter & Teal (Black Labradors)

An imposing mansion set in landscaped grounds by the River Till. Gracious public rooms include a stunning galleried lounge with a drawing room adjacent. The quiet, elegant dining room overlooks the gardens, whilst lunches and early dinners are available in the bistro. Bedrooms retain much traditional character and include several magnificent master rooms.

Rooms 14 (2 annexe) (4 smoking) S £70-£189; D £142-£205 (incl. bkfst)* Facilities FTV ⛳ Game shooting Fishing New Year Wi-fi Conf Class 20 Board 20 Thtr 50 Del from £160* Parking 50 Notes Closed 3 Jan-1 Apr Civ Wed 50

EMBLETON

Dunstanburgh Castle Hotel

★★ 79% HOTEL

☎ 01665 576111 🖹 01665 576203
NE66 3UN
e-mail: stay@dunstanburghcastlehotel.co.uk
web: www.dunstanburghcastlehotel.co.uk
dir: From A1, take B1340 to Denwick past Rennington & Masons Arms. Take next right signed Embleton

PETS: Bedrooms unattended Public areas Grounds Exercise area 10mtrs Resident Pet: Uncle Bob (dog)

The focal point of the village, this friendly, family-run hotel has a dining room and grill room that offer different menus, plus a cosy bar and two lounges. In addition to the main bedrooms, a barn conversion houses three stunning suites, each with a lounge and gallery bedroom above.

Rooms 20 (4 fmly) S £41.50-£55.50; D £83-£125 (incl. bkfst)* Parking 16 Notes LB Closed Dec-Jan

FALSTONE

The Blackcock Inn

★★★ INN

☎ 01434 240200
NE48 1AA
e-mail: thebcinn@yahoo.co.uk
dir: From Hexham take A6079 to Bellingham,
then left at church. In village centre, towards
Kielder Water

PETS: Bedrooms unattended Charges Public
areas except restaurant Grounds Exercise area
adjacent Facilities food (pre-bookable) food
bowl water bowl Resident Pets: Pooch (dog),
Eyefull, Cello, Banjo & Sno (cats), Rosso (rabbit),
Hallo (fish)

This traditional family-run village inn lies close
to Kielder Water. A cosy pub, it has a very homely
atmosphere, with welcoming fires in the colder
weather. The bedrooms are very comfortable
and well equipped, with family rooms available.
Evening meals are served here or in the cosy
restaurant. The inn is closed during the day on
Tuesdays throughout winter.

Rooms 6 rms (4 en suite) (2 pri facs) (1 fmly)
S £35-£60; D £70-£80* Facilities tea/coffee
Dinner available Cen ht Wi-fi Fishing Pool Table
Children's play area Parking 15 Notes LB RS Tue
closed during low season

NOTTINGHAM

Best Western Bestwood Lodge

★★★ 71% HOTEL

☎ 0115 920 3011 📄 0115 964 9678
Bestwood Country Park, Arnold NG5 8NE
e-mail: bestwoodlodge@btconnect.com
web: www.bw-bestwoodlodge.co.uk
dir: 3m N off A60. Left at lights into Oxclose Ln,
right at next lights into Queens Bower Rd. 1st
right. Keep right at fork in road

PETS: Bedrooms unattended Charges Public
areas Grounds Exercise area nearby country
park Facilities food bowl water bowl Other
please phone for details of further facilities for
dogs

Set in 700 acres of parkland this Victorian
building, once a hunting lodge, has stunning
architecture that includes Gothic features and
high vaulted ceilings. Bedrooms include all
modern comforts, suitable for both business and
leisure guests, and the popular restaurant serves
an extensive menu.

Rooms 39 (5 fmly) Facilities ♨ Guided walks
Xmas Wi-fi Conf Class 65 Board 50 Thtr 200
Parking 120 Notes RS 25 Dec & 1 Jan Civ Wed 80

NOTTINGHAM

The Nottingham Gateway Hotel
★★★ 67% HOTEL

☎ 0115 979 4949 📠 0115 979 4744
Nuthall Rd, Cinderhill NG8 6AZ
e-mail: sales@nottinghamgatewayhotel.co.uk
web: www.nottinghamgatewayhotel.co.uk
dir: M1 junct 26, A610, hotel on 3rd rdbt on left

PETS: Bedrooms unattended Charges Public
areas Grounds Exercise area

Located approximately three miles from the city
centre, and with easy access to the M1. This
modern hotel provides spacious public areas,
with a popular restaurant and lounge bar, and
the contemporary accommodation is suitably well
equipped. Ample parking is a bonus.

Rooms 108 (18 fmly) (10 smoking) S £49-£85;
D £49-£90 (incl. bkfst) Facilities STV FTV Xmas
New Year Wi-fi Conf Class 150 Board 60 Thtr 250
Del from £90 to £140 Services Lift Parking 250
Notes LB Civ Wed 250

WORKSOP

Best Western Lion Hotel
★★★ 78% HOTEL

☎ 01909 477925 📠 01909 479038
112 Bridge St S80 1HT
e-mail: reception@thelionworksop.co.uk
web: www.thelionworksop.co.uk
dir: A57 to town centre, turn right at Sainsburys,
follow to Norfolk Arms, turn left

PETS: Bedrooms unattended Charges Public
areas Grounds Exercise area 2 mins

This former coaching inn lies on the edge of
the main shopping precinct, with a car park to
the rear. It has been extended to offer modern
accommodation that includes excellent executive
rooms. A wide range of interesting dishes is
offered in both the restaurant and bar.

Rooms 46 (3 fmly) (7 GF) S £55-£85; D £65-£115
(incl. bkfst)* Facilities STV FTV Xmas New
Year Wi-fi Conf Class 80 Board 70 Thtr 160
Del from £88 to £145* Services Lift Parking 50
Notes LB Civ Wed 150

BLETCHINGDON

The Oxfordshire Inn

★★★ 72% HOTEL

☎ 01869 351444   📠 01869 351555
Heathfield Village OX5 3DX
e-mail: staff@oxfordshireinn.co.uk
web: www.oxfordshireinn.co.uk
dir: M40 junct 9, A34 towards Oxford, then A4027 towards Bletchingdon. Hotel signed 0.7m on right

PETS: Bedrooms unattended Charges Public areas Grounds Exercise area large grounds & fields surrounding

A converted farmhouse with additional outbuildings that is located close to major motorway networks. Accommodation is set around an open courtyard, and includes suites that have four-poster beds. There is a spacious bar and restaurant.

Rooms 28 (4 fmly) (15 GF) S £49-£97; D £59-£104 (incl. bkfst) Facilities Putt green Golf driving range Xmas New Year Wi-fi Conf Class 80 Board 30 Thtr 140 Parking 50 Notes LB

BURFORD

The Inn For All Seasons

★★ 75% HOTEL

☎ 01451 844324   📠 01451 844375
The Barringtons OX18 4TN
e-mail: sharp@innforallseasons.com
web: www.innforallseasons.com
dir: 3m W of Burford on A40 towards Cheltenham

PETS: Bedrooms unattended Charges Public areas except restaurant & breakfast room Grounds Exercise area adjacent Facilities food water bowl Other prior notice required Resident Pets: Bob (Black Labrador), Guscot (Springer Spaniel)

This 16th-century coaching inn is conveniently located near Burford. Bedrooms are comfortable, and public areas retain much period charm with original fireplaces and oak beams still remaining. A good selection of bar meals is available at lunchtime, while the evening menu includes an appetising selection of fresh fish.

Rooms 10 (1 annexe) (2 fmly) (1 GF) S £35-£68; D £50-£95 (incl. bkfst)* Facilities Xmas New Year Wi-fi Conf Class 30 Board 30 Thtr 25 Del from £125 to £155* Parking 62 Notes LB

DORCHESTER (ON THAMES)

White Hart Hotel

★★★ 77% @ HOTEL

☎ 01865 340074 📄 01865 341082
High St OX10 7HN
e-mail: whitehart@oxfordshire-hotels.co.uk
web: www.oxfordshire-hotels.co.uk
dir: M40 junct 6, take B4009 through Watlington
& Benson to A4074. Follow signs to Dorchester.
Hotel on right

PETS: Bedrooms unattended **Charges Public
areas** except bar & restaurant **Grounds Exercise
area** 200mtrs **Facilities** food bowl water bowl

Period charm and character are plentiful
throughout this 17th-century coaching inn,
which is situated in the heart of a picturesque
village. The spacious bedrooms are individually
decorated and thoughtfully equipped. Public
rooms include a cosy bar, a choice of lounges
and an atmospheric restaurant, complete with
vaulted timber ceiling.

Rooms 26 (4 annexe) (2 fmly) (9 GF) **Facilities**
Xmas Wi-fi **Conf** Class 20 Board 18 Thtr 30
Del from £100 to £130 **Parking** 36

FARINGDON

Best Western Sudbury House Hotel & Conference Centre

★★★ 74% HOTEL

☎ 01367 241272 📄 01367 242346
London St SN7 8AA
e-mail: stay@sudburyhouse.co.uk
web: www.sudburyhouse.co.uk
dir: Off A420, signed Folly Hill

PETS: Bedrooms unattended **Charges Public
areas Grounds Exercise area Facilities** food
bowl water bowl

Situated on the edge of the Cotswolds and set in
nine acres of pleasant grounds, this hotel offers
spacious and well-equipped bedrooms that are
attractively decorated in warm colours. Dining
options include the comfortable restaurant for a
good selection of carefully presented dishes, and
also the bar for lighter options. A comprehensive
room service menu is available.

Rooms 49 (2 fmly) (10 GF) (2 smoking)
Facilities STV ⬆ Gym Badminton Boules New
Year Wi-fi **Conf** Class 30 Board 34 Thtr 100
Services Lift **Parking** 100 **Notes** Civ Wed 160

GORING

The Miller of Mansfield

★★★★★ ֍ RESTAURANT WITH ROOMS

☎ 01491 872829 🖷 01491 873100
High St RG8 9AW
e-mail: reservations@millerofmansfield.com
web: www.millerofmansfield.com

PETS: Bedrooms unattended Charges Public
areas except restaurant Grounds Exercise area
approx 0.5m Facilities water bowl

The frontage of this former coaching inn hides
sumptuous rooms with a distinctive and
individual style, an award-winning restaurant
that serves appealing dishes using locally
sourced ingredients and a comfortable bar, which
serves real ales, fine wines, afternoon tea and a
bar menu for a quick bite.

Rooms 13 en suite (2 fmly) S £100-£125; D
£125-£225* Facilities FTV tea/coffee Dinner
available Direct Dial Cen ht Wi-fi Conf Max 14
Thtr 14 Class 14 Board 14 Parking 2 Notes LB

HENLEY-ON-THAMES

The Baskerville

★★★★ INN

☎ 0118 940 3332
Station Rd, Lower Shiplake RG9 3NY
e-mail: enquiries@thebaskerville.com
dir: 2m S of Henley in Lower Shiplake. Off A4155
onto Station Rd, B&B signed

PETS: Bedrooms unattended Charges Public
areas except public bar Grounds Exercise area
village lanes & river banks nearby Facilities
water bowl

Located close to Shiplake station and just a short
drive from Henley, this smart accommodation
is perfect for a business or leisure break. It
is a good base for exploring the Oxfordshire
countryside, and the enjoyable hearty meals
served in the cosy restaurant use good local
produce.

Rooms 4 en suite (1 fmly) S £75; D £85*
Facilities tea/coffee Dinner available Cen ht
Wi-fi Conf Max 15 Thtr 15 Class 15 Board 15
Parking 15 Notes RS 23 Dec-2 Jan room only
No coaches

KINGHAM

Mill House Hotel & Restaurant

★★★ 78% ☺ HOTEL

☎ 01608 658188 🖹 01608 658492
OX7 6UH

e-mail: stay@millhousehotel.co.uk
web: www.millhousehotel.co.uk
dir: Off A44 onto B4450. Hotel indicated by
tourist sign

PETS: Bedrooms unattended Charges Public
areas Grounds 7-acres Facilities food (pre-
bookable) food bowl water bowl Other chews &
treats on request

This Cotswold-stone, former mill house has
been carefully converted into a comfortable and
attractive hotel. It is set in well-kept grounds
bordered by its own trout stream. Bedrooms are
comfortable and provide thoughtfully equipped
accommodation. There is a peaceful lounge
and bar, plus an atmospheric restaurant where
the imaginative, skilfully cooked dishes are a
highlight of any stay.

Rooms 23 (2 annexe) (1 fmly) (7 GF) S £65-£75;
D £80-£120 (incl. bkfst) Facilities STV FTV
Fishing ⛵ Xmas New Year Wi-fi Conf Class 24
Board 24 Thtr 70 Parking 62 Notes LB
Civ Wed 100

KINGHAM

The Tollgate Inn & Restaurant

★★★★ ⊜ INN

☎ 01608 658389
Church St OX7 6YA
e-mail: info@thetollgate.com

PETS: Bedrooms unattended Charges Public
areas except restaurant & lounge Grounds
Exercise area Other please phone for details
of further facilities for dogs Resident Pets:
Guinness (Black Labrador), Tinker (cat)

Situated in the idyllic Cotswold village of
Kingham, this Grade II-listed Georgian building
has been lovingly restored to provide a complete
home-from-home among some of the most
beautiful and historic countryside in Britain. The
Tollgate provides comfortable, well-equipped
accommodation in pleasant surroundings. A good
choice of menu for lunch and dinner is available
with fine use made of fresh and local produce.
You can also be sure of a hearty breakfast
provided in the modern, well-equipped dining
room.

Rooms 5 en suite 4 annexe en suite (1 fmly) (4
GF) Facilities tea/coffee Dinner available Cen ht
Wi-fi Conf Max 15 Parking 12

MILTON COMMON

The Oxford Belfry
★★★★ 76% HOTEL

☎ 01844 279381 📠 01844 279624
OX9 2JW
e-mail: oxfordbelfry@qhotels.co.uk
web: www.qhotels.co.uk
dir: M40 junct 7 onto A329 to Thame. Left onto
A40, hotel 300yds on right

PETS: Bedrooms unattended Charges Public
areas except food areas (assist dogs only)
Grounds Exercise area fields adjacent
Restrictions max 2 small or 1 large dog per
booking

This modern hotel has a relatively rural location
and enjoys lovely views of the countryside to the
rear. The hotel is built around two very attractive
courtyards and has a number of lounges and
conference rooms, as well as indoor leisure
facilities and outdoor tennis courts. Bedrooms
are large and feature a range of extras.

Rooms 154 (20 fmly) (66 GF) S £59-£180;
D £69-£190 (incl. bkfst) Facilities Spa STV ③
♨ ♨ Gym Steam room Sauna Aerobics studio
Xmas New Year Wi-fi Conf Class 180 Board 100
Thtr 450 Del from £130 to £215 Services Lift
Parking 350 Notes LB Civ Wed 300

OXFORD

Old Parsonage Hotel
★★★★ 75% ⊛ TOWN HOUSE HOTEL

☎ 01865 310210 📠 01865 311262
1 Banbury Rd OX2 6NN
e-mail: info@oldparsonage-hotel.co.uk
web: www.oldparsonage-hotel.co.uk
dir: From Oxford ring road to city centre via
Summertown. Hotel on right by St Giles Church

PETS: Bedrooms unattended Charges Public
areas except restaurant Grounds Exercise area
2 mins walk Facilities food (pre-bookable) food
bowl water bowl Other dog baskets available
& special menus on request Restrictions well
behaved dogs only

Dating back in parts to the 16th century, this
stylish hotel offers great character and charm
and is conveniently located at the northern edge
of the city centre. Bedrooms are attractively
styled and particularly well appointed. The focal
point of the operation is the busy all-day bar and
restaurant; the small garden areas and terraces
prove popular in summer months.

Rooms 30 (4 fmly) (10 GF) S £125-£190;
D £175-£260* Facilities FTV Beauty treatments
Free use of nearby leisure facilities, punt &
house bikes ♫ Xmas Wi-fi Conf Class 8 Board 12
Thtr 20 Del from £200 to £250* Services Air con
Parking 14 Notes LB Civ Wed 20

WALLINGFORD

Shillingford Bridge Hotel

★★★ 74% HOTEL

☎ 01865 858567 📠 01865 858636
Shillingford OX10 8LZ
e-mail: shillingford.bridge@forestdale.com
web: www.shillingfordbridgehotel.com
dir: M4 junct 10, A329 through Wallingford towards Thame, then B4009 through Watlington. Right on A4074 at Benson, then left at Shillingford rdbt (unclass road) Wallingford road

PETS: Bedrooms unattended **Charges Public areas** except restaurant **Grounds Facilities** food (pre-bookable) food bowl water bowl

This hotel enjoys a superb position right on the banks of the River Thames, and benefits from private moorings and has a waterside open-air swimming pool. Public areas are stylish with a contemporary feel and have large picture windows making the best use of the view. Bedrooms are well equipped and furnished with guest comfort in mind.

Rooms 40 (8 annexe) (6 fmly) (9 GF) **S** £70-£95; **D** £102-£154 (incl. bkfst)* **Facilities** FTV ↲ supervised Fishing Table tennis ♫ Xmas New Year Wi-fi **Conf** Class 40 Board 36 Thtr 80 **Parking** 100 **Notes** Civ Wed 150

WITNEY

The Fleece

★★★ INN

☎ 01993 892270 📠 0871 8130458
11 Church Green OX28 4AZ
e-mail: fleece@peachpubs.com
dir: A40 to Witney town centre, on Church Green

PETS: Bedrooms unattended **Charges Public areas Grounds Exercise area** village green **Facilities** water bowl **Other** please ask about any specific requirements for dogs

Set in the centre of Witney overlooking the church green, The Fleece offers ten well equipped, en suite, modern bedrooms. The popular destination pub offers food all day including breakfast, and a great selection of wines and real ales.

Rooms 7 en suite 3 annexe en suite (1 fmly) (1 GF) **S** fr £80; **D** fr £90* **Facilities** tea/coffee Dinner available Direct Dial Cen ht Wi-fi **Conf** Max 30 Thtr 25 Class 16 Board 22 **Parking** 12 **Notes** LB Closed 25 Dec

WOODSTOCK

Macdonald Bear Hotel
★★★★ 76% 🏵🏵 HOTEL

☎ 0844 879 9143 📄 01993 813380
Park St OX20 1SZ
e-mail: gm.bear@macdonaldhotels.co.uk
web: www.macdonaldhotels.co.uk
dir: M40 junct 9 follow signs for Oxford &
Blenheim Palace. A44 to town centre hotel on left

PETS: Bedrooms unattended Charges Public
areas except restaurant Exercise area Facilities
water bowl Restrictions small dogs only

With its ivy-clad façade, oak beams and open
fireplaces, this 13th-century coaching inn exudes
charm and cosiness. The bedrooms are decorated
in a modern style that remains in keeping with
the historic character of the building. Public
rooms include a variety of function rooms, an
intimate bar area and an attractive restaurant
where attentive service and good food are
offered.

Rooms 54 (18 annexe) (1 fmly) (8 GF)
Facilities STV Xmas New Year Wi-fi Conf Class 12
Board 24 Thtr 40 Parking 40

WOODSTOCK

Feathers Hotel
★★★ 83% 🏵🏵 HOTEL

☎ 01993 812291 📄 01993 813158
Market St OX20 1SX
e-mail: enquiries@feathers.co.uk
dir: From A44 (Oxford to Woodstock), 1st left after
lights. Hotel on left

PETS: Bedrooms unattended Charges Public
areas except restaurant Grounds Exercise area
0.5m Facilities food bowl water bowl Resident
Pet: Johann (African Grey parrot)

This intimate and unique hotel enjoys a town
centre location with easy access to nearby
Blenheim Palace. Public areas are elegant
and full of traditional character from the cosy
drawing room to the atmospheric restaurant.
Individually styled bedrooms are appointed to a
high standard and are furnished with attractive
period and reproduction furniture.

Rooms 20 (5 annexe) (4 fmly) (2 GF)
S £109-£219; D £169-£279 (incl. bkfst)
Facilities FTV 1 suite has steam room Xmas
New Year Wi-fi Conf Class 20 Board 30 Thtr 20
Notes LB

OAKHAM

Barnsdale Lodge Hotel

★★★ 78% ⊛ HOTEL

☎ 01572 724678 🖹 01572 724961
The Avenue, Rutland Water, North Shore
LE15 8AH
e-mail: enquiries@barnsdalelodge.co.uk
web: www.barnsdalelodge.co.uk
dir: Off A1 onto A606. Hotel 5m on right, 2m E
of Oakham

PETS: **Bedrooms** unattended **Charges Public
areas** in bar area only **Grounds Exercise area
Facilities** food bowl water bowl **Resident Pets:**
Coco & Maisie (Norfolk Terriers)

A popular and interesting hotel converted from
a farmstead overlooking Rutland Water. The
public areas are dominated by a very successful
food operation with a good range of appealing
meals on offer for either formal or informal
dining. Bedrooms are comfortably appointed with
excellent beds enhanced by contemporary soft
furnishings and thoughtful extras.

Rooms 44 (2 fmly) (15 GF) **S** £80-£90;
D £90-£145 (incl. bkfst) **Facilities** FTV Fishing
🌙 Archery Beauty treatments Golf Shooting
Xmas New Year **Conf** Class 120 Board 76
Thtr 330 Del from £112.50 **Parking** 200 **Notes** LB
Civ Wed 160

BRIDGNORTH

Bearwood Lodge Guest House

★★★★ GUEST ACCOMMODATION

☎ 01746 762159
10 Kidderminster Rd WV15 6BW
dir: On A442, 50yds S of Bridgnorth bypass
island

PETS: **Bedrooms** unattended **Public areas
Exercise area** 100yds to river walk & park

This friendly guest house is situated on the
outskirts of Bridgnorth. It provides soundly
maintained modern accommodation, including
one bedroom on the ground floor. The bright
and pleasant breakfast room has an adjacent
conservatory, which opens onto the attractive
and colourful garden. There is also a comfortable
lounge.

Rooms 5 en suite (1 GF) **S** £45; **D** £60*
Facilities TVL tea/coffee Cen ht **Parking** 8
Notes LB ⊛

CHURCH STRETTON

Longmynd Hotel
★★★ 73% HOTEL

☎ 01694 722244 📠 01694 722718
Cunnery Rd SY6 6AG
e-mail: info@longmynd.co.uk
web: www.longmynd.co.uk
dir: A49 into town centre on Sandford Ave, left at
Lloyds TSB, over mini-rdbt, 1st right into Cunnery
Rd, hotel at top of hill on left

PETS: Bedrooms unattended Charges Public
areas Grounds Exercise area Facilities food
(pre-bookable)

Built in 1901 as a spa, this family-run hotel
overlooks this country town, and the views
from many of the rooms and public areas are
breathtaking. The attractive wooded grounds
include a unique wood sculpture trail. Bedrooms,
with smart modern bathrooms, are comfortable
and well equipped; suites are available. Facilities
include a choice of relaxing lounges. An ethical
approach to climatic issues is observed, and a
warm welcome is assured.

Rooms 50 (6 fmly) S £50-£65; D £100-£130
(incl. bkfst)* Facilities ⤳ Putt green Pitch and
putt Sauna Xmas New Year Wi-fi Conf Class 50
Board 40 Thtr 100 Services Lift Parking 100
Notes LB Civ Wed 100

CRAVEN ARMS

Castle View
★★★★ BED AND BREAKFAST

☎ 01588 673712
Stokesay SY7 9AL
e-mail: castleviewb_b@btinternet.com
dir: On A49 S of Craven Arms opposite turning to
Stokesay Castle

PETS: Bedrooms unattended Charges Public
areas assist dogs in dining room only Grounds
Exercise area Facilities food (pre-bookable)
food bowl water bowl Resident Pet: Cindy
(Bearded Collie)

The Victorian cottage, extended about 20 years
ago, stands in delightful gardens on the southern
outskirts of Craven Arms, close to Stokesay
Castle. Bedrooms are thoughtfully furnished, and
breakfasts, featuring local produce, are served in
the cosy, traditionally-furnished dining room.

Rooms 3 rms (1 en suite) (2 pri facs)
Facilities tea/coffee Cen ht Parking 4 Notes LB
No Children 3yrs 🐾

KNOCKIN

Top Farm House

★★★★ GUEST HOUSE

☎ 01691 682582   📠 01691 682070
SY10 8HN
e-mail: p.a.m@knockin.freeserve.co.uk
web: www.topfarmknockin.co.uk
dir: Off B4396 in village centre

PETS: Bedrooms unattended **Charges Public areas** except dining room **Grounds Exercise area** 200mtrs

This impressive half-timbered Tudor house, set amid pretty gardens, retains many original features including a wealth of exposed beams and open fires. Bedrooms are equipped with many thoughtful extras, and the open-plan ground-floor area includes a comfortable sitting room and elegant dining section, where imaginative comprehensive breakfasts are served.

Rooms 3 en suite (1 fmly) **Facilities** TVL tea/coffee Cen ht **Parking** 6

LUDLOW

Fishmore Hall

★★★ 85% ⊚⊚ SMALL HOTEL

☎ 01584 875148   📠 01584 877907
Fishmore Rd SY8 3DP
e-mail: reception@fishmorehall.co.uk
web: www.fishmorehall.co.uk
dir: A49 onto Henley Rd. 1st right, Weyman Rd, at bottom of hill right onto Fishmore Rd

ETS: Bedrooms unattended **Charges Public areas** except restaurant **Grounds Exercise area** adjacent **Facilities** water bowl **Resident Pets:** Fidget & Nismo (cats)

Located in a rural area within easy reach of town centre, this Palladian styled Georgian house has been sympathetically renovated and extended to provide high standards of comfort and facilities. A contemporary styled interior highlights the many retained period features and public areas include a comfortable lounge and restaurant, the setting for imaginative cooking.

Rooms 15 (1 GF) **S** £100-£210; **D** £140-£250 (incl. bkfst) **Facilities** FTV ⤴ Beauty treatments Massage Xmas New Year Wi-fi **Conf** Class 20 Board 30 Thtr 40 **Services** Lift **Parking** 48 **Notes** LB Civ Wed 80

LUDLOW

The Charlton Arms
★★★★ ⊜ INN

☎ 01584 872813
Ludford Bridge SY8 1PJ
dir: From town centre onto Broad St, over Ludford Bridge, Charlton Arms on right

PETS: Bedrooms unattended **Charges Public areas** except top terrace, restaurant & eating area **Grounds Exercise area** adjacent **Facilities** water bowl

This refurbished riverside inn is situated in the historic market town of Ludlow. The restaurant provides fresh locally-sourced ingredients and as a free house also offers a fine selection of local beers. The accommodation reflects the character of this historic building whilst offering all the comforts of modern life. There is one bedroom which has a private terrace and hot tub, and there are decking areas to enjoy drinks or a meal on warmer days.

Rooms 11 en suite (2 fmly); **D** £80-£180*
Facilities TVL tea/coffee Dinner available Cen ht Fishing **Conf** Max 100 Thtr 100 Class 80 Board 70 **Parking** 25

LUDLOW

Church Inn
★★★★ INN

☎ 01584 872174 📄 01584 877146
The Buttercross SY8 1AW
web: www.thechurchinn.com
dir: In town centre at top of Broad St

PETS: Bedrooms unattended **Public areas** except in breakfast area **Facilities** water bowl **Other** prior notice required; owners must bring dog's own bedding if required

Set right in the heart of the historic town, this Grade II listed inn has been renovated to provide quality accommodation with smart modern bathrooms, some with spa baths. Other areas include a small lounge, a well-equipped meeting room, and cosy bar areas where imaginative food and real ales are served.

Rooms 8 en suite (3 fmly) **Facilities** TVL tea/coffee Dinner available Direct Dial Cen ht **Conf** Max 38 **Notes** No coaches

LUDLOW

Moor Hall

★★★★ GUEST HOUSE

☎ 01584 823209 📄 08715 041324
Cleedownton SY8 3EG
e-mail: enquiries@moorhall.co.uk
dir: A4117 Ludlow to Kidderminster, left to
Bridgnorth. B4364, follow for 3.2m, Moor Hall
on right

PETS: Bedrooms unattended **Public areas**
except dining room **Grounds Exercise area** fields
Resident Pets: 2 dogs & 5 cats

This impressive Georgian house, once the home
of Lord Boyne, is surrounded by extensive gardens
and farmland. Bedrooms are richly decorated,
well equipped, and one room has a sitting area.
Public areas are spacious and comfortably
furnished. There is a choice of sitting rooms
and a library bar. Guests dine family-style in an
elegant dining room.

Rooms 3 en suite (1 fmly) S £40-£45; D
£60-£70* **Facilities** tea/coffee Dinner available
Cen ht Licensed Fishing **Conf** Max 14 Thtr 14

OSWESTRY

Pen-y-Dyffryn Country Hotel

★★★ 83% ⊛⊛ HOTEL

☎ 01691 653700 📄 01978 211004
Rhydycroesau SY10 7JD
e-mail: stay@peny.co.uk
web: www.peny.co.uk
dir: A5 into town centre. Follow signs to Llansilin
on B4580, hotel 3m W of Oswestry before
Rhydycroesau

PETS: Bedrooms unattended **Public areas** not
after 6pm **Grounds Exercise area Facilities** food
bowl water bowl

Peacefully situated in five acres of grounds, this
charming old house dates back to around 1840,
when it was built as a rectory. The tastefully
appointed public rooms have real fires during
cold weather, and the accommodation includes
several mini-cottages, each with its own patio.
This hotel attracts many guests for its food and
attentive, friendly service.

Rooms 12 (4 annexe) (1 fmly) (1 GF) S £85-£86;
D £112-£164 (incl. bkfst)* **Facilities** STV Guided
walks Xmas New Year Wi-fi **Parking** 18 **Notes** LB
No children 3yrs Closed 18 Dec-19 Jan

SHREWSBURY

Albright Hussey Manor Hotel & Restaurant

★★★★ 73% ⊛ HOTEL

☎ 01939 290571 & 290523 📠 01939 291143
Ellesmere Rd SY4 3AF
e-mail: info@albrighthussey.co.uk
web: www.albrighthussey.co.uk
dir: 2.5m N of Shrewsbury on A528, follow signs
for Ellesmere

PETS: Bedrooms unattended Charges Public
areas Exercise area

First mentioned in the Domesday Book, this
enchanting medieval manor house is complete
with a moat. Bedrooms are situated in either
the sumptuously appointed main house or in
the more modern wing. The intimate restaurant
displays an abundance of original features and
there is also a comfortable cocktail bar and
lounge.

Rooms 26 (4 fmly) (8 GF) S £79-£130;
D £95-£190 (incl. bkfst)* Facilities ➥ Xmas
New Year Wi-fi Conf Class 180 Board 80 Thtr 250
Parking 100 Notes LB Civ Wed 180

SHREWSBURY

Mytton & Mermaid

★★★ 77% ⊛⊛ HOTEL

☎ 01743 761220 📠 01743 761292
Atcham SY5 6QG
e-mail: admin@myttonandmermaid.co.uk
web: www.myttonandmermaid.co.uk
dir: From Shrewsbury over old bridge in Atcham.
Hotel opposite main entrance to Attingham Park

PETS: Bedrooms unattended Charges Public
areas Grounds Exercise area Facilities food
bowl water bowl Resident Pets: dogs

Convenient for Shrewsbury, this ivy-clad former
coaching inn enjoys a pleasant location beside
the River Severn. Some bedrooms, including
family suites, are in a converted stable block
adjacent to the hotel. There is a large lounge bar,
a comfortable lounge, and a brasserie that has
gained a well-deserved local reputation for the
quality of its food.

Rooms 18 (7 annexe) (1 fmly) S £85-£95;
D £110-£175 (incl. bkfst)* Facilities Fishing ♫
New Year Wi-fi Conf Class 24 Board 28 Thtr 70
Del from £150 to £170* Parking 50 Notes LB ⊗
Closed 25 Dec Civ Wed 80

BATH

The Royal Crescent

★★★★★ 84% ⍟⍟ HOTEL

☎ 01225 823333 📠 01225 339401
16 Royal Crescent BA1 2LS
e-mail: info@royalcrescent.co.uk
web: www.vonessenhotels.co.uk
dir: From A4, right at lights. 2nd left (Bennett St).
Into The Circus, 2nd exit onto Brock St

PETS: Bedrooms unattended Charges Public
areas except restaurant Grounds Exercise area
park adjacent Facilities food (pre-bookable) food
bowl water bowl Other please contact hotel to
confirm which dog breeds are accepted Resident
Pets: Tilly & Toby (cats)

John Wood's masterpiece of fine Georgian
architecture provides the setting for this elegant
hotel in the centre of the world famous Royal
Crescent. Spacious, air-conditioned bedrooms
are individually designed and furnished with
antiques. Delightful central grounds lead to a
second house, with further rooms, the award-
winning Dower House restaurant and the Bath
House which offers therapies and treatments.

Rooms 45 (8 fmly) (7 GF) Facilities Spa STV
FTV ⍟⍟ Gym 1920s river launch Xmas
New Year Wi-fi Conf Class 25 Board 24
Thtr 50 Services Lift Air con Parking 27
Notes Civ Wed 50

BATH

Pratt's Hotel

★★★ 74% HOTEL

☎ 01225 460441 📠 01225 448807
South Pde BA2 4AB
e-mail: pratts@forestdale.com
web: www.prattshotel.co.uk
dir: A46 into city centre. Left at 1st lights (Curfew
Pub), right at next lights. 2nd exit at next rdbt,
right at lights, left at next lights, 1st left into
South Pde

PETS: Bedrooms unattended Charges Public
areas except restaurant Exercise area 2-minute
walk Facilities food food bowl water bowl

Built in 1743 this popular Georgian hotel still has
many original features and is centrally placed
for exploring Bath. The bedrooms, each with their
own individual character and style, offer great
comfort. The lounge has original open fireplaces
and offers a relaxing venue for afternoon tea.

Rooms 46 (2 fmly) S £70-£100; D £90-£155
(incl. bkfst)* Facilities FTV Xmas New Year Wi-fi
Conf Class 12 Board 20 Thtr 50 Services Lift

CASTLE CARY

The George Hotel
★★ 67% HOTEL

☎ 01963 350761 📠 01963 350035
Market Place BA7 7AH
e-mail: castlecarygeorge@aol.co.uk
dir: A303 onto A371. Signed Castle Cary, 2m
on left

PETS: Bedrooms unattended Charges Public
areas Exercise area park, numerous walks
Facilities food (pre-bookable) food bowl water
bowl

This 15th-century coaching inn provides well-
equipped bedrooms that are generally spacious.
Most rooms are at the back of the house, enjoying
a quiet aspect, and some are on the ground floor;
one is suitable for less able guests. Diners can
choose to eat in the more formal dining room, or
in one of the two cosy bars.

Rooms 17 (5 annexe) (1 fmly) (5 GF)
S £59.50-£62.50; D £79.50-£95 (incl. bkfst)
Facilities Xmas New Year Wi-fi Conf Class 40
Board 20 Thtr 50 Del from £109 to £200
Parking 7 Notes LB

CHARD

Lordleaze Hotel
★★★ 77% HOTEL

☎ 01460 61066 📠 01460 66468
Henderson Dr, Forton Rd TA20 2HW
e-mail: info@lordleazehotel.co.uk
web: www.lordleazehotel.co.uk
dir: From Chard take A358, at St Mary's Church
turn left to Forton & Winsham on B3162. Follow
signs to hotel

PETS: Bedrooms unattended Charges Public
areas Grounds Exercise area Resident Pet:
West Highland Terrier

Conveniently and quietly located, this hotel is
close to the Devon, Dorset and Somerset borders,
and only minutes from Chard. All bedrooms are
well equipped and comfortable. The friendly
lounge bar has a wood-burning stove and serves
tempting bar meals. The conservatory restaurant
offers more formal dining.

Rooms 25 (2 fmly) (7 GF) S £70-£75;
D £105-£110 (incl. bkfst)* Facilities FTV Xmas
New Year Wi-fi Conf Class 60 Board 40 Thtr 180
Del from £115 to £125* Parking 55 Notes LB
Civ Wed 100

CLUTTON

The Hunters Rest

★★★★ INN

☎ 01761 452303 📠 01761 453308
King Ln, Clutton Hill BS39 5QL
e-mail: paul@huntersrest.co.uk
web: www.huntersrest.co.uk
dir: Off A37 onto A368 towards Bath, 100yds
right onto lane, left at T-junct, inn 0.25m on left

PETS: Bedrooms unattended Charges Public
areas Grounds Exercise area adjacent Facilities
food (pre-bookable) food bowl water bowl Other
dogs allowed in certain bedrooms only Resident
Pet: Reg (Black Labrador)

This establishment was originally built around
1750 as a hunting lodge for the Earl of Warwick.
Set in delightful countryside, it is ideally
located for Bath, Bristol and Wells. Bedrooms
and bathrooms are furnished and equipped
to excellent standards, and the ground floor
combines the character of a real country inn with
an excellent range of home-cooked meals.

Rooms 5 en suite (1 fmly) Facilities tea/
coffee Dinner available Direct Dial Cen ht
Wi-fi Conf Max 40 Thtr 40 Class 25 Board 25
Parking 90

DUNSTER

The Luttrell Arms Hotel

★★★ 73% HOTEL

☎ 01643 821555 📠 01643 821567
High St TA24 6SG
e-mail: info@luttrellarms.fsnet.co.uk
web: www.luttrellarms.co.uk/main.htm
dir: A39/A396 S toward Tiverton. Hotel on left
opposite Yarn Market

PETS: Bedrooms unattended Charges Public
areas except restaurant Grounds Exercise area
adjacent Resident Pets: Merlin & Mordred (cats)

Occupying an enviable position on the high
street, this 15th-century hotel looks up towards
the town's famous castle. Beautifully renovated
and decorated, high levels of comfort can
be found throughout. Some of the spacious
bedrooms have four-poster beds. The warm
and friendly staff provide attentive service in a
relaxed atmosphere.

Rooms 28 (3 fmly) S £70-£102; D £104-£140
(incl. bkfst)* Facilities Exmoor safaris Historic
tours Walking tours New Year Conf Class 20
Board 20 Thtr 35 Notes LB

EXFORD

Crown Hotel

★★★ 75% ◉ HOTEL

☎ 01643 831554   📠 01643 831665
TA24 7PP
e-mail: info@crownhotelexmoor.co.uk
web: www.crownhotelexmoor.co.uk
dir: M5 junct 25, follow Taunton signs. Take A358
from Taunton, then B3224 via Wheddon Cross
to Exford

PETS: Bedrooms unattended Charges Public
areas except restaurant Grounds Exercise area
25mtrs Facilities water bowl Resident Pet: Oscar
(Patterdale Terrier)

Guest comfort is certainly the hallmark here.
Afternoon tea is served in the lounge beside
a roaring fire and tempting menus in the bar
and restaurant are all part of the charm of this
delightful old coaching inn that specialises in
breaks for shooting and other country sports.
Bedrooms retain a traditional style yet offer a
range of modern comforts and facilities, many
with views of this pretty moorland village.

Rooms 17 (3 fmly) S £70; D £110-£140
(incl. bkfst)* Facilities Xmas New Year
Wi-fi Conf Board 15 Del from £115 to £150*
Parking 30 Notes LB

HIGHBRIDGE

The Greenwood

★★★★ GUEST ACCOMMODATION

☎ 01278 795886   📠 01278 795886
76 Main Rd, West Huntspill TA9 3QU
e-mail: info@the-greenwood.co.uk
web: www.the-greenwood.co.uk
dir: On A38 in West Huntspill, between Orchard
Inn & Sundowner Hotel

PETS: Bedrooms unattended Charges Public
areas except restaurant Grounds Exercise area
adjacent Facilities water bowl

Set in two acres of land, this 18th-century former
farmhouse and family home offers comfortable
accommodation in a friendly environment.
Breakfast, featuring home-made preserves, is
served in the dining room and home-cooked
dinners are available by arrangement. There is a
lounge for relaxation.

Rooms 7 rms (6 en suite) (1 pri facs) (3 fmly) (1
GF) S £47.50; D £68* Facilities TVL tea/coffee
Dinner available Cen ht Licensed Wi-fi Treatment
room Conf Max 30 Thtr 30 Class 20 Board 12
Parking 8 Notes LB

ILMINSTER

Best Western Shrubbery Hotel

★★★ 78% HOTEL

☎ 01460 52108 📄 01460 53660
TA19 9AR
e-mail: stuart@shrubberyhotel.com
web: www.shrubberyhotel.com
dir: 0.5m from A303 towards Ilminster town centre

PETS: Bedrooms unattended Charges Public areas except restaurant Grounds Exercise area nature reserve 0.25m Facilities food bowl water bowl Resident Pet: Oscar (Collie)

Set in attractive terraced gardens, the Shrubbery is a well established hotel in this small town. Bedrooms are well equipped and bright, and include three ground-floor rooms and impressive executive rooms. Bar meals or full meals are available in the bar, lounges and restaurant. Additional facilities include a range of function rooms.

Rooms 21 (3 fmly) (3 GF) S £60-£100;
D £80-£140 (incl. bkfst)* Facilities STV ﾃ New Year Wi-fi Conf Class 100 Board 60 Thtr 200 Del from £110 to £140* Parking 70 Notes LB Closed 24-26 Dec Civ Wed 200

MINEHEAD

Best Western Northfield Hotel

★★★ 74% HOTEL

☎ 01643 705155 & 0845 1302678
📄 01643 707715
Northfield Rd TA24 5PU
e-mail: reservations@northfield-hotel.co.uk
web: www.northfield-hotel.co.uk
dir: M5 junct 23, follow A38 to Bridgwater then A39 to Minehead

PETS: Bedrooms unattended Charges Public areas Grounds

Located conveniently close to the town centre and the seafront, this hotel is set in delightfully maintained gardens and has a loyal following. A range of comfortable sitting rooms and leisure facilities, including an indoor, heated pool is provided. A fixed-price menu is served every evening in the oak-panelled dining room. The attractively co-ordinated bedrooms vary in size and are equipped to a good standard.

Rooms 30 (7 fmly) (4 GF) (6 smoking)
Facilities STV FTV ﾃ Putt green Gym Steam room Xmas New Year Wi-fi Conf Class 45 Board 30 Thtr 70 Services Lift Parking 34

MINEHEAD

Alcombe House Hotel
★★ 85% HOTEL

☎ 01643 705130 📄 01643 705130
Bircham Rd, Alcombe TA24 6BG
e-mail: alcombe.house@virgin.net
web: www.alcombehouse.co.uk
dir: On A39 on outskirts of Minehead opposite
West Somerset Community College

PETS: Bedrooms unattended Public areas
Grounds Exercise area 0.25m Facilities water
bowl Other prior notice required

Located midway between Minehead and Dunster
on the coastal fringe of Exmoor National Park,
this Grade II listed, Georgian hotel offers a
delightful combination of efficient service
and genuine hospitality delivered by the very
welcoming resident proprietors. Public areas
include a comfortable lounge and a candlelit
dining room where a range of carefully prepared
dishes is offered from a daily-changing menu.

Rooms 7 S £44; D £68 (incl. bkfst)* Facilities
Xmas Parking 9 Notes No children 15yrs Closed
8 Nov-18 Mar

RUDGE

The Full Moon Inn
★★★ INN

☎ 01373 830936
BA11 2QF
e-mail: info@thefullmoon.co.uk
dir: From A36 S from Bath, 10m, left at
Standerwick by The Bell pub. 4m from
Warminster

PETS: Bedrooms unattended Charges Public
areas except restaurant Grounds Exercise area
local walks

Peacefully located in the quiet village of Rudge,
this traditional inn offers a warm welcome and
a proper country pub atmosphere. In the bar
area, guests mix well with the locals to enjoy a
selection of real ales and a log fire in the colder
months. In addition to bar meals, a comfortable
restaurant serving excellent home cooked dishes
is available. Bedrooms include some at the main
inn and more in an adjacent annexe - all are
comfortable and well equipped.

Rooms 5 en suite 12 annexe en suite (2 fmly)
(3 GF) S £57.50-£62.50; D £79.50-£85*
Facilities tea/coffee Dinner available Cen ht
🕙 Conf Max 65 Thtr 30 Class 12 Board 18
Parking 25 Notes LB

STANTON DREW

Greenlands
★★★★ FARMHOUSE

☎ 01275 333487 📠 01275 331211
BS39 4ES
Mrs J Cleverley
dir: A37 onto B3130, on right before Stanton
Drew Garage

PETS: Bedrooms unattended **Public areas** except
dining room **Grounds Exercise area** adjacent
Resident Pets: Spoof & Magic (Labradors)

Situated near the ancient village of Stanton Drew
in the heart of the Chew Valley, Greenlands is
convenient for Bristol Airport and Bath, Bristol
and Wells. There are comfortable, well-equipped
bedrooms and a downstairs lounge, and
breakfast is the highlight of any stay here.

Rooms 4 en suite **Facilities** STV FTV TVL tea/
coffee Cen ht **Parking** 8 **Notes** No Children 12yrs
🐾 3 acres Hobby Farming - Poultry

TAUNTON

The Mount Somerset Hotel
★★★ 77% ☺☺ HOTEL

☎ 01823 442500 📠 01823 442900
Lower Henlade TA3 5NB
e-mail: info@mountsomersethotel.co.uk
web: www.vonessenhotels.co.uk
dir: M5 junct 25, A358 towards Chard/Ilminster,
at Henlade right into Stoke Rd, left at T-junct at
end, then right into drive

PETS: Bedrooms unattended **Charges Public
areas** except restaurant & conservatory **Facilities**
food bowl water bowl

From its elevated and rural position, this
impressive Regency house has wonderful views
over Taunton Vale. Some of the well-appointed
bedrooms have feature bathrooms, and the
elegant public rooms are stylish with an intimate
atmosphere. In addition to the daily-changing,
fixed-price menu, a carefully selected seasonal
carte is available in the restaurant.

Rooms 11 (1 fmly) S £110-£150; D £125-£280
(incl. bkfst)* **Facilities** 🧖 Beauty treatments
Xmas New Year Wi-fi Conf Class 30 Board 20
Thtr 60 Del from £195 to £205* **Services** Lift
Parking 100 **Notes** Civ Wed 60

WELLS

Coxley Vineyard

★★ 72% HOTEL

☎ 01749 670285   📠 01749 679708
Coxley BA5 1RQ
e-mail: max@orofino.freeserve.co.uk
dir: A39 from Wells signed Coxley. Village halfway
between Wells & Glastonbury. Hotel off main road
at end of village

PETS: Bedrooms unattended Public areas except
restaurant & lounge bar Grounds Exercise area
surrounding area Facilities water bowl

This privately owned and personally run hotel
was built on the site of an old cider farm. It was
later part of a commercial vineyard and some of
the vines are still in evidence. It provides well
equipped, modern bedrooms; most are situated
on the ground floor. There is a comfortable bar
and a spacious restaurant with an impressive
lantern ceiling. The hotel is a popular venue for
conferences and other functions.

Rooms 9 (5 fmly) (8 GF) S £60-£70;
D £65-£89.50 (incl. bkfst)* Facilities ⌇
Xmas Wi-fi Conf Class 50 Board 40 Thtr 90
Del from £70 to £80* Parking 50 Notes LB

WELLS

The Crown at Wells

★★★★ INN

☎ 01749 673457   📠 01749 679792
Market Place BA5 2RP
e-mail: stay@crownatwells.co.uk
web: www.crownatwells.co.uk
dir: In city centre

PETS: Bedrooms unattended Charges Public
areas Exercise area Facilities food bowl water
bowl

Retaining its original features and period charm,
this historic inn is situated in the heart of the
city, just a short stroll from the cathedral. The
building's frontage has been used for many film
sets. Bedrooms, all with modern facilities, vary in
size and style. Public areas focus around Anton's,
the popular bistro, which offers a light and airy
environment and relaxed atmosphere. The Penn
Bar offers an alternative eating option and real
ales.

Rooms 15 en suite (2 fmly) S £45-£90; D
£90-£110* Facilities FTV tea/coffee Dinner
available Cen ht Parking 10 Notes LB

WESTON-SUPER-MARE

Ynishir B&B

★★★ BED AND BREAKFAST

☎ 01934 412703 & 0771 495 0023
74 Uphill Way BS23 4TN
e-mail: simon.bilkus@homecall.co.uk
dir: A370 follow signs to hospital (Grange Rd),
right at mini-rdbt, left onto Uphill Way

PETS: Bedrooms unattended Charges Public
areas Exercise area opposite Other dogs
allowed in one bedroom only Resident Pets:
Polly & Bella (Labradors), Immy & Maisy (Jack
Russells), 1 cat, 2 goats, 1 horse

Set in pleasant countryside in the quiet village
of Uphill, just a short distance from the Channel,
Ynishir has one bedroom with private facilities,
and would be ideal for anyone who wants to walk
the Mendip Way.

Rooms 1 en suite (1 fmly) (1 GF) Facilities FTV
TVL tea/coffee Cen ht Parking 1 Notes 🐾

WINCANTON

Holbrook House

★★★ 79% ⊛⊛ COUNTRY HOUSE HOTEL

☎ 01963 824466 & 828844 📄 01963 32681
Holbrook BA9 8BS
e-mail: enquiries@holbrookhouse.co.uk
web: www.holbrookhouse.co.uk
dir: From A303 at Wincanton left onto A371
towards Castle Cary & Shepton Mallet

PETS: Bedrooms unattended Charges Public
areas except restaurant areas Grounds Exercise
area 50mtrs Facilities food bowl water bowl

This handsome country house offers a unique
blend of quality and comfort combined with a
friendly atmosphere. Set in 17 acres of peaceful
gardens and wooded grounds, Holbrook House
makes a perfect retreat. The restaurant provides
a selection of innovative dishes prepared with
enthusiasm and served by a team of caring staff.

Rooms 21 (5 annexe) (2 fmly) (5 GF)
D £140-£250 (incl. bkfst) Facilities Spa FTV ⊛
⊛ ⊛ Gym Beauty treatment Exercise classes
Sauna Steam room Fitness suite 🎵 Xmas New
Year Wi-fi Conf Class 50 Board 55 Thtr 200
Parking 100 Notes LB Civ Wed 150

WINSFORD

Karslake House
★★★★ ◉ GUEST HOUSE

☎ 01643 851242 📄 01643 851242
Halse Ln TA24 7JE
e-mail: enquiries@karslakehouse.co.uk
web: www.karslakehouse.co.uk
dir: In village centre, past pub, up hill

PETS: Bedrooms unattended Charges Public
areas Exercise area 50yds Resident Pets: Cassa
(Staffordshire Bull Terrier), Molly (cat)

The 15th-century Karslake House stands in a
peaceful Exmoor village. Its public rooms feature
original beams and fireplaces, and an interesting
menu of delicious dishes is available in the
dining room. Bedrooms are thoughtfully furnished
and have a number of extra touches.

Rooms 6 rms (5 en suite) (1 pri facs) (1 GF)
Facilities tea/coffee Dinner available Cen ht
Licensed Aromatherapist & Masseuse Parking 15
Notes No Children 12yrs Closed Feb & Mar RS
Nov-Jan Limited opening by request

YEOVIL

Little Barwick House
★★★★★ ◉◉◉ RESTAURANT WITH ROOMS

☎ 01935 423902 📄 01935 420908
Barwick Village BA22 9TD
e-mail: littlebarwick@hotmail.com
dir: From Yeovil A37 towards Dorchester, left at
1st rdbt, 1st left, 0.25m on left

PETS: Bedrooms unattended Charges Public
areas except restaurant Grounds Exercise area
fields & footpaths accessed from house Other
dogs allowed in lounge if acceptable to other
guests Resident Pets: Ellie (Pointer), Rossi &
Casey (cats), Pip & Bugsy (Hanovarian event
horses)

Situated in a quiet hamlet in three and half acres
of gardens and grounds, this listed Georgian
dower house is an ideal retreat for those seeking
peaceful surroundings and good food. Just one
of the highlights of a stay here is a meal in the
restaurant, where good use is made of local
ingredients. Each bedroom has its own character,
and a range of thoughtful extras such as fresh
flowers, bottled water and magazines.

Rooms 6 en suite Facilities tea/coffee Dinner
available Direct Dial Cen ht Parking 30 Notes LB
No Children 5yrs RS Sun eve & Mon Closed No
coaches

YEOVIL

The Helyar Arms
★★★★ @ INN

☎ 01935 862332 📠 01935 864129
Moor Ln, East Coker BA22 9JR
e-mail: info@helyar-arms.co.uk
dir: 3m S of Yeovil. Off A30 or A37 into East Coker

PETS: **Bedrooms** unattended **Charges Public
areas Grounds Exercise area** 0.5m

A charming 15th-century inn, serving real
food in the heart of a pretty Somerset village.
The traditional friendly bar with hand-drawn
ales retains many original features while
the bedrooms offer well equipped, attractive
accommodation and modern facilities.

Rooms 6 en suite (3 fmly) **S** £65; **D** £89*
Facilities tea/coffee Dinner available Direct Dial
Cen ht Wi-fi Skittle alley **Conf** Max 40 Thtr 40
Class 20 Board 30 **Parking** 40 **Notes** LB

ALDEBURGH

Wentworth Hotel
★★★ 88% @@ HOTEL

☎ 01728 452312 📠 01728 454343
Wentworth Rd IP15 5BD
e-mail: stay@wentworth-aldeburgh.co.uk
web: www.wentworth-aldeburgh.com
dir: Off A12 onto A1094, 6m to Aldeburgh, with
church on left, left at bottom of hill

PETS: **Bedrooms** unattended **Charges Public
areas** except restaurant **Grounds Exercise area**
300mtrs **Facilities** water bowl **Restrictions** no
breed larger than a Labrador accepted

A delightful privately owned hotel overlooking the
beach. The attractive, well-maintained public
rooms include three stylish lounges as well as a
cocktail bar and elegant restaurant. Bedrooms
are smartly decorated with co-ordinated fabrics
and have many thoughtful touches; some rooms
have superb sea views. Several very spacious
Mediterranean-style rooms are located across
the road.

Rooms 35 (7 annexe) (5 GF) **S** £58-£100;
D £98-£232 (incl. bkfst)* **Facilities** FTV Xmas
New Year Wi-fi **Conf** Class 12 Board 12 Thtr 15
Del from £95 to £115 **Parking** 30 **Notes** LB

ALDEBURGH

The Brudenell
★★★ 87% ⊛⊛ HOTEL

☎ 01728 452071 🖹 01728 454082
The Parade IP15 5BU
e-mail: info@brudenellhotel.co.uk
web: www.brudenellhotel.co.uk
dir: A12/A1094, on reaching town, turn right at
junct into High St. Hotel on seafront adjoining
Fort Green car park

PETS: **Bedrooms** unattended **Charges Public
areas** except bar & restaurant (assist dogs only)
Exercise area Facilities food (pre-bookable)
food bowl water bowl **Restrictions** well behaved
dogs only

Situated at the far end of the town centre just
a step away from the beach, this hotel has a
contemporary appearance, enhanced by subtle
lighting and quality soft furnishings. Many
of the bedrooms have superb sea views; they
include deluxe rooms with king-sized beds and
superior rooms suitable for families. The informal
restaurant showcases skilfully prepared dishes
that use fresh, seasonal produce especially local
fish, seafood and game.

Rooms 42 (15 fmly) S £64-£115; D £114-£238
(incl. bkfst)* **Facilities** Xmas New Year Wi-fi
Services Lift Parking 16 **Notes** LB

ALDEBURGH

Best Western White Lion Hotel
★★★ 83% ⊛ HOTEL

☎ 01728 452720 🖹 01728 452986
Market Cross Place IP15 5BJ
e-mail: info@whitelion.co.uk
web: www.whitelion.co.uk
dir: A12 onto A1094, follow signs to Aldeburgh at
junct on left. Hotel on right

PETS: **Bedrooms** unattended **Charges Public
areas** except restaurant **Exercise area** beach
adjacent (Oct-Apr only) **Facilities** food bowl
water bowl **Other** well behaved dogs only; dogs
allowed in certain bedrooms only

A popular 15th-century hotel situated at the quiet
end of town overlooking the sea. Bedrooms are
pleasantly decorated and thoughtfully equipped,
many rooms have lovely sea views. Public areas
include two lounges and an elegant restaurant,
where locally-caught fish and seafood are served.
There is also a modern brasserie.

Rooms 38 (1 fmly) S £68-£99.50; D £110-£214
(incl. bkfst)* **Facilities** STV Xmas New Year Wi-fi
Conf Class 50 **Board** 50 **Thtr** 120 **Parking** 15
Notes LB Civ Wed 100

BILDESTON

The Bildeston Crown
★★★ @@@ HOTEL

☎ 01449 740510 📠 01449 741843
104 High St IP7 7EB
e-mail: hayley@thebildestoncrown.co.uk
web: www.thebildestoncrown.co.uk
dir: A12 junct 31, right onto B1070, follow
signs to Hadleigh. At T-junct left onto A1141,
immediately right onto B1115. Hotel 0.5m

PETS: Bedrooms unattended Charges Public
areas except restaurant Grounds Exercise area
Facilities food bowl water bowl

A charming inn situated in a peaceful village
close to historic Lavenham. Public areas,
including bars, a lounge and a restaurant
feature beams and exposed brickwork, along with
contemporary decor. The bedrooms have lovely
co-ordinated fabrics, and facilities that include
a Yamaha music system and LCD TVs. Food here
is the real draw; guests can expect fresh, high-
quality local produce and accomplished technical
skills in both modern and classic dishes.

Rooms 13 S £80-£150; D £150-£250
(incl. bkfst)* Facilities STV FTV Xmas New
Year Wi-fi Conf Class 25 Board 16 Thtr 40
Del from £135 to £175* Services Lift Parking 30
Notes Civ Wed 50

BUNGAY

Kings Head Hotel
★★ 60% HOTEL

☎ 01986 893583
2 Market Place NR35 1AW
e-mail: info@kingsheadhotel.biz
web: www.kingsheadhotel.biz
dir: A143 to town centre

PETS: Bedrooms unattended Public areas bar
only Grounds Exercise area

This 18th-century coaching inn is situated in the
heart of town, amid a range of antique shops.
The spacious bedrooms are furnished with
pine pieces and have a good range of useful
extras; one room has a superb four-poster bed.
Public rooms include a restaurant, the Duke of
Wellington lounge bar and Oddfellows bar.

Rooms 13 (1 fmly) (4 smoking) Conf Class 50
Board 50 Thtr 100 Parking 29

BURY ST EDMUNDS

Angel Hotel

★★★★ 82% ◎◎ TOWN HOUSE HOTEL

☎ 01284 714000 🖹 01284 714001
Angel Hill IP33 1LT
e-mail: staying@theangel.co.uk
web: www.theangel.co.uk
dir: From A134, left at rdbt into Northgate St.
Continue to lights, right into Mustow St, left into
Angel Hill. Hotel on right

PETS: Bedrooms unattended Charges Public
areas lounge only Exercise area Abbey Gardens,
1 min walk

An impressive building situated just a short
walk from the town centre. One of the Angel's
more notable guests over the last 400 years was
Charles Dickens who is reputed to have written
part of the *Pickwick Papers* whilst in residence.
The hotel offers a range of individually designed
bedrooms that includes a selection of four-poster
rooms and a suite.

Rooms 75 (7 fmly) (15 GF) D £90-£150 (incl.
bkfst)* Facilities FTV Xmas New Year Wi-fi
Conf Class 20 Board 30 Thtr 90 Services Lift
Parking 20 Notes LB Civ Wed 80

BURY ST EDMUNDS

Ravenwood Hall

★★★ 88% ◎◎ COUNTRY HOUSE HOTEL

☎ 01359 270345 🖹 01359 270788
Rougham IP30 9JA
e-mail: enquiries@ravenwoodhall.co.uk
web: www.ravenwoodhall.co.uk
dir: 3m E off A14, junct 45. Hotel on left

PETS: Bedrooms unattended Charges Public
areas except restaurant Grounds Other please
phone for details of further facilities for dogs
Resident Pet: Minx (Labrador)

Delightful 15th-century property set in seven
acres of woodland and landscaped gardens. The
building has many original features including
carved timbers and inglenook fireplaces. The
spacious bedrooms are attractively decorated,
tastefully furnished with well-chosen pieces and
equipped with many thoughtful touches. Public
rooms include an elegant restaurant and a smart
lounge bar with an open fire.

Rooms 14 (7 annexe) (5 GF) Facilities ⚞ ⚟
Shooting fishing & horse riding can be arranged
Xmas New Year Wi-fi Conf Class 80 Board 40
Thtr 130 Parking 150 Notes Civ Wed 130

155

Best Western Priory

★★★ 83% ◉◉ HOTEL

☎ 01284 766181 📠 01284 767604

Mildenhall Rd IP32 6EH

e-mail: reservations@prioryhotel.co.uk

web: www.prioryhotel.co.uk

dir: From A14 take Bury St Edmunds W slip road. Follow signs to Brandon. At mini-rdbt turn right. Hotel 0.5m on left

PETS: **Bedrooms** unattended **Charges Public areas Grounds**

An 18th-century Grade II listed building set in landscaped grounds on the outskirts of town. The attractively decorated, tastefully furnished and thoughtfully equipped bedrooms are split between the main house and garden wings, which have their own sun terraces. Public rooms feature a smart restaurant, a conservatory dining room and a lounge bar.

Rooms 39 (30 annexe) (1 fmly) (30 GF) **Facilities** FTV Xmas New Year Wi-fi **Conf** Class 20 Board 20 Thtr 40 **Parking** 60 **Notes** Civ Wed 50

The Fox & Hounds

★★★★ INN

☎ 01284 386379

Felsham Rd, Bradfield St George IP30 0AB

dir: From A134 (Sudbury road), turn left just past Rushbrook Inn. Follow signs for Bradfield St George

PETS: **Bedrooms** unattended **Charges Public areas** except restaurant & lounge **Grounds Exercise area Facilities** water bowl **Resident Pet:** Cody (Jack Russell cross)

Charming inn situated in a peaceful rural location surrounded by open countryside. The well equipped bedrooms are located in a converted barn to the rear of the property; each one has lovely pine furniture and co-ordinated soft furnishings. Public rooms include a cosy bar, a smart dining room and a small conservatory.

Rooms 2 annexe en suite (2 GF); D £65* **Facilities** FTV tea/coffee Dinner available Cen ht **Parking** 25 **Notes** No Children RS Mon closed

HADLEIGH

Edge Hall

★★★★★ GUEST ACCOMMODATION

☎ 01473 822458 🖷 01473 822458
2 High St IP7 5AP
e-mail: r.rolfe@edgehall.co.uk
dir: B1070 into Hadleigh. 1st property in High
St on right

PETS: Bedrooms unattended Charges Public
areas Grounds Exercise area 100yds Facilities
water bowl Resident Pet: Truffles (Standard
Poodle)

This imposing 16th-century building is situated
at the quiet end of High Street and has been
run by the same family for over 25 years. The
spacious bedrooms are individually decorated
and carefully furnished in period style - one room
has a superb four-poster bed. Breakfast is served
in the elegant dining room and there is also a
comfortable lounge.

Rooms 6 en suite 4 annexe en suite (2 fmly) (1
GF) S £57.5-£67.5; D £85-£110 Facilities tea/
coffee Cen ht 🐾 Conf Max 12 Parking 20
Notes LB 🐾

HORRINGER

The Ickworth Hotel & Apartments

★★★★ 72% ◉◉ COUNTRY HOUSE HOTEL

☎ 01284 735350 🖷 01284 736300
IP29 5QE
e-mail: info@ickworthhotel.co.uk
web: www.ickworthhotel.co.uk
dir: A14 exit for Bury St Edmunds, follow Ickworth
House signs, 4th exit at rdbt, on at staggered
x-rds to T-junct, right into village, right into
Estate

PETS: Bedrooms unattended Public areas except
restaurant & food areas Grounds Other prior
notice required; please contact hotel to confirm
which dog breeds are accepted

Gifted to the National Trust in 1956 this
stunning property is in part a luxurious hotel that
combines the glorious design and atmosphere
of the past with a reputation for making
children very welcome. The staff are friendly
and easy going, there is a children's play area,
crèche, horses and bikes to ride, and wonderful
'Capability' Brown gardens to roam in.

Rooms 39 (12 annexe) (35 fmly) (4 GF)
Facilities Spa STV FTV 🐾 🏊 🐾 Adventure
playground Vineyard Xmas New Year Wi-fi
Child facilities Conf Class 30 Board 20 Thtr 35
Services Lift Parking 40 Notes Civ Wed 40

IPSWICH

Novotel Ipswich Centre
★★★ 82% HOTEL

☎ 01473 232400 📄 01473 232414
Greyfriars Rd IP1 1UP
e-mail: h0995@accor.com
web: www.novotel.com
dir: From A14 towards Felixstowe. Left onto A137, follow for 2m into town centre. Hotel on double rdbt by Stoke Bridge

PETS: Bedrooms unattended Charges Public areas except restaurant Grounds Exercise area marina & parks nearby

A modern, red brick hotel perfectly placed in the centre of town close to shops, bars and restaurants. The open-plan public areas include a Mediterranean-style restaurant and a bar with a small games area. The bedrooms are smartly appointed and have many thoughtful touches; three rooms are suitable for less mobile guests.

Rooms 101 (8 fmly) Facilities Gym Pool table Sauna Xmas New Year Wi-fi Conf Class 75 Board 45 Thtr 180 Services Lift Air con Parking 53 Notes LB Civ Wed 75

LAVENHAM

The Swan
★★★★ 82% ⊛⊛ HOTEL

☎ 01787 247477 📄 01787 248286
High St CO10 9QA
e-mail: info@theswanatlavenham.co.uk
web: www.theswanatlavenham.co.uk
dir: From Bury St Edmunds take A134 (S), then A1141 to Lavenham

PETS: Bedrooms unattended Charges Public areas except food service areas Grounds Exercise area 400yds Facilities water bowl Other well behaved dogs only

A delightful collection of listed buildings dating back to the 14th century, lovingly restored to retain their original charm. Public rooms include comfortable lounge areas, a charming rustic bar, an informal brasserie and a fine-dining restaurant. Bedrooms are tastefully furnished and equipped with many thoughtful touches. The friendly staff are helpful, attentive and offer professional service.

Rooms 45 (11 fmly) (13 GF) S £75-£85; D £160-£280 (incl. bkfst)* Facilities STV FTV Xmas New Year Wi-fi Conf Class 36 Board 30 Thtr 50 Del from £145 to £165* Parking 62 Notes LB Civ Wed 100

LONG MELFORD

The Black Lion Hotel
★★★ 79% HOTEL

☎ 01787 312356 📄 01787 374557
Church Walk, The Green CO10 9DN
e-mail: enquiries@blacklionhotel.net
web: www.blacklionhotel.net
dir: At junct of A134 & A1092

PETS: **Bedrooms** unattended **Charges Public
areas** except restaurant **Grounds Exercise area**
opposite **Facilities** water bowl

This charming 15th-century hotel is situated on
the edge of this bustling town overlooking the
green. Bedrooms are generally spacious and each
is attractively decorated, tastefully furnished and
equipped with useful extras. An interesting range
of dishes is served in the lounge bar or guests
may choose to dine from the same innovative
menu in the more formal restaurant.

Rooms 10 (1 fmly) **S** £99.50-£132.50;
D £153-£199 (incl. bkfst)* **Facilities** Xmas
New Year Wi-fi **Conf** Class 28 Board 28 Thtr 50
Parking 10 **Notes** LB Civ Wed 50

NEWMARKET

Best Western Heath Court Hotel
★★★ 78% HOTEL

☎ 01638 667171 📄 01638 666533
Moulton Rd CB8 8DY
e-mail: quality@heathcourthotel.com
dir: Leave A14 at Newmarket & Ely exit onto
A142. Follow town centre signs over mini rdbt. At
clocktower left into Moulton Rd

ETS: **Bedrooms** unattended **Charges Public
areas Grounds Exercise area** 200yds **Facilities**
food (pre-bookable) food bowl water bowl

Modern red-brick hotel situated close to
Newmarket Heath and perfectly placed for the
town centre. Public rooms include a choice of
dining options - informal meals can be taken
in the lounge bar or a modern carte menu is
offered in the restaurant. The smartly presented
bedrooms are mostly spacious and some have air
conditioning.

Rooms 41 (2 fmly) **Facilities** STV New Year
Wi-fi **Conf** Class 50 Board 40 Thtr 130
Del from £85 to £145* **Services** Lift **Parking** 60
Notes Civ Wed 80

NEWMARKET

The Garden Lodge
★★★★ BED AND BREAKFAST

☎ 01638 731116
11 Vicarage Ln, Woodditton CB8 9SG
e-mail: swedishgardenlodge@hotmail.com
web: www.gardenlodge.net
dir: 3m S of Newmarket in Woodditton

PETS: Bedrooms unattended Public areas
Grounds Facilities food bowl water bowl
Restrictions no Bull Terriers

A warm welcome is assured in this home-from-
home, not far from the famous racecourse. The
accommodation, in quality chalets, is very well
equipped and features a wealth of thoughtful
extras. Freshly prepared home-cooked breakfasts
are served in an elegant dining room in the main
house.

Rooms 3 en suite (3 GF) S £35-£40; D £60-£70*
Facilities tea/coffee Dinner available Cen ht
Parking 6 Notes 🐕

ORFORD

The Crown & Castle
★★★ 85% ⊛⊛ HOTEL

☎ 01394 450205
IP12 2LJ
e-mail: info@crownandcastle.co.uk
web: www.crownandcastle.co.uk
dir: Turn right from B1084 on entering village,
towards castle

PETS: Bedrooms unattended Charges Public
areas Grounds Exercise area Other 1 dog-
friendly table in restaurant Resident Pets: Jack,
Teddy & Ande (Wire-Haired Fox Terriers)

Delightful inn situated adjacent to the Norman
castle keep. Contemporary style bedrooms are
spilt between the main house and the garden
wing; the latter are more spacious and have
patios with access to the garden. The restaurant
has an informal atmosphere with polished tables
and local artwork; the menu features quality,
locally sourced produce.

Rooms 19 (12 annexe) (1 fmly) (11 GF)
S £92-£164; D £115-£205 (incl. bkfst)* Facilities
Xmas New Year Wi-fi Conf Board 10 Parking 20
Notes LB No children 4yrs Closed 4-7 Jan

SOUTHWOLD

Blyth Hotel

★★ 85% ® SMALL HOTEL

☎ 01502 722632 & 0845 348 6867
Station Rd IP18 6AY
e-mail: reception@blythhotel.com

PETS: Bedrooms unattended Charges Public
areas except restaurant & lounge Grounds
Exercise area 5 mins

Expect a warm welcome at this delightful family
run hotel which is situated just a short walk
from the town centre. The spacious public rooms
include a smart residents' lounge, an open-
plan bar and a large restaurant. Bedrooms are
tastefully appointed with co-ordinated fabrics
and have many thoughtful touches.

Rooms 13 S £65-£75; D £95-£115 (incl. bkfst)*
Facilities FTV Xmas New Year Wi-fi Conf Class 20
Board 12 Thtr 20 Del from £90 to £150*
Parking 8 Notes LB

WOODBRIDGE

Best Western Ufford Park Hotel
Golf & Spa

★★★ 82% HOTEL

☎ 01394 383555 📠 0844 4773727
Yarmouth Rd, Ufford IP12 1QW
e-mail: mail@uffordpark.co.uk
web: www.uffordpark.co.uk
dir: A12 N to A1152, in Melton left at lights,
follow B1438, hotel 1m on right

PETS: Bedrooms unattended Charges Public
areas except restaurant Grounds Exercise area
0.5m Facilities food bowl water bowl

A modern hotel set in open countryside boasting
superb leisure facilities including a challenging
golf course. The spacious public rooms provide
a wide choice of areas in which to relax and
include a busy lounge bar, a carvery restaurant
and the Vista Restaurant. Bedrooms are smartly
appointed; many overlook the golf course.

Rooms 87 (20 fmly) (32 GF) S £90-£120;
D £110-£170 (incl. bkfst)* Facilities Spa FTV
🏊 supervised ₤ 18 Putt green Fishing 🏋 Gym
Golf Academy with PGA tuition 2 storey floodlit
driving range Dance Studio Xmas New Year Wi-fi
Conf Class 120 Board 120 Thtr 300 Del from £99
to £116* Services Lift Parking 250 Notes LB
Civ Wed 120

DORKING

Mercure White Horse Hotel
★★★ 66% HOTEL

☎ 0870 400 8282 📄 01306 887241
High St RH4 1BE
web: www.mercure-uk.com
dir: M25 junct 9, A24 S towards Dorking. Hotel in
town centre

PETS: Bedrooms unattended Charges Public
areas Grounds Exercise area 100yds

The hotel was first established as an inn in 1750,
although parts of the building date back as far
as the 15th century. Its town centre location and
Dickensian charm have long made this a popular
destination for travellers. There's beamed
ceilings, open fires and four-poster beds; more
contemporary rooms can be found in the garden
wing.

Rooms 78 (41 annexe) (2 fmly) (5 GF) Facilities
Xmas Conf Class 30 Board 30 Thtr 50 Parking 73

ALFRISTON

Deans Place
★★★ 82% ◉ HOTEL

☎ 01323 870248 📄 01323 870918
Seaford Rd BN26 5TW
e-mail: mail@deansplacehotel.co.uk
web: www.deansplacehotel.co.uk
dir: Off A27, signed Alfriston & Drusillas Zoo
Park. Continue south through village

PETS: Bedrooms unattended Charges Public
areas except restaurant & function rooms
Grounds Facilities water bowl

Situated on the southern fringe of the village,
this friendly hotel is set in attractive gardens.
Bedrooms vary in size and are well appointed
with good facilities. A wide range of food is
offered including an extensive bar menu and a
fine dining option in Harcourt's Restaurant.

Rooms 36 (4 fmly) (8 GF) S £80-£90;
D £120-£170 (incl. bkfst) Facilities STV FTV
⚲ Putt green 😊 Boules Xmas New Year Wi-fi
Conf Class 100 Board 60 Thtr 200 Parking 100
Notes LB Civ Wed 150

ALFRISTON

The Star Inn
★★★ 70% HOTEL

☎ 01323 870495 📠 01323 870922
BN26 5TA
e-mail: bookings@thestaralfriston.co.uk
dir: 2m off A27, at Drusillas rdbt follow Alfriston signs. Hotel on right in centre of High St

PETS: Bedrooms unattended Charges Public areas except restaurant Exercise area 0.2m

Built in the 13th century and reputedly one of the country's oldest inns, this charming establishment is ideally situated for walking the South Down or exploring the Sussex coast. Bedrooms, including two feature rooms and mini suite, are traditionally decorated but with comfortable, modern facilities. Public areas include cosy lounges with open log fires, a bar and a popular restaurant serving a wide choice of dishes using mainly local produce. Guests can also enjoy luxury spa treatments by appointment.

Rooms 37 (1 fmly) (11 GF) S £70-£80;
D £110-£125 (incl. bkfst)* Facilities Xmas New Year Wi-fi Conf Class 60 Board 76 Thtr 120 Del from £110 to £135* Parking 35 Notes Civ Wed

BATTLE

Powder Mills
★★★ 79% ◉ HOTEL

☎ 01424 775511 📠 01424 774540
Powdermill Ln TN33 0SP
e-mail: powdc@aol.com
web: www.powdermillshotel.com
dir: M25 junct 5, A21 towards Hastings. At St Johns Cross take A2100 to Battle. Pass Abbey on right, 1st right into Powdermills Ln. 1m, hotel on right

PETS: Bedrooms unattended Charges Public areas except restaurant Grounds Resident Pets: Holly & Gemma (English Springer Spaniels)

A delightful 18th-century country-house hotel set amidst 150 acres of landscaped grounds with lakes and woodland. The individually decorated bedrooms are tastefully furnished and thoughtfully equipped; some rooms have sun terraces with lovely lake views. Public rooms include a cosy lounge bar, music room, drawing room, library, restaurant and conservatory.

Rooms 40 (10 annexe) (5 GF) S £87.50-£115;
D £140-£350 (incl. bkfst)* Facilities ⚄
🎣 Fishing Jogging trails Woodland walks Clay pigeon shooting Xmas New Year Wi-fi Conf Class 50 Board 16 Thtr 250 Del from £135 to £145* Parking 101 Notes LB Civ Wed 100

BEXHILL

Cooden Beach Hotel
★★★ 80% HOTEL

☎ 01424 842281 📠 01424 846142
Cooden Beach TN39 4TT
e-mail: jk@thecoodenbeachhotel.co.uk
web: www.thecoodenbeachhotel.co.uk
dir: A259 towards Cooden. Signed at rdbt in Little
Common Village. Hotel at end of road

PETS: Bedrooms unattended Public areas except
restaurant (tavern/bar only) Grounds Exercise
area beach adjacent Facilities water bowl Other
dogs to be left unattended only for short periods
Restrictions well behaved dogs only

This privately owned hotel is situated in two
acres of private gardens that have direct access
to the beach. With a train station within walking
distance the location is perfectly suited for both
business and leisure guests. Bedrooms are
comfortably appointed, and public areas include
a spacious restaurant, lounge, bar and leisure
centre with swimming pool.

Rooms 41 (8 annexe) (10 fmly) (4 GF)
Facilities FTV ⊙ Gym Sauna Steam room ♫
Xmas New Year Wi-fi Conf Class 40 Board 40
Thtr 120 Parking 60 Notes Civ Wed 120

BRIGHTON & HOVE

The Oriental
★★★★ GUEST ACCOMMODATION

☎ 01273 205050 📠 01273 205050
9 Oriental Place BN1 2LJ
e-mail: info@orientalbrighton.co.uk
dir: A23 right onto A259 at seafront, right into
Oriental Place, on right

PETS: Bedrooms unattended Public areas
Exercise area 50mtrs Facilities food bowl water
bowl Restrictions well behaved dogs only

The Oriental is situated close to the seafront
and enjoys easy access to all areas. The
accommodation is comfortable and modern, and
there is a licensed bar. A tasty Sussex breakfast
using locally sourced produce is offered in a
friendly, relaxed atmosphere.

Rooms 9 en suite (4 fmly) (1 GF) S £49-£75;
D £65-£195* Facilities FTV tea/coffee Cen ht
Licensed Wi-fi Massage & Aromatherapy
Conf Max 10 Thtr 10 Class 10 Board 10

BRIGHTON & HOVE

Avalon

★★★ GUEST ACCOMMODATION

☎ 01273 692344 📠 01273 692344
7 Upper Rock Gardens BN2 1QE
e-mail: info@avalonbrighton.co.uk
dir: A23 to Brighton Pier, left onto Marine Parade,
300yds at lights left onto Lower Rock Gdns, over
lights Avalon on left

PETS: **Bedrooms** unattended **Charges Public
areas Exercise area** parks & beach nearby
Facilities food bowl water bowl

A warm welcome is assured at this guest house
just a short walk from the seafront and The
Lanes. The en suite bedrooms vary in size and
style but all are attractively presented with plenty
of useful accessories including free Wi-fi. Parking
vouchers are available for purchase from the
proprietor.

Rooms 7 en suite (3 fmly) (1 GF) S £49-£55; D
£69-£95* **Facilities** FTV tea/coffee Cen ht Wi-fi

EASTBOURNE

The Royal

★★★★ GUEST ACCOMMODATION

☎ 01323 649222 📠 0560 1500 0658-9
Marine Pde BN21 3DX
e-mail: info@royaleastbourne.org.uk
web: www.royaleastbourne.org.uk
dir: East of pier

PETS: **Bedrooms** unattended **Charges Public
areas** except breakfast room **Exercise area**
beach (20mtrs) **Facilities** food (pre-bookable)
food bowl water bowl

This property enjoys a central seafront location
close to the pier and within easy walking
distance of the town centre. Spectacular
uninterrupted sea views are guaranteed. Now
fully renovated and eco-friendly, the comfortable
bedrooms are modern with flat-screen TVs and
free Wi-fi. One of the ten rooms has private
facilities, while the others are fully en suite. A
substantial continental breakfast is served. The
Royal offers a full pet-sitting service.

Rooms 10 rms (9 en suite) (1 pri facs) (1 fmly)
S £35-£47; D £70-£84* **Facilities** STV FTV tea/
coffee Cen ht Wi-fi Golf Wi-fi available **Notes** LB
No Children 14yrs

PEASMARSH

Best Western Flackley Ash Hotel
★★★ 78% HOTEL

☎ 01797 230651 📠 01797 230510
TN31 6YH
e-mail: enquiries@flackleyashhotel.co.uk
web: www.flackleyashhotel.co.uk
dir: Exit A21 onto A268 to Newenden, next left
A268 to Rye. Hotel on left on entering Peasmarsh

PETS: Bedrooms unattended **Charges Public
areas** except restaurant, leisure centre & bar
Grounds Exercise area 10mtrs

Five acres of beautifully kept grounds make a
lovely setting for this elegant Georgian country
house. The hotel is superbly situated for exploring
the many local attractions, including the ancient
Cinque Port of Rye. Stylishly decorated bedrooms
are comfortable and boast many thoughtful
touches. A sunny conservatory dining room,
luxurious beauty spa and a swimming pool are
available.

Rooms 45 (5 fmly) (19 GF) (10 smoking)
S £85-£100; **D** £120-£160 (incl. bkfst)
Facilities Spa STV 🕐 supervised Putt green ⛳
Gym Beauty salon Steam room Saunas Xmas
New Year Wi-fi **Conf** Class 60 Board 40 Thtr 100
Parking 80 **Notes** Civ Wed 100

ARUNDEL

Norfolk Arms
★★★ 74% HOTEL

☎ 01903 882101 📠 01903 884275
High St BN18 9AB
e-mail: norfolk.arms@forestdale.com
web: www.norfolkarmshotel.com
dir: On High St in city centre

PETS: Bedrooms unattended **Charges Public
areas** except restaurant

Built by the 10th Duke of Norfolk, this Georgian
coaching inn enjoys a superb setting beneath the
battlements of Arundel Castle. Bedrooms vary in
sizes and character - all are comfortable and well
equipped. Public areas include two bars serving
real ales, comfortable lounges with roaring log
fires, a traditional restaurant and a range of
meeting and function rooms.

Rooms 33 (13 annexe) (4 fmly) (8 GF) **S** £70-£89;
D £90-£125 (incl. bkfst)* **Facilities** FTV Xmas
New Year Wi-fi **Conf** Class 36 Board 40 Thtr 100
Parking 34 **Notes** Civ Wed 60

CHICHESTER

The Horse and Groom
★★★★ INN

☎ 01243 575339 📠 01243 575560
East Ashling PO18 9AX
e-mail: info@thehorseandgroomchichester.co.uk
web: www.thehorseandgroomchichester.co.uk
dir: 3m N of Chichester, on B2178 towards
Rowland's Castle

PETS: Bedrooms unattended Public areas except
restaurant Grounds Exercise area adjacent
Facilities water bowl

The Horse and Groom is a unique 17th-century
country pub and restaurant offering spacious and
comfortable accommodation and warm, friendly
hospitality. The substantial, freshly prepared
breakfasts, lunches and dinners make good
use of freshly caught fish and locally sourced
ingredients.

Rooms 11 en suite (11 GF) Facilities tea/coffee
Dinner available Cen ht Parking 40 Notes RS Sun
eve Bar & Restaurant close 6pm

CLIMPING

Bailiffscourt Hotel & Spa
★★★ ◉◉ HOTEL

☎ 01903 723511 📠 01903 723107
Climping St BN17 5RW
e-mail: bailiffscourt@hshotels.co.uk
web: www.hshotels.co.uk
dir: A259, follow Climping Beach signs.

PETS: Bedrooms unattended Charges Public
areas except restaurant Grounds Exercise area,
beach Facilities food (pre-bookable) food bowl
water bowl room service dog menu

A delightful moated 'medieval manor' dating
back only to the 1920s that sits in 30 acres of
delightful parkland that leads to the beach.
Bedrooms vary from atmospheric feature rooms
to spacious, stylish and contemporary rooms
located in the grounds. The Tapestry Restaurant
serves award-winning cuisine, and in summer
the Courtyard offers informal light lunches and
afternoon tea. Superb health spa facilities.

Rooms 39 (30 annexe) (25 fmly) (16 GF)
S £200-£485; D £215-£545 (incl. bkfst)*
Facilities Spa STV FTV ⓣ supervised ⚲
supervised ⚲⛱ Gym Sauna Steam room Dance/
fitness studio Yoga/pilates/gym inductions Xmas
New Year Wi-fi Conf Class 20 Board 26 Thtr 40
Parking 100 Notes LB Civ Wed 60

MIDHURST

Spread Eagle Hotel and Spa

★★★ 80% @@ HOTEL

☎ 01730 816911 📠 01730 815668
South St GU29 9NH
e-mail: spreadeagle@hshotels.co.uk
web: www.hshotels.co.uk/spread/spreadeagle-main.htm
dir: M25 junct 10, A3 to Milford, take A286 to Midhurst. Hotel adjacent to market square

PETS: Bedrooms unattended Charges Public areas except restaurant Grounds Exercise area Facilities food (pre-bookable) food bowl water bowl Restrictions very large breeds not accepted; dogs not allowed on beds Resident Pet: Boxer dog

Offering accommodation since 1430, this historic property is full of character, evident in its sloping floors and inglenook fireplaces. Individually styled bedrooms provide modern comforts; those in the main house include some spacious feature rooms. Noteworthy food is served in the oak beamed restaurant.

Rooms 36 (8 GF) S £80-£495; D £100-£495 (incl. bkfst)* Facilities Spa STV FTV ⏲ Gym Health & beauty treatment rooms Steam room Sauna Fitness trainer Xmas New Year Wi-fi Conf Class 40 Board 34 Thtr 80 Del from £135 to £280* Parking 75 Notes LB Civ Wed 120

SELSEY

St Andrews Lodge

★★★★ GUEST ACCOMMODATION

☎ 01243 606899 📠 01243 607826
Chichester Rd PO20 0LX
e-mail: info@standrewslodge.co.uk
web: www.standrewslodge.co.uk
dir: B2145 into Selsey, on right just before church

PETS: Bedrooms unattended Charges Public areas except restaurant/lounge Grounds Exercise area 200yds Facilities food bowl water bowl Resident Pet: Pepper (cat)

This friendly lodge is just half a mile from the seafront. The refurbished bedrooms are bright and spacious, and have a range of useful extras. Five ground-floor rooms, one with easier access, overlook the large south-facing garden, which is perfect for a drink on a summer evening.

Rooms 5 en suite 5 annexe en suite (3 fmly) (5 GF) S £38-£55; D £68-£85 Facilities TVL tea/coffee Direct Dial Cen ht Licensed Wi-fi Conf Max 15 Parking 14 Notes LB Closed 21 Dec-11 Jan

WORTHING

Cavendish Hotel
★★ 61% HOTEL

☎ 01903 236767 📠 01903 823840
115 Marine Pde BN11 3QG
e-mail: reservations@cavendishworthing.co.uk
web: www.cavendishworthing.co.uk
dir: On seafront, 600yds W of pier

PETS: Bedrooms unattended Public areas except
restaurant Exercise area countryside walks &
beach opposite

This popular, family-run hotel enjoys a prominent
seafront location. Bedrooms are well equipped
and soundly decorated. Guests have an extensive
choice of meal options, with a varied bar
menu, and carte and daily menus offered in the
restaurant. Limited parking is available at the
rear of the hotel.

Rooms 17 (4 fmly) (1 GF) (6 smoking) S £45-£49;
D £69.50-£85 (incl. bkfst)* Facilities STV Wi-fi
Services Air con Parking 5

BAGINGTON

The Oak
★★★ INN

☎ 024 7651 8855 📠 024 7651 8866
Coventry Rd CV8 3AU
e-mail: thebagintonoak@aol.com
web: http://theoak.greatpubs.net

PETS: Bedrooms unattended Charges Public
areas Grounds Exercise area adjacent Facilities
water bowl pet washing facilities on request
Resident Pets: Beau & Jasper (Border Collies)

Located close to major road links and Coventry
Airport, this popular inn provides a wide range
of food throughout the themed, open-plan public
areas. Families are especially welcome. Modern,
well-equipped bedrooms are situated in a
separate accommodation building.

Rooms 13 annexe en suite (1 fmly) (6 GF) S
£40-£60; D £40-£60* Facilities FTV tea/coffee
Dinner available Cen ht Wi-fi Free use of local
gym Conf Max 40 Thtr 40 Class 40 Board 25
Parking 110

COLESHILL

Grimstock Country House

★★★ 71% COUNTRY HOUSE HOTEL

☎ 01675 462121 & 462161 📄 01675 467646
Gilson Rd, Gilson B46 1LJ
e-mail: enquiries@grimstockhotel.co.uk
web: www.grimstockhotel.co.uk
dir: Off A446 at rdbt onto B4117 to Gilson, hotel
100yds on right

PETS: Bedrooms unattended Charges Public
areas Grounds Exercise area adjacent field

This privately owned hotel is convenient for
Birmingham International Airport and the NEC,
and benefits from a peaceful rural setting.
Bedrooms are spacious and comfortable. Public
rooms include two restaurants, a wood-panelled
bar, good conference facilities and a gym
featuring the latest cardiovascular equipment.

Rooms 44 (1 fmly) (13 GF) S £65-£95;
D £75-£125 (incl. bkfst) Facilities STV Gym Xmas
New Year Wi-fi Conf Class 60 Board 50 Thtr 100
Del from £125 to £140 Parking 100 Notes LB
Civ Wed 100

CORLEY MOTORWAY SERVICE AREA (M6)

Days Inn Corley - NEC

BUDGET HOTEL

☎ 01676 543800 & 540111 📄 01676 540128
Junction 3-4, M6 North, Corley CV7 8NR
e-mail: corley.hotel@welcomebreak.co.uk
dir: On M6 between juncts 3 & 4 N'bound

PETS: Bedrooms unattended Charges Public
areas except main service area Grounds
Exercise area Facilities food (pre-bookable)
water bowl Other dog training school within
walking distance

This modern building offers accommodation in
smart, spacious and well-equipped bedrooms,
suitable for families and business travellers,
and all with en suite bathrooms. Continental
breakfast is available and other refreshments
may be taken at the nearby family restaurant.

Rooms 50 (13 fmly) (24 GF) (44 smoking)
S £29-£59; D £39-£69*

STRATFORD-UPON-AVON

Barceló Billesley Manor Hotel
★★★★ 77% ⚜⚜ HOTEL

☎ 01789 279955 📠 01789 764145
Billesley, Alcester B49 6NF
e-mail: billesleymanor@barcelo-hotels.co.uk
web: www.barcelo-hotels.co.uk
dir: A46 towards Evesham. Over 3 rdbts, right for Billesley after 2m

PETS: Bedrooms unattended Charges Public areas Grounds

This 16th-century manor is set in peaceful grounds and parkland with a delightful yew topiary garden and fountain. The spacious bedrooms and suites, most in traditional country-house style, are thoughtfully designed and well equipped. Conference facilities and some of the bedrooms are found in the cedar barns. Public areas retain many original features, such as oak panelling, fireplaces and exposed stone.

Rooms 72 (29 annexe) (5 GF) Facilities Spa
🕭 supervised 🏊 💪 Gym Steam room Beauty treatments Yoga studio Xmas New Year
Conf Class 60 Board 50 Thtr 100 Del from £125*
Parking 100 Notes Civ Wed 75

STRATFORD-UPON-AVON

Mercure Shakespeare
★★★★ 72% ⚜ HOTEL

☎ 01789 294997 📠 01789 415411
Chapel St CV37 6ER
e-mail: h6630@accor.com
web: www.mercure-uk.com
dir: M40 junct 15. Follow signs for Stratford town centre on A439. Follow one-way system onto Bridge St. Left at rdbt, hotel 200yds on left opp HSBC bank

PETS: Bedrooms (unattended) Charges Public areas Exercise area park 300yds

Dating back to the early 17th century, The Shakespeare is one of the oldest hotels in this historic town. The hotel name represents one of the earliest exploitations of Stratford as the birthplace of one of the world's leading playwrights. With exposed beams and open fires, the public rooms retain an ambience reminiscent of this era. Bedrooms are appointed to a good standard and remain in keeping with the style of the property.

Rooms 74 (11 annexe) (3 GF) (3 smoking)
S £60-£150; D £60-£200 (incl. bkfst)* Facilities Xmas New Year Wi-fi Conf Class 60 Board 40
Thtr 80 Del from £120 to £160 Services Lift
Parking 34 Notes LB Civ Wed 100

BALSALL COMMON

Haigs

★★★ 72% HOTEL

☎ 01676 533004 📠 01676 535132
Kenilworth Rd CV7 7EL
e-mail: info@haigshotel.co.uk
dir: A45 towards Coventry, at Stonebridge Island turn right, 4m S of M42 junct 6

PETS: Bedrooms unattended **Charges Public areas Grounds Exercise area** 500yds **Facilities** water bowl

Conveniently located just five miles from Birmingham Airport and twelve miles from Stratford-upon-Avon. This hotel offers a comfortable stay at a small family run operation. Enjoyable meals can be taken in Mckees Brasserie.

Rooms 23 (2 fmly) (5 GF) **Facilities** Xmas New Year Wi-fi **Conf** Board 20 Thtr 25 **Parking** 23 **Notes** Civ Wed 60

BIRMINGHAM

Hotel du Vin Birmingham

★★★★ 78% ⊛ TOWN HOUSE HOTEL

☎ 0121 200 0600 📠 0121 236 0889
25 Church St B3 2NR
e-mail: info@birmingham.hotelduvin.com
web: www.hotelduvin.com
dir: M6 junct 6/A38(M) to city centre, over flyover. Keep left,exit at St Chads Circus signed Jewellery Quarter. At lights & rdbt take 1st exit, follow Colmore Row signs, opposite cathedral. Right into Church St, across Barwick St. Hotel on right

PETS: Bedrooms unattended **Charges Public areas** except bar & bistro **Facilities** food bowl water bowl dog bed & dog blanket available

The former Birmingham Eye Hospital has become a chic and sophisticated hotel. The stylish, high-ceilinged rooms, all with a wine theme, are luxuriously appointed and feature stunning bathrooms, sumptuous duvets and Egyptian cotton sheets. The Bistro offers relaxed dining and a top-notch wine list, while other attractions include a champagne bar, a wine boutique and a health club.

Rooms 66 **Facilities** Spa STV Gym Treatment rooms Steam room Sauna Xmas New Year Wi-fi **Conf** Class 40 Board 40 Thtr 84 **Services** Lift Air con **Notes** LB Civ Wed 84

BIRMINGHAM

Ibis Birmingham City Centre
BUDGET HOTEL

☎ 0121 622 6010 📠 0121 622 6020
Arcadian Centre, Ladywell Walk B5 4ST
e-mail: h1459@accor-hotels.com
web: www.ibishotel.com
dir: From motorways follow city centre signs.
Then follow Bullring or Indoor Market signs. Hotel
adjacent to market

PETS: Bedrooms unattended Charges Public
areas Restrictions small dogs only

Modern, budget hotel offering comfortable and
pactial bedrooms. Breakfast is self-service and
dinner is available in the restaurant.

Rooms 159 (5 fmly) D £50-£95* Conf Class 60
Board 50 Thtr 120 Del from £85 to £115*

COVENTRY

Ibis Coventry South Whitley
BUDGET HOTEL

☎ 024 7663 9922 📠 024 7630 6898
Abbey Rd, Whitley CV3 4BJ
e-mail: H2094@accor-hotels.com
web: www.ibishotel.com
dir: Signed from A46/A423 rdbt. Take A423
towards A45. Follow signs for Esporta Health
Club and Jaguar Engineering Plant

PETS: Bedrooms unattended Charges Public
areas except restaurant Grounds Exercise area
0.1m

Modern, budget hotel offering comfortable and
pactial bedrooms. Breakfast is self-service and
dinner is available in the restaurant.

Rooms 51 (25 GF) S £42-£62; D £42-£62*
Conf Class 20 Board 16 Thtr 20

MERIDEN

Manor Hotel
★★★★ 82% ◉ HOTEL

☎ 01676 522735   🖷 01676 522186
Main Rd CV7 7NH
e-mail: reservations@manorhotelmeriden.co.uk
web: www.manorhotelmeriden.co.uk
dir: M42 junct 6, A45 towards Coventry then A452
signed Leamington. At rdbt take B4102 signed
Meriden, hotel on left

PETS: Bedrooms unattended **Public areas** assist
dogs only **Grounds Exercise area**

A sympathetically extended Georgian manor in
the heart of a sleepy village is just a few minutes
away from the M6, M42 and National Exhibition
Centre. The Regency Restaurant offers modern
dishes, while Houston's serves lighter meals
and snacks. The bedrooms are smart and well
equipped.

Rooms 110 (20 GF) **S** £70-£140; **D** £80-£180
(incl. bkfst)* **Facilities** Wi-fi **Conf** Class 150
Board 60 Thtr 250 Del from £100 to £160*
Services Lift **Parking** 200 **Notes** LB RS 24 Dec-2
Jan Civ Wed 150

SOLIHULL

Corus
★★★ 68% HOTEL

☎ 0844 736 8605   & 0121 745 0400
🖷 0121 733 3801
Stratford Rd, Shirley B90 4EB
e-mail: solihull@corushotels.com
web: www.corushotels.com
dir: M42 junct 4 onto A34 for Shirley, cross 1st 3
rdbts, then double back along dual carriageway,
hotel on left

PETS: Bedrooms unattended **Charges Public
areas** except restaurant & lounge **Grounds
Exercise area Facilities** food bowl ,water bowl

A large, friendly hotel attracting both corporate
and leisure guests. It is ideally located within a
few minutes of the major transportation links and
benefits from its own extensive leisure centre that
includes a lagoon pool, sauna and gym.

Rooms 111 (11 fmly) (13 GF) **S** £49-£109;
D £49-£189 **Facilities** ◈ Gym Steam room
Plunge pool Sauna ♫ Xmas New Year Wi-fi
Conf Class 80 Board 60 Thtr 180 Del from £69
to £189 **Services** Lift **Parking** 275 **Notes** LB
RS Xmas Civ Wed 150

SUTTON COLDFIELD

Ramada Birmingham, Sutton Coldfield

★★★ 73% HOTEL

☎ 0121 351 3111   📠 0844 815 9022
Penns Ln, Walmley B76 1LH
e-mail: sales.birmingham@ramadajarvis.co.uk
web: www.ramadajarvis.co.uk
dir: A5127 towards Sutton Coldfield for 2m, through lights, 4th right into Penns Lane. Hotel 1m on right follow brown tourist signs

PETS: **Bedrooms** unattended **Public areas Grounds Exercise area**

Conveniently located for both M42 and M6 this large hotel is set in private grounds overlooking a lake. Bedrooms are comfortably appointed for both business and leisure guests. Public areas include the Club Restaurant and bar, a leisure club and extensive conference facilities.

Rooms 170 (13 annexe) (20 fmly) (20 GF) (7 smoking) **Facilities** Spa 🕲 supervised Fishing Gym Squash Hairdressing salon Xmas New Year Wi-fi **Conf** Class 200 Board 40 Thtr 500 **Services** Lift **Parking** 500 **Notes** Civ Wed 150

WOLVERHAMPTON

Novotel Wolverhampton

★★★ 75% HOTEL

☎ 01902 871100   📠 01902 870054
Union St WV1 3JN
e-mail: H1188@accor.com
web: www.novotel.com
dir: 6m from M6 junct 10. A454 to Wolverhampton. Hotel on main ring road

PETS: **Bedrooms** unattended **Charges Public areas Grounds Exercise area** 1m **Facilities** water bowl

This large, modern, purpose-built hotel stands close to the town centre. It provides spacious, smartly presented and well-equipped bedrooms, all of which contain convertible bed settees for family occupancy. In addition to the open-plan lounge and bar area, there is an attractive brasserie-style restaurant, which overlooks an attractive patio garden.

Rooms 132 (9 fmly) (15 smoking) **S** £50-£130; **D** £50-£130* **Facilities** STV Wi-fi **Conf** Class 100 Board 80 Thtr 200 Del from £99 to £145* **Services** Lift **Parking** 120 **Notes** LB RS 23 Dec-4 Jan Civ Wed 200

BONCHURCH

Winterbourne Country House

★★★★★ ☖ GUEST HOUSE

☎ 01983 852535 ▤ 01983 857529
Bonchurch Village Rd PO38 1RQ
e-mail: info@winterbournehouse.co.uk
dir: 1m E of Ventnor. Off A3055 into Bonchurch
village

PETS: **Bedrooms** unattended **Charges Public
areas** except breakfast room **Grounds Exercise
area Facilities** food bowl water bowl **Resident
Pets:** Boots & Indie (Bassett Hounds)

During his stay in 1849, Charles Dickens
described Winterbourne as 'the prettiest place I
ever saw in my life, at home or abroad'. Today,
the comfortable bedrooms are all well equipped
and differ in size, and include luxurious rooms
with sea views. There are two lounges and a
secluded terrace.

Rooms 7 rms (6 en suite) (1 pri facs) **S**
£65-£150; **D** £110-£190* **Facilities** TVL tea/
coffee Direct Dial Cen ht Licensed ⚹ **Parking** 8
Notes No Children 11yrs Closed Dec-Mar

COWES

Best Western New Holmwood

★★★ 70% HOTEL

☎ 01983 292508 ▤ 01983 295020
Queens Rd, Egypt Point PO31 8BW
e-mail: reception@newholmwoodhotel.co.uk
dir: From A3020 at Northwood Garage lights, left
& follow to rdbt. 1st left then sharp right into
Baring Rd, 4th left into Egypt Hill. At bottom turn
right, hotel on right

PETS: **Bedrooms** unattended **Charges Public
areas** except restaurant **Exercise area** 2 mins
walk to beach **Facilities** water bowl **Resident
Pet:** Mya (German Shepherd)

Just by the Esplanade, this hotel has an enviable
outlook. Bedrooms are comfortable and very well
equipped, and the light and airy, glass-fronted
restaurant looks out to sea and serves a range of
interesting meals. The sun terrace is delightful in
the summer and there is a small pool area.

Rooms 26 (1 fmly) (9 GF) **Facilities** STV ⚹ Xmas
New Year Wi-fi **Conf** Class 60 Board 50 Thtr 120
Parking 20

FRESHWATER

Farringford

★★★ 76% ☺ HOTEL

☎ 01983 752500 📠 01983 756515

Bedbury Ln PO40 9PE

e-mail: enquiries@farringford.co.uk
web: www.farringford.co.uk
dir: A3054, left to Norton Green down Pixlie Hill.
Left to Freshwater Bay. At bay turn right into
Bedbury Lane, hotel on left

PETS: Bedrooms unattended Charges Public
areas Grounds Exercise area

Upon seeing Farringford, Alfred Lord Tennyson is
said to have remarked "we will go no further, this
must be our home" and so it was for some forty
years. Some 150 years later, the hotel provides
bedrooms ranging in style and size, from large
rooms in the main house to adjoining chalet-style
rooms. The atmosphere is relaxed, and dinner
features fresh local produce.

Rooms 18 (4 annexe) (5 fmly) (4 GF) Facilities ✎
⚐ 9 ⛳ Putt green ❤ Beauty treatment room
Bowling Green ♫ Conf Class 50 Board 50
Thtr 120 Parking 55 Notes Closed Nov-Mar
Civ Wed 130

SHANKLIN

Hayes Barton

★★★★ ☞ GUEST ACCOMMODATION

☎ 01983 867747
7 Highfield Rd PO37 6PP
e-mail: williams.2000@virgin.net
web: www.hayesbarton.co.uk
dir: A3055 onto A3020 Victoria Av, 3rd left

PETS: Bedrooms unattended Charges Public
areas except dining room Grounds Exercise area
200yds Resident Pet: Katy (Labrador cross)

Hayes Barton has the relaxed atmosphere of
a family home and provides well-equipped
bedrooms and a range of comfortable public
areas. Dinner is available from a short selection
of home-cooked dishes and there is a cosy bar
lounge. The old village, beach and promenade are
all within walking distance.

Rooms 9 en suite (4 fmly) (2 GF) Facilities TVL
tea/coffee Dinner available Cen ht Licensed Wi-fi
Parking 9 Notes LB Closed Nov-Mar

TOTLAND BAY

The Hermitage

★★★ GUEST ACCOMMODATION

☎ 01983 752518
Cliff Rd PO39 0EW
e-mail: blake_david@btconnect.com
web: www.thehermitagebnb.co.uk
dir: Church Hill B3322, right onto Eden Rd, left
onto Cliff Rd, 0.5m on right

PETS: Bedrooms unattended Charges Public
areas except dining area Grounds Exercise area
Facilities water bowl Resident Pets: 1 German
Shepherd, 3 cats, 2 lovebirds

The Hermitage is an extremely pet and people
friendly establishment which occupies a
stunning and unspoilt location near to the
cliff top in Totland Bay. Extensive gardens
are well maintained and off-road parking is
a bonus. Accommodation is comfortable and
you are assured of a genuinely warm welcome
and friendly service at this traditionally styled
establishment. A range of delicious items at
breakfast provide a substantial start to the day.

Rooms 4 rms (3 en suite) (1 pri facs) (1 fmly) S
£25-£35; D £50-£70* Facilities TVL tea/coffee
Dinner available Parking 6 Notes LB

ALDBOURNE

The Crown Inn

★★★★ INN

☎ 01672 540214
2 The Square SN8 2DU
e-mail: gant12@hotmail.co.uk
web: www.crownataldbourne.co.uk
dir: M4 junct 15, N on A419, signed to Aldbourne

PETS: Bedrooms unattended Public areas
except restaurant Grounds Exercise area 100yds
Facilities food bowl water bowl Resident Pet: 1
Border Terrier

With a traditional village inn atmosphere, The
Crown offers a relaxed ambience and genuine
welcome. The comfortable bar and dining room
provide a very good selection of home-cooked
dishes with good quality produce used at both
dinner and breakfast. Bedrooms and bathrooms
come in a range of shapes and sizes but are all
well decorated and nicely furnished.

Rooms 4 en suite (1 fmly) S £49.95; D £69.95
Facilities FTV TVL tea/coffee Dinner available
Cen ht Wi-fi Conf Max 22 Thtr 16 Class 22 Board
22 Parking 9 Notes LB

BRADFORD-ON-AVON

Woolley Grange

★★★ 82% @@ HOTEL

☎ 01225 864705 📠 01225 864059
Woolley Green BA15 1TX
e-mail: info@woolleygrangehotel.co.uk
web: www.woolleygrangehotel.co.uk
dir: A4 onto B3109. Bradford Leigh, left at
x-roads, hotel 0.5m on right at Woolley Green

PETS: **Bedrooms** unattended **Charges Public
areas** except dining areas **Grounds Facilities**
food bowl water bowl **Other** dogs should be
kept on leads due to children staying at hotel
Resident Pet: Peanut (Cocker Spaniel)

This splendid Cotswold manor house is set in
beautiful countryside, and children are made
especially welcome here. The hotel is charmingly
appointed in true country-house style, with many
thoughtful touches and luxurious extras. the
varied menus include ingredients from the hotel's
own garden.

Rooms 26 (14 annexe) (20 fmly) (3 GF)
S £145-£200; D £200-£510 (incl. bkfst &
dinner)* **Facilities** FTV ⌇ 🏊 Beauty treatments
Football Table tennis Trampoline Boules
Cricket Xmas New Year Wi-fi Child facilities
Conf Class 12 Board 22 Thtr 35 Del from £155 to
£165* **Parking** 40 **Notes** LB Civ Wed 30

CASTLE COMBE

Manor House Hotel and Golf Club

★★★★ @@@ COUNTRY HOUSE HOTEL

☎ 01249 782206 📠 01249 782159
SN14 7HR
e-mail: enquiries@manorhouse.co.uk
web: www.exclusivehotels.co.uk
dir: M4 junct 17 follow Chippenham signs onto
A420 Bristol, right onto B4039. Through village,
right after bridge

PETS: **Bedrooms** unattended **Charges Public
areas** except food areas **Grounds Other** dogs
allowed in cottage bedrooms only **Resident Pets:**
1 cat, 6 pigs, 6 chickens

This delightful hotel is situated in 365-acre
grounds complete with an Italian garden and
a golf course. Bedrooms have been superbly
furnished, and public rooms include a number
of cosy lounges with roaring fires. Service
is a pleasing blend of professionalism and
friendliness. The award-winning food utilises top
quality local produce.

Rooms 48 (26 annexe) (8 fmly) (12 GF)
S £150-£600; D £180-£600 (incl. bkfst)*
Facilities STV ⌀ 18 ⛳ Putt green Fishing 🏊
Jogging track Hot air ballooning Xmas New
Year Wi-fi **Conf** Class 70 Board 30 Thtr 100
Parking 100 **Notes** LB Civ Wed 110

179

LACOCK

At the Sign of the Angel
★★★★ 🔒 🍽 GUEST ACCOMMODATION

☎ 01249 730230 📠 01249 730527
6 Church St SN15 2LB
e-mail: angel@lacock.co.uk
dir: Off A350 into Lacock, follow 'Local Traffic' sign

PETS: Bedrooms unattended Charges Public areas except restaurant Grounds Exercise area walks in surrounding area Facilities water bowl Resident Pet: Felix (cat)

Visitors will be impressed by the character of this 15th-century former wool merchant's house, set in the National Trust village of Lacock. Bedrooms come in a range of sizes and styles including the atmospheric rooms in the main house and others in an adjacent building. Excellent dinners and breakfasts are served in the beamed dining rooms, and there is also a first-floor lounge and a pleasant rear garden.

Rooms 6 en suite 4 annexe en suite (3 GF) S £82; D £120* Facilities FTV tea/coffee Dinner available Direct Dial Cen ht Licensed Wi-fi Conf Max 14 Board 14 Parking 6 Notes Closed 23-27 Dec RS Mon (ex BHs) Closed for lunch Civ Wed 24

LOWER CHICKSGROVE

Compasses Inn
★★★★ ◉ INN

☎ 01722 714318 📠 01722 714318
SP3 6NB
e-mail: thecompasses@aol.com
web: www.thecompassesinn.com
dir: Off A30 signed Lower Chicksgrove, 1st left onto Lagpond Ln, single-track lane to village

PETS: Bedrooms unattended Public areas Grounds Exercise area adjacent Facilities food bowl water bowl

This charming 17th-century inn, within easy reach of Bath, Salisbury, Glastonbury and the Dorset coast, offers comfortable accommodation in a peaceful setting. Carefully prepared dinners are enjoyed in the warm atmosphere of the bar-restaurant, while breakfast is served in a separate dining room.

Rooms 5 en suite (1 fmly) S £65-£90; D £85-£90* Facilities FTV tea/coffee Dinner available Cen ht Wi-fi Conf Max 14 Parking 40 Notes LB Closed 25-26 Dec

MALMESBURY

Old Bell Hotel
★★★ 80% ◉◉ HOTEL

☎ 01666 822344 🖷 01666 825145
Abbey Row SN16 0BW
e-mail: info@oldbellhotel.com
web: www.oldbellhotel.com
dir: M4 junct 17, follow A429 north. Left at 1st
rdbt. Left at T-junct. Hotel next to Abbey

PETS: **Bedrooms** unattended **Charges Public
areas** except restaurants **Grounds Exercise area**
250mtrs **Facilities** water bowl **Restrictions** no
large dogs (eg Newfoundland, Great Dane, Irish
Wolfhound)

Dating back to 1220, the Old Bell is reputed to
be the oldest purpose-built hotel in England.
Bedrooms vary in size and style; those in the
main house tend to be more spacious and are
traditionally furnished with antiques, while
the newer bedrooms of the coach house have
a contemporary feel. Guests have a choice of
comfortable sitting areas and dining options
including the main restaurant where the
award-winning cuisine is based on high quality
ingredients.

Rooms 33 (15 annexe) (7 GF) **S** £90;
D £110-£235 (incl. bkfst)* **Facilities** FTV Xmas
New Year Wi-fi **Conf** Class 32 Board 32 Thtr 60
Parking 33 **Notes** LB Civ Wed 80

MALMESBURY

Best Western Mayfield House
★★★ 72% ◉ HOTEL

☎ 01666 577409 🖷 01666 577977
Crudwell SN16 9EW
e-mail: reception@mayfieldhousehotel.co.uk
web: www.mayfieldhousehotel.co.uk
dir: M4 junct 17, A429 to Cirencester. 3m N of
Malmesbury on left in Crudwell

PETS: **Bedrooms** unattended **Charges Public
areas Exercise area** paddock opposite &
bridleway

This popular hotel is in an ideal location for
exploring many of the nearby attractions of
Wiltshire and The Cotswolds. Bedrooms come in a
range of shapes and sizes, and include some on
the ground-floor level in a cottage adjacent to the
main hotel. In addition to outdoor seating, guests
can relax with a drink in the comfortable lounge
area where orders are taken for the carefully
prepared dinner to follow.

Rooms 28 (8 annexe) (4 fmly) (8 GF) **S** £50-£75;
D £80-£138 (incl. bkfst)* **Facilities** FTV Xmas
New Year Wi-fi **Conf** Class 30 Board 25 Thtr 40
Del from £99 to £135* **Parking** 50 **Notes** LB

181

SWINDON

Campanile Swindon
BUDGET HOTEL

☎ 01793 514777 📠 01793 514570
Delta Business Park, Great Western Way
SN5 7XG
e-mail: swindon@campanile.com
web: www.campanile-swindon.co.uk
dir: M4 junction 16, A3102 towards Swindon. After 2nd rdbt, 2nd exit onto Welton Rd (Delta Business Park), 1st left

PETS: **Bedrooms** unattended **Charges Public areas** except restaurant & bar **Grounds Exercise area Other** dogs may be left unattended in bedrooms for short periods only **Restrictions** no large dogs

This modern building offers accommodation in smart, well-equipped bedrooms, all with en suite bathrooms. Refreshments may be taken at the informal bistro.

Rooms 120 (6 fmly) (22 GF) **S** £46.95-£120; **D** £46.95-£120* **Conf** Class 40 Board 40 Thtr 70 Del from £100*

WARMINSTER

Bishopstrow House
★★★★ 77% ⊛⊛ HOTEL

☎ 01985 212312 📠 01985 216769
BA12 9HH
e-mail: info@bishopstrow.co.uk
web: www.vonessenhotels.co.uk
dir: A303, A36, B3414, hotel 2m on right

PETS: **Bedrooms** unattended **Charges Public areas** except restaurant, conservatory, pool area **Other** please contact hotel to confirm which dog breeds are accepted

This is a fine example of a Georgian country home, situated in 27 acres of grounds. Public areas are traditional in style and feature antiques and open fires. Most bedrooms offer DVD players. A spa, a tennis court and several country walks ensure there is something for all guests. The restaurant serves top quality, contemporary cuisine.

Rooms 32 (2 annexe) (2 fmly) (7 GF) **Facilities** Spa 🏊 ↖ 🎣 Fishing 🏋 Gym Clay pigeon shooting Archery Cycling Xmas New Year Wi-fi **Conf** Class 32 Board 36 Thtr 65 **Parking** 100 **Notes** LB Civ Wed 65

ABBERLEY

The Elms Hotel & Restaurant
★★★ 88% ◉◉ HOTEL

☎ 01299 896666 📠 01299 896804
Stockton Rd WR6 6AT
e-mail: info@theelmshotel.co.uk
web: www.theelmshotel.co.uk
dir: On A443, 2m beyond Great Witley

PETS: Bedrooms unattended Charges Public
areas except restaurants Grounds Resident
Pets: Tickle (Chocolate Labrador), George (cat)

This imposing Queen Anne mansion set in
delightful grounds dates back to 1710 and
offers a sophisticated yet relaxed atmosphere
throughout. The spacious public rooms and
generously proportioned bedrooms offer elegance
and charm. The hotel is particularly well geared
for families, with a host of child friendly facilities
and features including a crèche, a play area
and wonderful high teas. Imaginative cooking is
served in the elegant restaurant.

Rooms 23 (6 annexe) (1 fmly) (3 GF)
D £215-£495 (incl. bkfst & dinner)*
Facilities Spa FTV 🕲 ॐ 🏊 Gym Xmas New
Year Wi-fi Conf Class 30 Board 30 Thtr 70
Del from £175 to £205* Parking 100
Notes Civ Wed 70

BEWDLEY

Royal Forester Country Inn
★★★★ ◉ INN

☎ 01299 266286
Callow Hill DY14 9XW
e-mail: contact@royalforesterinn.co.uk

PETS: Bedrooms unattended Charges Public
areas except restaurant Grounds Exercise area
Facilities food (pre-bookable) food bowl water
bowl

Located opposite The Wyre Forest on the town's
outskirts, this inn dates back to 1411 and has
been sympathetically restored to provide high
standards of comfort. Stylish modern bedrooms
are complemented by smart bathrooms and
equipped with many thoughtful extras. Decor
styles throughout the public areas highlight the
many retained period features and the restaurant
serves imaginative food featuring locally sourced
produce.

Rooms 7 en suite (2 fmly) Facilities STV FTV tea/
coffee Dinner available Cen ht Wi-fi Parking 40
Notes No coaches

The Broadway Hotel
★★★ 78% HOTEL

☎ 01386 852401 📠 01386 853879
The Green, High St WR12 7AA
e-mail: info@broadwayhotel.info
web: www.cotswold-inns-hotels.co.uk
dir: Follow signs to Evesham, then Broadway

PETS: **Bedrooms** unattended **Charges Public areas** except eating areas **Grounds Facilities** water bowl

A half-timbered Cotswold stone property, built in the 15th century as a retreat for the Abbots of Pershore. The hotel combines modern, attractive decor with original charm and character. Bedrooms are tastefully furnished and well equipped while public rooms include a relaxing lounge, cosy bar and charming restaurant; alfresco all-day dining in summer months proves popular.

Rooms 19 (1 fmly) (3 GF) **Facilities** Xmas New Year Wi-fi **Conf** Board 12 Thtr 20 **Parking** 20 **Notes** Civ Wed 50

BROADWAY

Horse & Hound
★★★★ 🛏 INN

☎ 01386 852287 📠 01386 853784
54 High St WR12 7DT
e-mail: k2mtk@aol.com
dir: Off A46 to Evesham

PETS: **Bedrooms** unattended **Charges Public areas** except restaurant **Exercise area** 100yds **Restrictions** small dogs only **Resident Pets:** Talisker & Rosie (Springer Spaniel)

The Horse & Hound is at the heart of this beautiful Cotswold village. A warm welcome is guaranteed whether dining in the inviting pub or staying overnight in the attractive and well-appointed bedrooms. Breakfast and dinner should not to be missed - both use carefully prepared local produce.

Rooms 5 en suite (1 fmly) **Facilities** tea/coffee Dinner available Cen ht **Parking** 15 **Notes** RS Winter Closed 3pm-6pm

DROITWICH

The Hadley Bowling Green Inn
★★★★ ⍟⍟ INN

☎ 01905 620294   📠 01905 620771
Hadley Heath WR9 0AR
e-mail: info@hadleybowlinggreen.com
web: www.hadleybowlinggreen.com

PETS: Bedrooms unattended **Charges Public areas** front bar only **Grounds Other** dogs allowed in cottage rooms only

Dating back to the 16th century and named after the UK's oldest bowling green, which is next door, much of the original coaching inn features have been retained. Reputedly this was one of the meeting places for Guy Fawkes and his fellow conspirators. The kitchen provides imaginative food from high quality local produce; service is both professional and friendly and there's a good selection of fine wines or real ales on offer. The spacious, en suite bedrooms are comfortable and include including some with four-poster beds.

Rooms 12 en suite (4 fmly) (1 GF) S £65-£75; D £75-£85* **Facilities** FTV TVL tea/coffee Dinner available Cen ht Lift Wi-fi Crown bowling green **Conf** Max 100 Thtr 100 Class 100 Board 100 **Parking** 80 **Notes** Civ Wed 100

MALVERN

The Cottage in the Wood Hotel
★★★ 85% ⍟⍟ HOTEL

☎ 01684 588860   📠 01684 560662
Holywell Rd, Malvern Wells WR14 4LG
e-mail: reception@cottageinthewood.co.uk
web: www.cottageinthewood.co.uk
dir: 3m S of Great Malvern off A449, 500yds N of B4209, on opposite side of road

PETS: Bedrooms unattended **Charges Public areas Grounds Exercise area** adjacent **Facilities** food bowl water bowl

Sitting high up on a wooded hillside, this delightful, family-run hotel boasts lovely views over the Severn Valley. The bedrooms are divided between the main house, Beech Cottage and the Pinnacles. The public areas are very stylishly decorated, and imaginative food is served in an elegant dining room, overlooking the immaculate grounds.

Rooms 30 (23 annexe) (9 GF) S £112-£115; D £185-£189 (incl. bkfst)* **Facilities** Direct access to Malvern Hills Xmas New Year Wi-fi **Conf** Board 14 Thtr 20 **Parking** 40

MALVERN

Four Hedges
★★ GUEST ACCOMMODATION

☎ 01684 310405
The Rhydd, Hanley Castle WR8 0AD
e-mail: fredgies@aol.com
dir: 4m E of Malvern at junct of B4211 & B4424

PETS: Bedrooms unattended Public areas
Grounds Exercise area adjoining Facilities food
bowl water bowl Resident Pets: Machu & Pichu
(cats)

Situated in a rural location, this detached house
stands in mature grounds with wild birds in
abundance. The bedrooms are equipped with
thoughtful extras. Tasty English breakfasts,
using free-range eggs, are served in a cosy
dining room at a table made from a 300-year-old
elm tree.

Rooms 4 rms (2 en suite) S fr £25; D fr £50
Facilities TVL tea/coffee Cen ht ⛵ Fishing
Parking 5 Notes No Children 1yr Closed Xmas 🐾

BRANDESBURTON

Burton Lodge
★★ 72% HOTEL

☎ 01964 542847   📠 01964 544771
YO25 8RU
e-mail: enquiries@burton-lodge.co.uk
dir: 7m from Beverley off A165, at Hainsworth
Park Golf Club

PETS: Bedrooms unattended Public areas
except dining room Grounds Facilities food
(pre-bookable) Resident Pets: Danny & Ollie
(Labradors)

A tennis court, sports play area and extensive
lawns are features of this friendly hotel, which
is situated in two acres of grounds adjoining a
golf course. The modern bedrooms look out either
onto the golf course or the countryside; there
is a comfortable lounge with a small bar and
a spacious restaurant that offers tasty home
cooking.

Rooms 9 (2 annexe) (3 fmly) (2 GF) Facilities ⛳
18 Putt green Pitch and putt Conf Class 20
Parking 15 Notes LB Closed 25-26 Dec

ALDBROUGH ST JOHN

Lucy Cross Farm
★★★ GUEST ACCOMMODATION

☎ 01325 374319 & 07931 545985
DL11 7AD
e-mail: sally@lucycross.co.uk
web: www.lucycross.co.uk
dir: A1 junct 56 onto B6275 at Barton, white
house 3m from Barton rdbt on left towards
Piercebridge

PETS: Bedrooms unattended Charges Public
areas Grounds Exercise area Facilities food
(pre-bookable) food bowl water bowl Other
dogs allowed in ground-floor bedroom only;
dogs must sleep in own basket; outside kennel
available; please phone for further details of
urther facilities for dogs Resident Pets: Spud
(Jack Russell)

Located close to major road links, a relaxed
atmosphere and friendly welcome is assured.
Traditionally furnished bedrooms are very
comfortably equipped; one is on the ground floor.
A lounge is available and hearty breakfasts are
served in the pleasant dining room.

Rooms 5 rms (3 en suite) (2 pri facs) (1 fmly)
(1 GF) S £35-£45; D £65-£75 Facilities FTV
TVL tea/coffee Dinner available Cen ht Wi-fi
Fishing Riding Conf Max 12 Board 12 Parking 10
Notes LB

BOLTON ABBEY

The Devonshire Arms Country House Hotel & Spa
★★★★ ⍟⍟⍟ HOTEL

☎ 01756 710441 & 718111 📄 01756 710564
BD23 6AJ
e-mail: res@thedevonshirehotels.co.uk
web: www.devonshirehotels.co.uk
dir: On B6160, 250yds N of junct with A59

PETS: Bedrooms unattended Public areas except
dining rooms Grounds Exercise area Facilities
food (pre-bookable) food bowl water bowl;
please phone for further details Resident Pets:
Dexter & Betsy (Cocker Spaniels)

With stunning views this beautiful hotel is
owned by the Duke and Duchess of Devonshire.
Bedrooms are elegantly furnished. The sitting
rooms are delightfully cosy with log fires, and the
dedicated staff deliver service with a blend of
friendliness and professionalism. The Burlington
Restaurant offers highly accomplished cuisine;
the Brasserie provides lighter options.

Rooms 40 (1 fmly) (17 GF) S £186-£342;
D £245-£420 (incl. bkfst) Facilities Spa STV
⍟ supervised ⌁ Fishing ⌁ Gym Classic cars
Falconry Laser pigeon shooting Fly fishing Cricket
Xmas New Year Wi-fi Conf Class 80 Board 30
Thtr 90 Parking 150 Notes LB Civ Wed 90

GREAT AYTON

Royal Oak
★★★ INN

☎ 01642 722361 & 723270
🖷 01642 724047
123 High St TS9 6BW
e-mail: info@royaloak-hotel.co.uk
dir: Off the A173, on High Street

PETS: **Bedrooms** unattended **Public areas** assist dogs only **Grounds Exercise area** local walks **Facilities** water bowl pet food on request

This 18th-century former coaching inn is very popular with locals and visitors to the village. Bedrooms are all comfortably equipped. The restaurant and public bar retain many original features and offer a good selection of fine ales; an extensive range of food is available all day and is served in the bar or the dining room.

Rooms 5 en suite **S** £35-£50; **D** £70*
Facilities tea/coffee Dinner available Direct Dial Cen ht Snooker **Conf** Max 30 Thtr 30 Class 30 Board 30

HARROGATE

The Boar's Head Hotel
★★★ 83% ◉◉ HOTEL

☎ 01423 771888 🖷 01423 771509
Ripley Castle Estate HG3 3AY
e-mail: reservations@boarsheadripley.co.uk
dir: On A61 (Harrogate to Ripon road). Hotel in town centre

PETS: **Bedrooms** unattended **Charges Public areas** except restaurant **Exercise area** 10mtrs **Facilities** food bowl water bowl

Part of the Ripley Castle estate, this delightful and popular hotel is renowned for its warm hospitality and as a dining destination. Bedrooms offer many comforts, and the luxurious day rooms feature works of art from the nearby castle. The banqueting suites in the castle are very impressive.

Rooms 25 (6 annexe) (2 fmly) **S** £105-£125; **D** £125-£150 (incl. bkfst)* **Facilities** ⏃ Fishing Clay pigeon shooting Tennis Fishing ♫ Xmas New Year Wi-fi **Conf** Class 80 Board 150 Thtr 150 Del from £155* **Parking** 50 **Notes** LB Civ Wed 120

HELMSLEY

Black Swan Hotel

★★★ 82% HOTEL

☎ 01439 770466 📠 01439 770174
Market Place YO62 5BJ
e-mail: enquiries@blackswan-helmsley.co.uk
web: www.blackswan-helmsley.co.uk
dir: A1 junct 49, A168, A170 east, hotel 14m
from Thirsk

PETS: Bedrooms unattended Charges Public
areas Grounds Exercise area 0.5m Facilities
food bowl water bowl

People have been visiting this establishment for
over 200 years and it has become a landmark
that dominates the market square. The hotel is
renowned for its hospitality and friendliness;
many of the staff are long-serving and dedicated.
The bedrooms are stylish and include a junior
suite and feature rooms. The hotel has a Tearoom
and Patisserie that is open daily.

Rooms 45 (4 fmly) Facilities STV ➴ Use of
leisure & spa facilities at nearby sister hotel
Xmas New Year Wi-fi Conf Class 30 Board 26
Thtr 50 Del from £145 to £165 Parking 50
Notes Civ Wed 130

HOVINGHAM

Worsley Arms Hotel

★★★ 72% HOTEL

☎ 01653 628234 📠 01653 628130
High St YO62 4LA
e-mail: worsleyarms@aol.com
dir: A64, signed York, towards Malton. At dual
carriageway left to Hovingham. At Slingsby left,
then 2m

PETS: Bedrooms unattended Charges Public
areas lounge only Ground Exercise area
Facilities food bowl water bowl dog biscuit on
arrival Resident Pet: Badger (Black Labrador)

Overlooking the village green, this hotel has
relaxing and attractive lounges with welcoming
open fires. Bedrooms are also comfortable and
several are contained in cottages across the
green. The restaurant provides interesting quality
cooking, with less formal dining in the Cricketers'
Bar and Bistro to the rear.

Rooms 20 (8 annexe) (2 fmly) (4 GF) S £65-£85;
D £90-£140 (incl. bkfst) Facilities FTV ➴
Shooting Xmas New Year Conf Class 40 Board 20
Thtr 40 Del from £150 to £170 Parking 25
Notes LB Civ Wed 100

MALHAM

Beck Hall
★★★ GUEST HOUSE

☎ 01729 830332
Cove Rd BD23 4DJ
e-mail: alice@beckhallmalham.com
web: www.beckhallmalham.com
dir: A65 to Gargrave, turn right to Malham. Beck Hall 100yds on right after mini rdbt

PETS: **Bedrooms** unattended **Public areas** with other guests' agreement **Grounds Exercise area** 10yds **Facilities** food bowl water bowl **Resident Pet:** Harvey (cat)

A small stone bridge over Malham Beck leads to this delightful property. Dating from 1710, the house has true character, with bedrooms carefully furnished with four-poster beds. Delicious afternoon teas are available in the colourful garden in warmer months, while roaring log fires welcome you in the winter.

Rooms 10 rms (9 en suite) (1 pri facs) 7 annexe en suite (4 fmly) (4 GF) S £25-£60; D £48-£76 **Facilities** STV tea/coffee Dinner available Cen ht Licensed Wi-fi Fishing Riding **Conf** Max 35 Thtr 30 Class 30 Board 30 **Parking** 40 **Notes** LB

MONK FRYSTON

Monk Fryston Hall Hotel
★★★ 81% COUNTRY HOUSE HOTEL

☎ 01977 682369 📄 01977 683544
LS25 5DU
e-mail: reception@monkfrystonhallhotel.co.uk
web: www.monkfrystonhallhotel.co.uk
dir: A1(M) junct 42/A63 towards Selby. Monk Fryston 2m, hotel on left

PETS: **Bedrooms** unattended **Charges Public areas** except restaurant **Grounds Exercise area**

This delightful 16th-century mansion house enjoys a peaceful location in 30 acres of grounds, yet is only minutes' drive from the A1. Many original features have been retained and the public rooms are furnished with antique and period pieces. Bedrooms are individually styled and thoughtfully equipped for both business and leisure guests.

Rooms 29 (2 fmly) (5 GF) S £75-£105; D £110-£175 (incl. bkfst) **Facilities** STV ⤳ Xmas New Year Wi-fi **Conf** Class 30 Board 25 Thtr 70 **Parking** 80 **Notes** LB Civ Wed 72

PICKERING

The White Swan Inn

★★★ 80% ® HOTEL

☎ 01751 472288 📄 01751 475554

Market Place YO18 7AA

e-mail: welcome@white-swan.co.uk

web: www.white-swan.co.uk

dir: In town, between church & steam railway station

PETS: Bedrooms unattended Public areas Grounds Exercise area 200mtrs Facilities food (pre-bookable) food bowl water bowl

This 16th-century coaching inn offers well-equipped, comfortable bedrooms, including suites, either of a more traditional style in the main building or modern rooms in the annexe. Service is friendly and attentive. Good food is served in the attractive restaurant, in the cosy bar and the lounge, where a log fire burns in cooler months. A comprehensive wine list focuses on many fine vintages. A private dining room is also available.

Rooms 21 (9 annexe) (3 fmly) (8 GF) D £145-£250 (incl. bkfst)* Facilities FTV Xmas New Year Wi-fi Conf Class 18 Board 25 Thtr 35 Parking 45 Notes LB Civ Wed 40

RIPON

Best Western Ripon Spa Hotel

★★★ 79% HOTEL

☎ 01765 602172 📄 01765 690770

Park St HG4 2BU

e-mail: sales@spahotelripon.co.uk

web: www.bw-riponspa.com

dir: From A61 to Ripon, follow Fountains Abbey signs. Hotel on left after hospital. Or from A1(M) junct 48, B6265 to Ripon, straight on at 2 rdbts. Right at lights towards city centre. Left at hill top. Left at Give Way sign. Hotel on left

PETS: Bedrooms unattended Public areas except food areas Grounds Exercise area 25yds Resident Pet: 1 Labrador

This privately owned hotel is set in extensive and attractive gardens just a short walk from the city centre. The bedrooms are well equipped to meet the needs of leisure and business travellers alike, while the comfortable lounges are complemented by the convivial atmosphere of the Turf Bar.

Rooms 40 (5 fmly) (4 GF) S £63-£118; D £79-£137 (incl. bkfst) Facilities STV ⚓ Xmas New Year Wi-fi Conf Class 35 Board 40 Thtr 150 Del from £130 to £140 Services Lift Parking 60 Notes LB Civ Wed 150

SALTBURN-BY-THE-SEA

Rushpool Hall Hotel
★★★ 73% HOTEL

☎ 01287 624111 📠 01287 625255
Saltburn Ln TS12 1HD
e-mail: enquiries@rushpoolhallhotel.co.uk
web: www.rushpoolhallhotel.co.uk
dir: A174 Redcar & Whitby, at 6th rdbt take 3rd
exit for Skelton, left at next 2 rdbts, hotel 0.5m

PETS: Bedrooms unattended Public areas except
restaurants Grounds 90-acre estate Facilities
Other dogs allowed in chalets only Restrictions
no Pit Bulls Resident Pets: Shaka (Rhodesian
Ridgeback), Humphrey (Miniature Shetland Pony),
peacocks

A grand Victorian mansion located in its own
grounds and woodlands. Stylish, elegant
bedrooms are well equipped and spacious; many
enjoy excellent sea views. The public rooms are
full of charm and character, and roaring fires
welcome guests in cooler months. The hotel is
an excellent wedding venue thanks to its superb
location and experienced event management.

Rooms 21 (3 smoking) S £65-£90; D £135-£165
(incl. bkfst)* Facilities STV FTV Fishing 🐟 Bird
watching Walking Jogging track Wi-fi Child
facilities Conf Class 75 Board 60 Thtr 100
Del from £75 to £110* Parking 120 Notes ⊗
Civ Wed 110

SCARBOROUGH

Delmont Hotel
★★ 64% HOTEL

☎ 01723 364500 📠 01723 363554
18/19 Blenheim Ter YO12 7HE
e-mail: enquiries@delmonthotel.co.uk
dir: Follow signs to North Bay. At seafront to top
of cliff. Hotel near castle

PETS: Bedrooms unattended Charges Public
areas except restaurant Grounds Exercise area
adjacent

Popular with groups, a friendly welcome is found
at this hotel on the North Bay. Bedrooms are
comfortable, and many have sea views. There are
two lounges, a bar and a spacious dining room
in which good-value, traditional food is served
along with entertainment on most evenings.

Rooms 51 (18 fmly) (5 GF) S £46-£56; D £46-£56
(incl. bkfst & dinner) Facilities Games Room Pool
table ♫ Xmas New Year Services Lift Parking 2

THORNTON WATLASS

Buck Inn
★★★ INN

☎ 01677 422461 📠 01677 422447
HG4 4AH
e-mail: innwatlass1@btconnect.com
web: www.thebuckinn.net
dir: From A1 at Leeming Bartake A684 towards
Bedale, B6268 towards Masham 2m, turn right at
x-rds to Thornton Watlass

PETS: **Bedrooms** unattended **Charges Public
areas** in residents' lounge only **Grounds Exercise
area** 300yds **Facilities** water bowl **Resident Pet:**
Tess (Border Collie)

This traditional country inn is on the village
green overlooking the cricket pitch. Cricket prints
and old photographs are found throughout and
an open fire in the bar adds to the warm and
intimate atmosphere. Wholesome lunches and
dinners, from an extensive menu, are served in
the bar or dining room. Bedrooms are brightly
decorated and well equipped.

Rooms 7 rms (5 en suite) (1 fmly) (1 GF) **S**
£65; **D** £80-£90* **Facilities** TVL tea/coffee
Dinner available Cen ht Wi-fi Fishing Pool Table
Quoits **Conf** Max 50 Thtr 50 Class 45 Board
30 **Parking** 10 **Notes** LB RS 24-25 Dec No
accommodation, no food 25 Dec

WEST WITTON

The Wensleydale Heifer
★★ 82% ◉◉ HOTEL

☎ 01969 622322 & 622725 📠 01969 624183
Main St DL8 4LS
e-mail: info@wensleydaleheifer.co.uk
web: www.wensleydaleheifer.co.uk
dir: A1 to Leeming Bar junct, A684 towards
Bedale for approx 10m to Leyburn, then towards
Hawes 3.5m to West Witton

PETS: **Bedrooms** unattended **Charges Public
areas** except bar & lounge **Grounds Exercise
area** adjacent **Facilities** food bowl water bowl

Describing itself as a boutique hotel, this 17th-
century coaching inn has been transformed in
recent years. The bedrooms (a four-poster room
and junior suite included) are each designed
with a unique and interesting theme - for
example, Chocolate, Malt Whisky, James Herriott
and Shooter. Food is very much the focus at the
Wensleydale Heifer whether it be in the informal
fish bar or the contemporary style restaurant. The
kitchen prides itself on sourcing the freshest fish
and locally reared meats.

Rooms 9 (3 fmly) **S** £70-£90; **D** £110-£140 (incl.
bkfst)* **Facilities** Xmas New Year **Parking** 40

YORK

The Grange

★★★★ 77% ◎◎ HOTEL

☎ 01904 644744 📄 01904 612453
1 Clifton YO30 6AA
e-mail: info@grangehotel.co.uk
web: www.grangehotel.co.uk
dir: On A19 York/Thirsk road

PETS: Bedrooms unattended **Charges Public areas Exercise area** 5 mins walk **Restrictions** small - medium size dogs only

This bustling Regency town house is just a few minutes' walk from the centre of York. A professional service is efficiently delivered by caring staff in a very friendly and helpful manner. Public rooms are comfortable and have been stylishly furnished; these include two dining options, the popular and informal Cellar Bar, and main hotel restaurant The Ivy Brasserie, which offers fine dining in a lavishly decorated environment. The individually designed bedrooms are comfortably appointed and have been thoughtfully equipped.

Rooms 36 (6 GF) **S** £117-£188; **D** £160-£225 (incl. bkfst) **Facilities** STV FTV Use of nearby health club Xmas New Year Wi-fi **Conf** Class 24 Board 24 Thtr 50 Del from £156.50 to £173.95 **Parking** 26 **Notes** LB Civ Wed 90

YORK

Best Western Monkbar

★★★ 79% HOTEL

☎ 01904 638086 📄 01904 629195
Monkbar YO31 7JA
e-mail: sales@monkbarhotel.co.uk
dir: A64 onto A1079 to city, turn right at city walls, take middle lane at lights. Hotel on right

PETS: Bedrooms unattended **Charges Public areas** except bar/restaurant **Grounds Exercise area** 100yds **Facilities** food food bowl water bowl; please phone for further details of facilities for dogs **Resident Pet:** Misty Monkbar (Golden Labrador)

This smart hotel enjoys a prominent position adjacent to the city walls, and just a few minutes' walk from the cathedral. Individually styled bedrooms are well equipped for both business and leisure guests. Spacious public areas include comfortable lounges, an American-style bar, an airy restaurant and impressive meeting and training facilities.

Rooms 99 (8 fmly) (2 GF) **S** £95-£125; **D** £105-£175 (incl. bkfst)* **Facilities** STV FTV Xmas New Year Wi-fi Child facilities **Conf** Class 80 Board 50 Thtr 140 Del from £130 to £175* **Services** Lift **Parking** 66 **Notes** LB Civ Wed 80

YORK

Ascot House
★★★★ GUEST ACCOMMODATION

☎ 01904 426826 🖹 01904 431077
80 East Pde YO31 7YH
e-mail: admin@ascothouseyork.com
web: www.ascothouseyork.com
dir: 0.5m NE of city centre. Off A1036 Heworth
Green onto Mill Ln, 2nd left

PETS: Bedrooms unattended Public areas
except dining room Grounds Exercise area
300yds Resident Pets: Gemma & Millie (Black
Labradors)

June and Keith Wood provide friendly service at
the 1869 Ascot House, a 15-minute walk from the
town centre. Bedrooms are thoughtfully equipped,
many with four-poster or canopy beds and other
period furniture. Reception rooms include a cosy
lounge that also retains its original features.

Rooms 13 rms (12 en suite) (1 pri facs) (3 fmly)
(2 GF) S £55-£70; D £70-£80 Facilities TVL tea/
coffee Cen ht Licensed Wi-fi Sauna Parking 13
Notes LB Closed 21-28 Dec

YORK

Greenside
★★★ GUEST HOUSE

☎ 01904 623631 🖹 01904 623631
124 Clifton YO30 6BQ
e-mail: greenside@surfree.co.uk
web: www.greensideguesthouse.co.uk
dir: A19 N towards city centre, over lights for
Greenside, on left opp Clifton Green

PETS: Bedrooms unattended Public areas
Exercise area 50yds Facilities food bowl water
bowl

Overlooking Clifton Green, this detached house
is just within walking distance of the city centre.
Accommodation consists of simply furnished
bedrooms and there is a cosy lounge and a
dining room, where dinners by arrangement and
traditional breakfasts are served. It is a family
home, and other families are welcome.

Rooms 6 rms (3 en suite) (2 fmly) (3 GF) S fr £30;
D fr £56* Facilities TVL tea/coffee Cen ht Wi-fi
Parking 6 Notes LB Closed Xmas & New Year 🐾

BARNSLEY

Best Western Ardsley House Hotel
★★★ 79% HOTEL

☎ 01226 309955 📄 01226 205374
Doncaster Rd, Ardsley S71 5EH
e-mail: ardsley.house@forestdale.com
web: www.ardsleyhousehotel.co.uk
dir: on A635, 0.75m from Stairfoot rdbt

PETS: Bedrooms unattended Charges Public
areas except restaurant

This late 18th-century building has retained
many of its original Georgian features. Bedrooms
are both comfortable and well equipped. The
excellent leisure facilities including a gym, pool
and beauty salon. The Allendale restaurant
with views of the nearby woodlands offers an
extensive menu.

Rooms 75 (12 fmly) (14 GF) Facilities Spa ☺
supervised Gym Beauty spa 3 treatment rooms
♫ Xmas New Year Wi-fi Conf Class 250 Board 40
Thtr 350 Parking 200 Notes LB Civ Wed 250

DONCASTER

Campanile Doncaster
BUDGET HOTEL

☎ 01302 370770 📄 01302 370813
Doncaster Leisure Park, Bawtry Rd DN4 7PD
e-mail: doncaster@campanile.com
dir: Follow signs to Doncaster Leisure Centre, left
at rdbt before Dome complex

PETS: Bedrooms unattended Charges Public
areas except restaurant (assist dogs only)
Grounds Exercise area surrounding area

This modern building offers accommodation in
smart, well-equipped bedrooms, all with en suite
bathrooms. Refreshments may be taken at the
informal bistro.

Rooms 50 Conf Class 15 Board 15 Thtr 25

ROTHERHAM

Hellaby Hall Hotel
★★★★ 71% HOTEL

☎ 01709 702701 📠 01709 700979
Old Hellaby Ln, Hellaby S66 8SN
e-mail: reservations@hellabyhallhotel.co.uk
web: www.hellabyhallhotel.co.uk
dir: 0.5m off M18 junct 1, onto A631 towards
Maltby. Hotel in Hellaby. (NB do not use postcode
for sat nav)

PETS: **Bedrooms** unattended **Charges Public
areas** except restaurant & bar **Grounds Exercise
area Facilities** food (pre-bookable) food bowl
water bowl **Resident Pet:** Savah (cat)

This 17th-century house was built to a Flemish
design with high, beamed ceilings, staircases
which lead off to private meeting rooms and a
series of oak-panelled lounges. Bedrooms are
elegant and well equipped, and guests can
dine in the formal Attic Restaurant. There are
extensive leisure facilities and conference areas,
and the hotel holds a licence for civil weddings.

Rooms 90 (2 fmly) (17 GF) **Facilities Spa** STV FTV
🏊 Gym Beauty room Exercise studio Xmas New
Year Wi-fi **Conf** Class 300 Board 150 Thtr 500
Services Lift **Parking** 250 **Notes** Civ Wed 200

WOODALL MOTORWAY SERVICE AREA (M1)

Days Inn Sheffield
BUDGET HOTEL

☎ 0114 248 7992 📠 0114 248 5634
Woodall Service Area S26 7XR
e-mail: woodall.hotel@welcomebreak.co.uk
web: www.welcomebreak.co.uk
dir: M1 southbound, at Woodall Services, between
juncts 30 & 31

PETS: **Bedrooms** unattended **Charges Public
areas Grounds Facilities** food bowl water bowl

This modern building offers accommodation in
smart, spacious and well-equipped bedrooms,
suitable for families and business travellers,
and all with en suite bathrooms. Continental
breakfast is available and other refreshments
may be taken at the nearby family restaurant.

Rooms 38 (32 fmly) **S** £29-£59; **D** £39-£69*
Conf Board 10 Del from £65 to £95*

BINGLEY

Five Rise Locks Hotel & Restaurant
★★ 74% SMALL HOTEL

☎ 01274 565296 🖷 01274 568828
Beck Ln BD16 4DD
e-mail: info@five-rise-locks.co.uk
dir: Off Main St onto Park Rd, 0.5m left onto Beck Ln

PETS: Bedrooms unattended Charges Public areas GroundsExercise area 300yds Resident Pets: Ruby & Tilly (Bassett Hounds)

A warm welcome and comfortable accommodation await guests at this impressive Victorian building. Bedrooms are of a good size and feature homely extras. The restaurant offers imaginative dishes and the bright breakfast room overlooks open countryside.

Rooms 9 (2 GF) S £60-£65; D £85-£105 (incl. bkfst)* Facilities FTV Wi-fi Conf Class 16 Board 18 Thtr 25 Del from £100 to £125* Parking 20

BRADFORD

Best Western Guide Post Hotel
★★★ 75% HOTEL

☎ 0845 409 1362 🖷 01274 671085
Common Rd, Low Moor BD12 0ST
e-mail: sue.barnes@guideposthotel.net
web: www.guideposthotel.net
dir: From M606 rdbt take 2nd exit (Little Chef on right). At next rdbt take 1st exit (Cleckheaton Rd). 0.5m, turn right at bollard into Common Rd

PETS: Bedrooms unattended Charges Public areas except restaurant & bar Exercise area 2 mins

Situated south of the city, this hotel offers attractively styled, modern, comfortable bedrooms. The restaurant offers an extensive range of food using fresh, local produce; lighter snack meals are served in the bar. There is also a choice of well-equipped meeting and function rooms. There is disabled access to the hotel, restaurant and one function room.

Rooms 42 (8 fmly) (13 GF) (8 smoking) S £50-£94; D £59-£105 Facilities STV FTV Complimentary use of nearby swimming & gym facilities Wi-fi Conf Class 80 Board 60 Thtr 120 Del from £119 to £129 Parking 100 Notes LB Civ Wed 120

DEWSBURY

Heath Cottage Hotel & Restaurant
★★★ 72% HOTEL

☎ 01924 465399 📠 01924 459405
Wakefield Rd WF12 8ET
e-mail: info@heathcottage.co.uk
dir: M1 junct 40/A638 for 2.5m towards
Dewsbury. Hotel before lights, opposite
Earlsheaton Cemetery

PETS: Bedrooms unattended Charges Public
areas Grounds Exercise area Other dog food
available only if pre-booked

tanding in an acre of grounds, Heath Cottage
is just two and a half miles from the M1. The
service is friendly and professional. All the
bedrooms are modern and well appointed, and
some are in a converted stable building. The
lounge bar and restaurant are air conditioned.
Extensive parking is available.

Rooms 28 (6 annexe) (3 fmly) (3 GF) S £39-£59;
D £49.50-£99 (incl. bkfst)* Facilities Wi-fi
Conf Class 56 Board 32 Thtr 100 Del from £79
to £99* Parking 60 Notes RS 23-27 Dec
Civ Wed 100

GARFORTH

Best Western Milford Hotel
★★★ 81% HOTEL

☎ 01977 681800 📠 01977 681245
A1 Great North Rd, Peckfield LS25 5LQ
e-mail: enquiries@mlh.co.uk
web: www.mlh.co.uk
dir: On A63, 1.5m W of A1(M) junct 42 & 4.5m E
of M1 junct 46

PETS: Bedrooms unattended Charges Public
areas Exercise area 200yds Facilities food
(pre-bookable) food bowl water bowl Other dogs
allowed in ground-floor bedrooms only

This friendly, family owned and run hotel is
conveniently situated on the A1, and provides
very comfortable, modern accommodation.
The air-conditioned bedrooms are particularly
spacious and well equipped, and ten boutique-
style superior rooms are now available. Public
areas include a relaxing lounge area and the
contemporary Watermill Restaurant and lounge
bar which has a working waterwheel.

Rooms 46 (13 GF) (6 smoking) S £46.40-£80;
D £46.40-£80* Facilities STV FTV Xmas New
Year Wi-fi Conf Class 35 Board 30 Thtr 60
Del from £99 to £135* Services Air con
Parking 80 Notes LB

GARFORTH

Holiday Inn Leeds Garforth
★★★ 80% HOTEL

☎ 0113 286 6556 📠 0113 286 8326
Wakefield Rd LS25 1LH
e-mail: reservations@hileedsgarforth.com
web: www.holidayinn.co.uk
dir: At junct of A63/A642. Hotel opposite rdbt

PETS: Bedrooms unattended Charges Public
areas Grounds Exercise area 200yds

Located just outside Leeds, this hotel has
excellent access to the M1 and M62 making
it an ideal base for exploring the area. Well-
equipped accommodation includes executive
bedrooms. Public areas are attractively
designed and include meeting rooms and leisure
club. Aioli's Restaurant serves contemporary
cuisine.

Rooms 144 (30 fmly) (35 GF) (15 smoking)
Facilities FTV ☜ supervised Gym New Year Wi-fi
Conf Class 120 Board 50 Thtr 350 Del from £99
to £145* Services Air con Parking 250
Notes Civ Wed 140

GOMERSAL

Gomersal Park
★★★ 79% HOTEL

☎ 01274 869386 📠 01274 861042
Moor Ln BD19 4LJ
e-mail: enquiries@gomersalparkhotel.com
web: www.gomersalparkhotel.com
dir: A62 to Huddersfield. At junct with A65, by
Greyhound Pub right, after 1m take 1st right after
Oakwell Hall

PETS: Bedrooms unattended Charges Public
areas Grounds Exercise area 100yds Facilities
food bowl water bowl Resident Pet: Teal (English
Pointer)

Constructed around a 19th-century house, this
stylish, modern hotel enjoys a peaceful location
and pleasant grounds. Deep sofas ensure comfort
in the open-plan lounge and imaginative meals
are served in the popular Brasserie 101. The
well-equipped bedrooms provide high quality and
comfort. Extensive public areas include a well-
equipped leisure complex and pool, and a wide
variety of air-conditioned conference rooms.

Rooms 100 (3 fmly) (32 GF) Facilities ☜
supervised Gym Wi-fi Conf Class 130 Board 60
Thtr 250 Del from £90 to £140* Services Lift
Parking 150 Notes Civ Wed 200

HARTSHEAD MOOR MOTORWAY
SERVICE AREA (M62)

Days Inn Bradford
BUDGET HOTEL

☎ 01274 851706   📠 01274 855169
Hartshead Moor Service Area, Clifton HD6 4JX
e-mail: hartshead.hotel@welcomebreak.co.uk
web: www.welcomebreak.co.uk
dir: M62 between juncts 25 & 26

PETS: **Bedrooms** unattended **Charges Public areas Exercise area** surrounding fields

This modern building offers accommodation in smart, spacious and well-equipped bedrooms, suitable for families and business travellers, and all with en suite bathrooms. Continental breakfast is available and other refreshments may be taken at the nearby family restaurant.

Rooms 38 (33 fmly) **S** £39-£59; **D** £39-£69*
Conf Board 10 Del from £65 to £95*

HUDDERSFIELD

The Old Golf House Hotel
★★★ 70% HOTEL

☎ 0844 736 8609   & 01422 379311
📠 01422 372694
New Hey Rd, Outlane HD3 3YP
e-mail: oldgolfhouse@corushotels.com
web: www.corushotels.com/old-golf-house-hotel-the
dir: M62 junct 23 (eastbound only), or junct 24. Follow A640 to Rochdale. Hotel on A640

PETS: **Bedrooms** unattended **Charges Public areas Grounds Facilities** food bowl water bowl

Situated close to the M62, this traditionally styled hotel offers well-equipped bedrooms. A wide choice of dishes is offered in the restaurant, and lighter meals are available in the lounge bar. The hotel, with lovely grounds, is a popular venue for weddings.

Rooms 52 (4 fmly) (19 GF) (10 smoking)
S £79-£89; **D** £79-£89* **Facilities** STV Putt green Mini golf Xmas New Year Wi-fi **Conf** Class 35 Board 30 Thtr 70 Del from £90 to £110*
Parking 100 **Notes** LB RS 25 Dec Civ Wed 100

HUDDERSFIELD

The Huddersfield Central Lodge
★★★★ GUEST ACCOMMODATION

☎ 01484 515551 📄 01484 432349
11/15 Beast Market HD1 1QF
e-mail: enquiries@centrallodge.com
web: www.centrallodge.com
dir: In town centre off Lord St, signs for Beast Market from ring road

PETS: Bedrooms unattended Charges Public areas except breakfast room during breakfast Grounds Exercise area 500mtrs

This friendly, family-run operation offers smart spacious bedrooms with modern en suites. Some rooms are in the main building, while new rooms, many with kitchenettes, are situated across a courtyard. Public rooms include a bar and a conservatory, and there are arrangements for local restaurants to charge meals to guests' accounts. Secure complimentary parking.

Rooms 9 en suite 13 annexe en suite (2 fmly) (6 smoking) S £52-£58; D £68* Facilities STV TVL tea/coffee Direct Dial Cen ht Licensed Wi-fi Parking 50

KEIGHLEY

Dalesgate Hotel
★★ 70% HOTEL

☎ 01535 664930 📄 01535 611253
406 Skipton Rd, Utley BD20 6HP
e-mail: stephen.e.atha@btinternet.com
dir: In town centre follow A629 over rdbt onto B6265. Right after 0.75m into St. John's Rd. 1st right into hotel car park

PETS: Bedrooms unattended Charges Public areas except bar & restaurant Exercise area 300yds Facilities food bowl water bowl Resident Pet: Max (German Shepherd cross)

Originally the residence of a local chapel minister, this modern, well-established hotel provides well-equipped, comfortable bedrooms. It also boasts a cosy bar and pleasant restaurant, serving an imaginative range of dishes. A large car park is provided to the rear.

Rooms 20 (2 fmly) (3 GF) S £40-£45; D £60-£65 (incl. bkfst)* Parking 25 Notes RS 22 Dec-4 Jan

LEEDS

Malmaison Hotel
★★★ 82% @ HOTEL

☎ 0113 398 1000 📄 0113 398 1002
1 Swingate LS1 4AG
e-mail: leeds@malmaison.com
web: www.malmaison.com
dir: M621/M1 junct 3, follow city centre signs. At KPMG building, right into Sovereign Street. Hotel at end on right

PETS: Bedrooms unattended **Charges Public areas** except bar & restaurant **Facilities** food (pre-bookable) food bowl water bowl

Close to the waterfront, this stylish property offers striking bedrooms with CD players and air conditioning. The popular bar and brasserie feature vaulted ceilings, intimate lighting and offer a choice of a full three-course meal or a substantial snack. Service is both willing and friendly. A small fitness centre and impressive meeting rooms complete the package.

Rooms 100 (4 fmly) **S** £79-£135; **D** £79-£170*
Facilities STV Gym Xmas New Year Wi-fi
Conf Class 20 Board 24 Thtr 45 Del from £145 to £185* **Services** Lift Air con **Notes** LB

WAKEFIELD

Campanile Wakefield
BUDGET HOTEL

☎ 01924 201054 📄 01924 290976
Monckton Rd WF2 7AL
e-mail: wakefield@campanile.com
dir: M1 junct 39, A636, 1m towards Wakefield, left into Monckton Rd, hotel on left

PETS: Bedrooms unattended **Charges Public areas** except buffet section of restaurant **Grounds Exercise area** canalside walk nearby **Facilities** food bowl water bowl

This modern building offers accommodation in smart, well-equipped bedrooms, all with en suite bathrooms. Refreshments may be taken at the informal bistro.

Rooms 76 (76 annexe) (4 fmly) (25 GF)
S £42-£46; **D** £42-£46* **Conf** Class 15 Board 15 Thtr 25 Del from £59 to £99*

GROUVILLE

The Beausite Hotel

★★★ 71% HOTEL

☎ 01534 857577 📠 01534 857211
Les Rue des Pres, Grouville Bay JE3 9DJ
e-mail: beausite@jerseymail.co.uk
web: www.southernhotels.com
dir: Opposite Royal Jersey Golf Course

PETS: Bedrooms unattended Charges Public
areas bar only Grounds Resident Pet: Benjy
(Terrier)

This hotel is situated on the south-east side of
the island; a short distance from the picturesque
harbour at Gorey. With parts dating back to 1636,
the public rooms retain original character and
charm; bedrooms are generally spacious and
modern in design. The indoor swimming pool,
fitness room, saunas and spa bath are an added
bonus.

Rooms 75 (5 fmly) (18 GF) S £49-£94.50;
D £82-£126 (incl. bkfst)* Facilities STV ③ Gym
Wi-fi Parking 60 Notes LB Closed Nov-Mar

ST BRELADE

Hotel La Place

★★★★ 73% ❀ HOTEL

☎ 01534 744261 📠 01534 745164
Route du Coin, La Haule JE3 8BT
e-mail: reservations@hotellaplacejersey.com
dir: Off main St Helier/St Aubin coast road at
La Haule Manor (B25). Up hill, 2nd left (to Red
Houses), 1st right. Hotel 100mtrs on right

PETS: Bedrooms unattended Charges Public
areas Grounds

Developed around a 17th-century farmhouse
and well placed for exploration of the island.
Attentive, friendly service is the ethos here. A
range of bedroom types is provided, some having
private patios and direct access to the pool area.
The cocktail bar is popular for pre-dinner drinks
and a traditional lounge has a log fire in colder
months. An interesting menu is offered.

Rooms 42 (1 fmly) (10 GF) Facilities ⅃ Discount
at Les Ormes Country Club, including golf, gym &
indoor tennis Xmas Wi-fi Conf Class 40 Board 40
Thtr 100 Parking 100 Notes Civ Wed 100

ST BRELADE

Hotel Miramar
★★ 72% HOTEL

☎ 01534 743831 📄 01534 745009
Mont Gras d'Eau JE3 8ED
e-mail: miramarjsy@localdial.com
dir: From airport take B36 at lights, turn left onto
A13, 1st right into Mont Gras d'Eau

PETS: Bedrooms unattended Public areas
Exercise area 100yds

A friendly welcome awaits at this family-run hotel
set in delightful sheltered gardens, overlooking
the beautiful bay. Accommodation is comfortable
with well-appointed bedrooms; some are on
the ground floor, and there are two on the lower
ground with their own terrace overlooking the
outdoor heated pool. The restaurant offers a
varied set menu.

Rooms 38 (2 fmly) (14 GF) S £32-£49.90;
D £64-£99.80 (incl. bkfst)* Facilities ₹
Parking 30 Notes Closed Oct-mid Apr

ST SAVIOUR

Longueville Manor
★★★★★ @@@ HOTEL

☎ 01534 725501 📄 01534 731613
JE2 7WF
e-mail: info@longuevillemanor.com
web: www.longuevillemanor.com
dir: A3 E from St Helier towards Gorey. Hotel 1m
on left

PETS: Bedrooms unattended Public areas
Grounds Exercise area beach 0.5m

Dating back to the 13th century, there is
something very special about Longueville Manor,
which is why so many guests return. It is set in
17 acres of grounds including woodland walks,
a spectacular rose garden and a lake. Bedrooms
have great style and individuality boasting fresh
flowers, fine embroidered bed linen and a host
of extras. The committed team of staff create a
welcoming atmosphere and every effort is made
to ensure a memorable stay. The accomplished
cuisine is also a highlight.

Rooms 30 (1 annexe) (7 GF) (6 smoking)
S £185-£380; D £210-£600 (incl. bkfst)*
Facilities STV ₹ ⚤ ⚥ Xmas New Year Wi-fi
Conf Class 30 Board 30 Thtr 45 Del from £245*
Services Lift Parking 40 Notes LB Civ Wed 40

PORT ERIN

Falcon's Nest

★★ 67% HOTEL

☎ 01624 834077 📠 01624 835370
The Promenade IM9 6AF
e-mail: falconsnest@enterprise.net
web: www.falconsnesthotel.co.uk
dir: Follow coast road, S from airport or ferry.
Hotel on seafront, immediately after steam
railway station

PETS: Bedrooms unattended Public areas except
food areas Grounds Exercise area 50mtrs to
beach/park

Situated overlooking the bay and harbour,
this Victorian hotel offers generally spacious
bedrooms. There is a choice of bars, one of which
attracts many locals. Meals can be taken in the
lounge bar, the conservatory or in the attractively
decorated main restaurant.

Rooms 35 (9 fmly) (15 smoking) S £35-£42.50;
D £70-£85 (incl. bkfst) Facilities FTV Xmas
New Year Wi-fi Conf Class 50 Board 50 Thtr 50
Del from £80 to £100* Parking 30

ABERDEEN

Malmaison Aberdeen

★★★ 86% ⑩⑩ HOTEL

☎ 01224 327370 📠 01224 327371
49-53 Queens Rd AB15 4YP
e-mail: info.aberdeen@malmaison.com
dir: A90, 3rd exit onto Queens Rd at 3rd rdbt,
hotel on right

PETS: Bedrooms unattended Public areas except
restaurant Exercise area 2m Facilities food bowl
water bowl

Popular with business travellers and as a
function venue, this well-established hotel lies
east of the city centre. Public areas include a
reception lounge and an intimate restaurant;
however the extensive bar menu remains a
preferred choice for many regulars. There are two
styles of accommodation, with the superior rooms
being particularly comfortable and well equipped.

Rooms 80 (8 fmly) (10 GF) D £95-£180
Facilities Spa STV FTV Gym Steam room Xmas
New Year Wi-fi Conf Board 12 Services Lift
Parking 50

KILCHRENAN
The Ardanaiseig Hotel
★★★ 86% ◉◉ COUNTRY HOUSE HOTEL

☎ 01866 833333 ▤ 01866 833222
by Loch Awe PA35 1HE
e-mail: ardanaiseig@clara.net
dir: From A85 at Taynuilt onto B845 to
Kilchrenan. Left in front of pub (road very narrow)
signed 'Ardanaiseig Hotel' & 'No Through Road'.
Continue for 3m

PETS: Bedrooms unattended Charges Public
areas Grounds Resident Pet: Patch (Jack
Russell)

Set amid lovely gardens and breathtaking
scenery beside the shore of Loch Awe, this
peaceful country-house hotel was built in a
Scottish baronial style in 1834. Many fine pieces
of furniture are evident in the bedrooms and
charming day rooms, which include a drawing
room, a library bar and an elegant dining room.
Dinner provides the highlight of any visit with
skilfully cooked dishes making excellent use of
local, seasonal produce.

Rooms 18 (4 fmly) (5 GF) S £64-£137;
D £128-£274 (incl. bkfst) Facilities FTV Fishing
⇘ Boating Clay pigeon shooting Bikes for hire
Xmas New Year Wi-fi Parking 20 Notes Closed 2
Jan-1 Feb Civ Wed 50

OBAN
Lancaster
★★ GUEST ACCOMMODATION

☎ 01631 562587 ▤ 01631 562587
Corran Esplanade PA34 5AD
e-mail: lancasteroban@btconnect.com
dir: On seafront next to Columba's Cathedral

PETS: Bedrooms unattended Public areas except
dining room Exercise area beach & woods
adjacent

A family-run establishment on the esplanade
that offers budget accommodation; many
bedrooms boast lovely views out over the bay
towards the Isle of Mull. Public areas include a
choice of lounges and bars that also benefit from
the panoramic views. A swimming pool, sauna
and jacuzzi are added benefits.

Rooms 27 rms (24 en suite) (3 fmly) (27
smoking) Facilities TVL tea/coffee Cen ht
Licensed ◐ Sauna Pool table Jacuzzi, Steam
room Conf Max 30 Thtr 30 Class 20 Board 12
Parking 20 Notes LB

TARBERT LOCH FYNE

Stonefield Castle

★★★★ 73% ⊛ HOTEL

☎ 01880 820836 📄 01880 820929
PA29 6YJ

e-mail: reservations.stonefieldcastle.@ohiml.com
web: www.oxfordhotelsandinns.com
dir: From Glasgow take M8 towards Erskine
Bridge, follow signs for Loch Lomond on A82.
From Arrochar follow signs for A83 through
Inveraray & Lochgilphead, hotel on left 2m before
Tarbert

PETS: **Bedrooms** unattended **Charges Public
areas** except restaurant & bar **Grounds
Facilities** food bowl water bowl

This fine baronial castle commands a superb
lochside setting amidst beautiful woodland
gardens renowned for their rhododendrons - visit
in late spring to see them at their best. Elegant
public rooms are a feature, and the picture-
window restaurant offers unrivalled views across
Loch Fyne. Bedrooms are split between the main
house and a purpose-built wing.

Rooms 32 (2 fmly) (10 GF) **S** £55-£140;
D £65-£180 (incl. bkfst)* **Facilities** Xmas New
Year Wi-fi **Conf** Class 40 Board 50 Thtr 120
Del from £135 to £195 **Services** Lift **Parking** 50
Notes LB Civ Wed 100

AUCHENCAIRN

Balcary Bay Hotel

★★★ 86% ⊛⊛ HOTEL

☎ 01556 640217 & 640311 📄 01556 640272
DG7 1QZ

e-mail: reservations@balcary-bay-hotel.co.uk
web: www.balcary-bay-hotel.co.uk
dir: On A711 between Dalbeattie & Kirkcudbright,
hotel 2m from village

PETS: **Bedrooms** unattended **Charges Public
areas Grounds Exercise area** beach adjacent
Facilities food bowl water bowl **Resident Pet:**
Rusty (Irish Red Setter)

Taking its name from the bay on which it
lies, this hotel has lawns running down to the
shore. The larger bedrooms enjoy stunning
views over the bay, whilst others overlook
the gardens. Comfortable public areas invite
relaxation. Imaginative dishes feature at dinner,
accompanied by a good wine list.

Rooms 20 (1 fmly) (3 GF) **S** £71; **D** £126-£156
(incl. bkfst) **Facilities** FTV **Parking** 50 **Notes** LB
Closed 1st Sun Dec-1st Fri Feb

KIRKCUDBRIGHT

Arden House Hotel

★★ 72% HOTEL

☎ 01557 330544 📠 01557 330742
Tongland Rd DG6 4UU
dir: Off A57, 4m W of Castle Douglas onto A711.
Follow Kirkcudbright, over Telford Bridge. Hotel
400mtrs on left

PETS: Bedrooms unattended **Public areas
Grounds Exercise area**

Set well back from the main road in extensive
grounds on the northeast side of town, this
spotlessly maintained hotel offers attractive
bedrooms, a lounge bar and adjoining
conservatory serving a range of popular dishes,
which are also available in the dining room.
It boasts an impressive function suite in its
grounds.

Rooms 9 (7 fmly) (5 smoking) **S** fr £55;
D £75-£80 (incl. bkfst)* **Conf Class** 175 **Thtr** 175
Parking 70 **Notes** LB

LOCKERBIE

Dryfesdale Country House

★★★★ 71% HOTEL

☎ 01576 202427 📠 01576 204187
Dryfebridge DG11 2SF
e-mail: reception@dryfesdalehotel.co.uk
web: www.dryfesdalehotel.co.uk
dir: From M74 junct 17 follow Lockerbie North
signs, 3rd left at 1st rdbt, 1st exit left at 2nd
rdbt, hotel 200yds on left

PETS: Bedrooms unattended **Charges Public
areas Grounds Facilities** food (pre-bookable)
food bowl water bowl **Resident Pet:** Buddy (Long
Haired German Shepherd)

Conveniently situated for the M74, yet discreetly
screened from it, this friendly hotel provides
attentive service. Bedrooms, some with access
to patio areas, vary in size and style; all offer
good levels of comfort and are well equipped.
Creative, good value dinners make use of local
produce and are served in the airy restaurant
that overlooks the manicured gardens and rolling
countryside.

Rooms 28 (5 fmly) (19 GF) **Facilities** STV FTV
Putt green 🦌 Clay pigeon shooting Fishing 🎵
Xmas New Year Wi-fi **Conf Class** 100 **Board** 100
Thtr 150 **Del from** £100 to £125 **Parking** 60
Notes Civ Wed 150

LOCKERBIE

Kings Arms Hotel

★★ 78% HOTEL

☎ 01576 202410   📠 01576 202410
High St DG11 2JL
e-mail: reception@kingsarmshotel.co.uk
web: www.kingsarmshotel.co.uk
dir: A74(M), 0.5m into town centre, hotel opposite town hall

PETS: Bedrooms unattended **Public areas** except restaurant & 1 bar **Exercise area** 1 min walk **Facilities** food bowl water bowl **Resident Pet:** Bailey (Yellow Labrador)

Dating from the 17th century this former inn lies in the town centre. Now a family-run hotel, it provides attractive well-equipped bedrooms with Wi-fi access. At lunch a menu ranging from snacks to full meals is served in both the two cosy bars and the restaurant at dinner.

Rooms 13 (2 fmly) S £47.50; D £80 (incl. bkfst)* **Facilities** FTV Xmas New Year Wi-fi **Conf** Class 40 Board 30 Thtr 80 **Parking** 8

MOFFAT

Barnhill Springs Country Guest House

★★ GUEST ACCOMMODATION

☎ 01683 220580
DG10 9QS
dir: A74(M) junct 15, A701 towards Moffat, Barnhill Rd 50yds on right

PETS: Bedrooms unattended **Public areas** except dining room **Grounds** 1.5 acres **Facilities** food bowl water bowl **Resident Pet:** Kim (Collie cross)

This former farmhouse has a quiet, rural location south of the town and within easy reach of the M74. Bedrooms are well proportioned; and have either en suite or private bathrooms. There is a comfortable lounge and separate dining room.

Rooms 5 rms (1 en suite) (2 pri facs) (1 fmly) (1 GF) S £30-£32; D £60-£64* **Facilities** TVL tea/coffee Dinner available Cen ht **Parking** 10 **Notes** ⊛

NEWTON STEWART

Bruce Hotel

★★★ 73% HOTEL

☎ 01671 402294   📠 01671 402294

88 Queen St DG8 6JL

e-mail: mail@the-bruce-hotel.com

web: www.the-bruce-hotel.com

dir: Off A75 Newton Stewart rdbt towards town. Hotel 800mtrs on right

PETS: Bedrooms unattended **Charges Public areas** except restaurant **Grounds Exercise area Restrictions** please phone for advice on which dog breeds are accepted

Named after the Scottish patriot Robert the Bruce, this welcoming hotel is just a short distance from the A75. One of the well-appointed bedrooms features a four-poster bed, and popular family suites contain separate bedrooms for children. Public areas include a traditional lounge, a formal restaurant and a lounge bar, both offering a good choice of dishes.

Rooms 20 (3 fmly) S £45-£49; D £80-£90 (incl. bkfst)* **Facilities** New Year Wi-fi **Conf** Class 50 Board 14 Thtr 100 Del from £75 to £95* **Parking** 14 **Notes** LB

EDINBURGH

Prestonfield

★★★★★ ⊛⊛ TOWN HOUSE HOTEL

☎ 0131 225 7800   📠 0131 220 4392

Priestfield Rd EH16 5UT

e-mail: reservations@prestonfield.com

web: www.prestonfield.com

dir: A7 towards Cameron Toll. 200mtrs beyond Royal Commonwealth Pool, into Priestfield Rd

PETS: Bedrooms unattended **Charges Public areas Grounds Facilities** food (pre-bookable) food bowl water bowl **Resident Pets:** Archie & Brodie (Jack Russells), Homer (Boxer), Highland cattle, peacocks

This centuries-old landmark has been lovingly restored and enhanced to provide deeply comfortable and dramatically furnished bedrooms. The building demands to be explored: from the tapestry lounge and the whisky room to the restaurant, where the walls are adorned with pictures of former owners. Facilities and services are up-to-the-minute, and carefully prepared meals are served in the award-winning Rhubarb restaurant.

Rooms 23 (6 GF) **Facilities** STV FTV ⅃ 18 Putt green ⛳ Free bike hire Xmas New Year Wi-fi **Conf** Class 500 Board 40 Thtr 700 **Services** Lift **Parking** 250 **Notes** LB Civ Wed 350

EDINBURGH

Novotel Edinburgh Centre
★★★★ 73% HOTEL

☎ 0131 656 3500 📠 0131 656 3510
Lauriston Place, Lady Lawson St EH3 9DE
e-mail: H3271@accor.com
web: www.novotel.com
dir: From Edinburgh Castle right onto George IV
Bridge from Royal Mile. Follow to junct, then right
onto Lauriston Place. Hotel 700mtrs on right

PETS: Bedrooms unattended Charges Public
areas except restaurant Exercise area park 5
mins walk

One of the new generations of Novotels, this
modern hotel is located in the centre of the
city, close to Edinburgh Castle. Smart and
stylish public areas include a cosmopolitan bar,
brasserie-style restaurant and indoor leisure
facilities. The air-conditioned bedrooms feature
a comprehensive range of extras and bathrooms
with baths and separate shower cabinets.

Rooms 180 (146 fmly) (17 smoking)
Facilities STV 🏊 Gym Sauna Steam room
Xmas Wi-fi Conf Class 50 Board 32 Thtr 80
Services Lift Air con Parking 15

EDINBURGH

Quality Hotel Edinburgh Airport
★★★ 77% HOTEL

☎ 0131 333 4331 📠 0131 333 4124
Ingliston EH28 8AU
e-mail: info@qualityhoteledinburgh.com
dir: From M8, M9 & Forth Road Bridge follow
signs for airport then follow brown tourist signs
to hotel

PETS: Bedrooms unattended Charges Public
areas except during food service Exercise area
field 5 mins walk

Just 20 minutes from the city centre, this modern
hotel is convenient for Edinburgh International
Airport, which is only two minutes away by
courtesy minibus. The spacious executive
bedrooms are the pick of the accommodation,
and there is a bright restaurant offering a range
of contemporary dishes.

Rooms 95 (15 fmly) (35 GF) S £60-£200;
D £60-£200 Facilities STV FTV Wi-fi
Conf Class 24 Board 24 Thtr 70 Services Lift
Parking 100 Notes LB Civ Wed 80

EDINBURGH

Arden Guest House

★★★ GUEST HOUSE

☎ 0131 664 3985   📠 0131 621 0866
126 Old Dalkeith Rd EH16 4SD
e-mail: ardenguesthouse@btinternet.com
dir: 2m SE of city centre nr Craigmillar Castle. On
A7 200yds W of hospital

PETS: Bedrooms unattended **Public areas**
Grounds Exercise area 0.25m **Facilities** food
(pre-bookable) food bowl water bowl

Well situated on the south side of the city, close
to the hospital. Benefiting from off-road parking
and refurbishment in a number of areas. Many
thoughtful extras are provided as standard
including Wi-fi. Attentive and friendly service
enhances the guest experience.

Rooms 8 en suite (2 fmly) (3 GF) S £35-£65; D
£55-£99* **Facilities** STV tea/coffee Cen ht Wi-fi
Parking 8 **Notes** Closed 22-27 Dec

GLASGOW

Malmaison Glasgow

★★★ 83% ◉ HOTEL

☎ 0141 572 1000   📠 0141 572 1002
278 West George St G2 4LL
e-mail: glasgow@malmaison.com
web: www.malmaison.com
dir: From S & E - M8 junct 18 (Charing Cross),
from W & N - M8 city centre

PETS: Bedrooms unattended **Charges Public**
areas except restaurant **Exercise area** 50yds
Facilities (pre-bookable) food bowl water bowl

Built around a former church in the historic
Charing Cross area, this hotel is a smart,
contemporary establishment offering impressive
levels of service and hospitality. Bedrooms are
spacious and feature a host of modern facilities,
such as CD players and mini bars. Dining is a
treat here, with French brasserie-style cuisine,
backed up by an excellent wine list, served in the
original crypt.

Rooms 72 (4 fmly) (19 GF) **Facilities** STV
Gym Cardiovascular equipment New Year
Wi-fi **Conf** Board 22 Thtr 30 **Services** Lift
Notes Civ Wed 80

BOAT OF GARTEN

Boat Hotel
★★★ 82% ◉◉ HOTEL

☎ 01479 831258 & 831696 📄 01479 831414
PH24 3BH
e-mail: info@boathotel.co.uk
dir: Off A9 N of Aviemore onto A95, follow signs to
Boat of Garten

PETS: **Bedrooms** unattended **Charges Public areas** except restaurant **Grounds Other** dogs accommodated in certain rooms only

This well established hotel is situated in the heart of the pretty village of Boat of Garten. The public areas include a choice of comfortable lounges and the restaurant has a well deserved reputation for fine dining; in addition the bistro serves meals until late. Individually styled bedrooms reflect the unique character of the hotel; all are comfortable, well equipped and have a host of thoughtful extras.

Rooms 34 (2 fmly) **Facilities** Xmas New Year Wi-fi **Conf** Class 30 Board 25 Thtr 40 **Parking** 36 **Notes** Civ Wed 40

CONTIN

Coul House Hotel
★★★ 79% ◉ COUNTRY HOUSE HOTEL

☎ 01997 421487 📄 01997 421945
IV14 9ES
e-mail: stay@coulhousehotel.com
dir: Exit A9 north onto A835. Hotel on right

PETS: **Bedrooms** unattended **Charges Public areas** except dining areas **Grounds Exercise area** adjacent

This imposing mansion house is set back from the road in extensive grounds. A number of the generally spacious bedrooms have superb views of the distant mountains and all are thoughtfully equipped. The Octagonal Restaurant offers guests the chance to enjoy contemporary Scottish cuisine.

Rooms 20 (3 fmly) (4 GF) S £45-£95; D £85-£190 (incl. bkfst)* **Facilities** 9 hole pitch & putt New Year Wi-fi Child facilities **Conf** Class 30 Board 30 Thtr 80 **Parking** 60 **Notes** LB Closed 24-26 Dec Civ Wed 100

GLENFINNAN

The Prince's House

★★★ 78% ◉◉ SMALL HOTEL

☎ 01397 722246 🖹 01397 722323
PH37 4LT
e-mail: princeshouse@glenfinnan.co.uk
web: www.glenfinnan.co.uk
dir: on A830, 0.5m on right past Glenfinnan
Monument. 200mtrs from railway station

PETS: Bedrooms unattended Charges Public
areas except restaurant Grounds Exercise area
250mtrs Resident Pet: Floren (cat)

This delightful hotel enjoys a well deserved
reputation for fine food and excellent hospitality.
The hotel has inspiring views and sits close to
where 'Bonnie' Prince Charlie raised the Jacobite
standard. Comfortably appointed bedrooms offer
pleasing decor. Excellent local game and seafood
can be enjoyed in the restaurant and the bar.

Rooms 9 (1 fmly) S £55-£65; D £95-£120 (incl.
bkfst)* Facilities Fishing New Year Conf Class 20
Thtr 40 Parking 18 Notes LB Closed Xmas & Jan-
Feb (ex New Year) RS Nov-Dec & Mar

LOCHINVER

Inver Lodge Hotel

★★★★ ◉◉ HOTEL

☎ 01571 844496 🖹 01571 844395
IV27 4LU
e-mail: stay@inverlodge.com
web: www.inverlodge.com
dir: A835 to Lochinver, through village, left after
village hall, follow private road for 0.5m

PETS: Bedrooms unattended Charges Public
areas front foyer lounge only Grounds Exercise
area Resident Pet: Sam (Cairn Terrier)

Genuine hospitality is a real feature at this
delightful, purpose-built hotel. Set high on the
hillside above the village all bedrooms and public
rooms enjoy stunning views. There is a choice of
lounges and a restaurant where chefs make use
of the abundant local produce. Bedrooms are
spacious, stylish and come with an impressive
range of accessories. There is no night service
between 11pm and 7am.

Rooms 20 (11 GF) S £110; D £200 (incl. bkfst)
Facilities FTV Fishing Sauna Wi-fi Conf Board 20
Thtr 30 Del from £125 to £150* Parking 30
Notes LB Closed Nov-Mar Civ Wed 50

MUIR OF ORD

Ord House
★★ 72% ◉ SMALL HOTEL

☎ 01463 870492 📄 01463 870297
IV6 7UH
e-mail: admin@ord-house.co.uk
dir: Off A9 at Tore rdbt onto A832. 5m, through
Muir of Ord. Left towards Ullapool (A832). Hotel
0.5m on left

PETS: Bedrooms unattended Charges Public
areas except restaurant Grounds Exercise area
adjacent Facilities food (pre-bookable) food
bowl water bowl Resident Pet: Poppy (Black
Labrador

Dating back to 1637, this country-house hotel
is situated peacefully in wooded grounds and
offers brightly furnished and well-proportioned
accommodation. Comfortable day rooms reflect
the character and charm of the house, with
inviting lounges, a cosy snug bar and an elegant
dining room where wide-ranging, creative menus
are offered.

Rooms 12 (3 GF) S £55-£80; D £100-£140 (incl.
bkfst)* Facilities Putt green ⛳ Clay pigeon
shooting Wi-fi Parking 30 Notes LB Closed
Nov-Apr

ONICH

Onich Hotel
★★★ 79% ◉ HOTEL

☎ 01855 821214 📄 01855 821484
PH33 6RY
e-mail: enquiries@onich-fortwilliam.co.uk
web: www.onich-fortwilliam.co.uk
dir: Beside A82, 2m N of Ballachulish Bridge

PETS: Bedrooms unattended Public areas except
food service areas Grounds Exercise area Other
damage charge £25

Genuine hospitality is part of the appeal of this
hotel, which lies right beside Loch Linnhe with
gardens extending to its shores. Nicely presented
public areas include a choice of inviting lounges
and contrasting bars, and views of the loch
can be enjoyed from the attractive restaurant.
Bedrooms, with pleasing colour schemes, are
comfortably modern.

Rooms 26 (6 fmly) S £49.50-£69.50; D £70-£199
(incl. bkfst) Facilities STV Games room ♫
Xmas New Year Wi-fi Conf Board 40 Thtr 150
Del from £110 to £189.50 Parking 50 Notes LB
Civ Wed 120

SCOURIE

Scourie Hotel
★★★ 73% SMALL HOTEL

☎ 01971 502396 📠 01971 502423
IV27 4SX
e-mail: patrick@scourie-hotel.co.uk
dir: N'bound on A894. Hotel in village on left

PETS: Bedrooms unattended **Charges Public areas** except dining areas **Grounds Exercise area** 200yds **Resident Pets:** Molly (Springer Spaniel), Jessie & Clemmie (cats), Minstrel & Angus (horses)

This well-established hotel is an angler's paradise with extensive fishing rights available on a 25,000-acre estate. Public areas include a choice of comfortable lounges, a cosy bar and a smart dining room offering wholesome fare. The bedrooms are comfortable and generally spacious. The resident proprietors and their staff create a relaxed and friendly atmosphere.

Rooms 20 (2 annexe) (2 fmly) (5 GF)
S £62-£73; D £114-£134 (incl. bkfst & dinner)*
Facilities Fishing Wi-fi **Parking** 30 **Notes** LB Closed mid Oct-end Mar RS winter evenings

SHIELDAIG

Tigh an Eilean
★ ◎◎ SMALL HOTEL

☎ 01520 755251 📠 01520 755321
IV54 8XN
e-mail: tighaneilean@keme.co.uk
dir: off A896 onto village road signed Shieldaig, hotel in centre

PETS: Bedrooms unattended **Public areas Grounds Exercise area** 400mtrs **Facilities** food (pre-bookable) food bowl water bowl; please phone for details of further facilities for dogs **Resident Pets:** Ella & Katy (Black Labradors), Woody (cat)

A splendid location by the sea, with views over the bay, is the icing on the cake for this delightful small hotel. It can be a long drive to reach Sheildaig but guests remark that the journey is more than worth the effort. The brightly decorated bedrooms are comfortable though don't expect television, except in one of the lounges. For many, it's the food that attracts, with fish and seafood featuring strongly.

Rooms 11 (1 fmly) **Facilities** Birdwatching Kayaks Wi-fi **Parking** 15 **Notes** LB Closed late Oct-mid Mar Civ Wed 40

SOUTH BALLACHULISH

The Isles of Glencoe Hotel & Leisure Centre

★★★ 71% HOTEL

☎ 0844 855 9134   📄 0871 222 3416
PH49 4HL
e-mail: reservations.glencoe@foliohotels.com
web: www.foliohotels.com/isleofglencoe
dir: A82 N, slip road on left into village, 1st right, hotel in 600yds

PETS: **Bedrooms** unattended **Charges Public areas** except restaurant **Grounds Exercise area Facilities** food bowl water bowl

This hotel enjoys a spectacular setting beside Loch Leven. This friendly modern establishment has spacious bedrooms and guests have a choice of Loch or Mountain View rooms. Public areas include a popular restaurant and a family friendly leisure centre.

Rooms 59 (21 fmly) (21 GF) **Facilities** STV ⏲ Gym Hydroseat Bio-sauna ♫ Xmas New Year Wi-fi **Conf** Class 40 Board 20 Thtr 40 **Notes** LB Civ Wed 65

FORRES

Ramnee Hotel

★★★ 75% HOTEL

☎ 01309 672410   📄 01309 673392
Victoria Rd IV36 3BN
e-mail: info@ramneehotel.com
dir: Off A96 at rdbt on E side of Forres, hotel 200yds on right

PETS: **Bedrooms** unattended **Public areas Grounds Exercise area** 200mtrs

Genuinely friendly staff ensure this well-established hotel remains popular with business travellers. Bedrooms, including a family suite, vary in size, although all are well presented. Hearty bar food provides a less formal dining option to the imaginative restaurant menu.

Rooms 19 (4 fmly) (2 smoking) **S** £80-£120; **D** £90-£150 (incl. bkfst)* **Facilities** STV Wi-fi **Conf** Class 30 Board 45 Thtr 100 Del from £135 to £150* **Parking** 50 **Notes** LB Closed 25 Dec & 1-3 Jan Civ Wed 100

CUMBERNAULD

The Westerwood Hotel & Golf Resort

★★★★ 80% HOTEL

☎ 01236 457171 🖹 01236 738478
1 St Andrews Dr, Westerwood G68 0EW
e-mail: westerwood@qhotels.co.uk
web: www.qhotels.co.uk

PETS: Bedrooms unattended **Charges Public areas** except leisure club & restaurant **Grounds Exercise area Other** pet food on request **Restrictions** small dogs only

This stylish, contemporary hotel enjoys an elevated position within 400 acres at the foot of the Camspie Hills. Accommodation is provided in spacious, bright bedrooms, many with super bathrooms, and day rooms include sumptuous lounges and an airy restaurant; extensive golf, fitness and conference facilities are available.

Rooms 148 (15 fmly) (49 GF) S £65-£125; D £75-£135 (incl. bkfst) **Facilities** Spa ⊙ ↓ 18 ⊜ Putt green Gym Beauty salon Jacuzzi Relaxation room Sauna Steam room Xmas New Year Wi-fi **Conf** Class 120 Board 60 Thtr 400 Del from £120 to £180* **Services** Lift **Parking** 250 **Notes** LB Civ Wed 400

ALYTH

Tigh Na Leigh Guesthouse

★★★★★ 🔝 GUEST ACCOMMODATION

☎ 01828 632372 🖹 01828 632279
22-24 Airlie St PH11 8AJ
e-mail: bandcblack@yahoo.co.uk
web: www.tighnaleigh.co.uk
dir: In town centre on B952

PETS: Bedrooms unattended **Charges Public areas** except dining room **Grounds Exercise area** 200yds **Facilities** food bowl water bowl **Resident Pets:** Tom & Bunny (cats)

Situated in the heart of this country town, Tigh Na Leigh is Gaelic for 'The House of the Doctor or Physician'. Its location and somewhat sombre façade are in stunning contrast to what lies inside. The house has been completely restored to blend its Victorian architecture with contemporary interior design. Bedrooms, including a superb suite, have state-of-the-art bathrooms. There are three entirely different lounges, while delicious meals are served in the conservatory/dining room overlooking a spectacular landscaped garden.

Rooms 5 en suite (1 GF) S £45; D £90-£115* **Facilities** FTV TVL tea/coffee Dinner available Cen ht Licensed Wi-fi **Parking** 5 **Notes** No Children 12yrs Closed Dec-Feb

COMRIE

Royal Hotel

★★★ 82% ❀ HOTEL

☎ 01764 679200 📠 01764 679219
Melville Square PH6 2DN
e-mail: reception@royalhotel.co.uk
web: www.royalhotel.co.uk
dir: off A9 on A822 to Crieff, then B827 to
Comrie. Hotel in main square on A85

PETS: Bedrooms unattended Charges Public
areas Grounds Exercise area 500yds Facilities
food bowl water bowl Resident Pets: Abby & Ella
(Labradors)

A traditional façade gives little indication of the
style and elegance inside this long-established
hotel located in the village centre. Public areas
include a bar and library, a bright modern
restaurant and a conservatory-style brasserie.
Bedrooms are tastefully appointed and furnished
with smart reproduction antiques.

Rooms 13 (2 annexe) S £85-£105; D £140-£180
(incl. bkfst) Facilities STV Fishing Shooting
arranged New Year Wi-fi Conf Class 10 Board 20
Thtr 20 Parking 22 Notes LB Closed 25-26 Dec

KINLOCH RANNOCH

Dunalastair Hotel

★★★ 77% ❀ HOTEL

☎ 01882 632323 & 632218 📠 01882 632371
PH16 5PW
e-mail: robert@dunalastair.co.uk
web: www.dunalastair.co.uk
dir: A9 to Pitlochry, at northern end take B8019 to
Tummel Bridge then A846 to Kinloch Rannoch

PETS: Bedrooms unattended Charges Public
areas except restaurant Grounds Exercise area
Facilities food (pre-bookable) food bowl water
bowl Resident Pets: Kiita (Blue Merle Border
Collie)

A traditional Highland hotel with inviting public
rooms full of character - log fires, stags' heads,
wood panelling and an extensive selection of
malt whiskies. Standard and superior bedrooms
are on offer. However, it is the friendly attentive
service by delightful staff and first-class dinners
that leave lasting impressions.

Rooms 28 (4 fmly) (9 GF) Facilities Fishing
4x4 safaris Rafting Clay pigeon shooting Bike
hire Archery Xmas New Year Child facilities
Conf Class 40 Board 40 Thtr 60 Parking 33
Notes LB Civ Wed 70

PERTH

The Anglers Inn
★★★ ֎ INN

☎ 01821 640329
Main Rd, Guildtown PH2 6BS
e-mail: info@theanglersinn.co.uk
web: www.theanglersinn.co.uk
dir: 6m N of Perth on A93

PETS: Bedrooms unattended **Public areas** in bar
only **Grounds Exercise area** 10mtrs **Facilities**
water bowl **Resident Pets:** Barney (Labrador);
Mocca (Spaniel) (at certain times)

This charming country inn enjoys a peaceful
rural setting and yet is only a short drive from
Perth city centre and is a favourite with race-
goers. The inn has been totally refurbished and
the accommodation comprises five tastefully
styled en suite bedrooms each equipped with
flat-screen TVs and complimentary Wi-fi. The
award-winning restaurant has a loyal following
and the dinner menu is supplemented by nightly
blackboard specials.

Rooms 5 en suite (1 fmly) **S** £50; **D** £100*
Facilities FTV TVL tea/coffee Dinner available
Cen ht Wi-fi ᴥ Pool Table **Parking** 40 **Notes** LB
No Children

PITLOCHRY

Green Park Hotel
★★★ 87% ֎ COUNTRY HOUSE HOTEL

☎ 01796 473248 📄 01796 473520
Clunie Bridge Rd PH16 5JY
e-mail: bookings@thegreenpark.co.uk
web: www.thegreenpark.co.uk
dir: turn off A9 at Pitlochry, follow signs 0.25m
through town

PETS: Bedrooms unattended **Public areas**
Grounds Exercise area 20yds **Facilities** food
bowl water bowl **Resident Pets:** Dan (Golden
Retriever), Squeaky & Speedy (Guinea Pigs)

Guests return year after year to this lovely hotel
that is situated in a stunning setting on the
shores of Loch Faskally. Most of the thoughtfully
designed bedrooms, including a splendid wing,
the restaurant and the comfortable lounges enjoy
these views. Dinner utilises fresh produce, much
of it grown in the kitchen garden.

Rooms 51 (16 GF) **S** £65-£93; **D** £130-£186 (incl.
bkfst & dinner)* **Facilities** Putt green New Year
Wi-fi **Parking** 51 **Notes** LB

ST FILLANS

The Four Seasons Hotel

★★★ 83% ◉◉ HOTEL

☎ 01764 685333 📠 01764 685444
Loch Earn PH6 2NF
e-mail: info@thefourseasonshotel.co.uk
web: www.thefourseasonshotel.co.uk
dir: on A85, towards W of village

PETS: Bedrooms unattended Charges Public areas except restaurants Grounds Exercise area behind hotel Facilities food (pre-bookable) food bowl water bowl Other pet concierge service Resident Pets: Sham & Pagne (Münsterlanders)

Set on the edge of Loch Earn, this welcoming hotel and many of its bedrooms benefit from fine views. There is a choice of lounges, including a library, warmed by log fires during winter. Local produce is used to good effect in both the Meall Reamhar restaurant and the more informal Tarken Room.

Rooms 18 (6 annexe) (7 fmly) S £55-£90; D £110-£130 (incl. bkfst)* Facilities Xmas New Year Wi-fi Conf Class 45 Board 38 Thtr 95 Del from £104 to £124 Parking 40 Notes LB Closed 2 Jan-Feb RS Nov, Dec, Mar Civ Wed 80

BROUGHTON

The Glenholm Centre

★★★ 🏠 GUEST ACCOMMODATION

☎ 01899 830408
ML12 6JF
e-mail: info@glenholm.co.uk
dir: 1m S of Broughton. Off A701 to Glenholm

PETS: Bedrooms unattended Public areas Grounds Exercise area adjacent Resident Pets: Tarry & Minty (Bearded Collies)

Surrounded by peaceful farmland, this former schoolhouse has a distinct African theme. The home-cooked meals and baking have received much praise and are served in the spacious lounge-dining room. The bright airy bedrooms are thoughtfully equipped, and the service is friendly and attentive. Computer courses are available.

Rooms 3 en suite 1 annexe en suite (1 fmly) (2 GF) Facilities TVL tea/coffee Dinner available Cen ht Licensed Wi-fi ♿ Conf Max 24 Thtr 24 Class 24 Board 24 Parking 14 Notes Closed 20 Dec-1 Feb

JEDBURGH

Ferniehirst Mill Lodge

★★ GUEST HOUSE

☎ 01835 863279TD8 6PQ
e-mail: ferniehirstmill@aol.com
web: www.ferniehirstmill.co.uk
dir: 2.5m S on A68, onto private track to end

PETS: **Bedrooms** unattended **Charges Public areas Grounds Exercise area** 30mtrs **Resident Pets:** Arctic-maremma (Sheepdog), Flight & Mac (Whippets), 11 horses

Reached by a narrow farm track and a rustic wooden bridge, this chalet-style house has a secluded setting by the River Jed. Bedrooms are small and functional but there is a comfortable lounge in which to relax. Home-cooked dinners are available by arrangement, and hearty breakfasts are served in the cosy dining room.

Rooms 7 en suite (1 GF) **S** £28; **D** £56* **Facilities** TVL tea/coffee Dinner available Direct Dial Cen ht Fishing Riding **Parking** 10

PEEBLES

Macdonald Cardrona Hotel Golf & Country Club

★★★★ 76% ● HOTEL

☎ 01896 833600 📄 01896 831166
Cardrona Mains EH45 6LZ
e-mail: general.cardrona@
macdonald-hotels.co.uk
web: www.macdonald-hotels.co.uk/cardrona
dir: On A72 between Peebles & Innerleithen, 3m S of Peebles

PETS: **Bedrooms** unattended **Charges** ublic areas lounge only **Grounds Exercise area**

The rolling hills of the Scottish Borders are a stunning backdrop for this modern, purpose-built hotel. Spacious bedrooms are traditional in style, equipped with a range of extras, and most enjoy fantastic countryside. The hotel features some impressive leisure facilities, including an 18-hole golf course, 18-metre indoor pool and state-of-the-art gym.

Rooms 99 (24 fmly) (16 GF) **S** £82-£169; **D** £92-£179 (incl. bkfst) **Facilities** Spa STV ⊕ ⅃ 18 Putt green Gym Sauna Steam room Xmas New Year Wi-fi **Conf** Class 120 Board 90 Thtr 250 Del from £130 to £160 **Services** Lift **Parking** 200 **Notes** LB Civ Wed 200

PEEBLES

Tontine

★★★ 81% HOTEL

☎ 01721 720892 📄 01721 729732
High St EH45 8AJ
e-mail: info@tontinehotel.com
web: www.tontinehotel.com
dir: In town centre

PETS: **Bedrooms** unattended **Charges Public areas** assist dogs only **Exercise area** Tweed Green behind hotel **Other** dogs allowed in certain bedrooms only **Restrictions** well behaved dogs only

Conveniently situated in the main street, this long-established hotel offers comfortable public rooms including an elegant Adam restaurant, inviting lounge and 'clubby' bar. Bedrooms, contained in the original house and the river-facing wing, offer a smart, classical style of accommodation. The lasting impression is of the excellent level of hospitality and guest care.

Rooms 36 (3 fmly) **S** £45-£65; **D** £65-£95 (incl. bkfst)* **Facilities** STV FTV Xmas New Year Wi-fi Child facilities **Conf** Class 24 Board 24 Thtr 40 Del from £85 to £115* **Parking** 24

PEEBLES

Park Hotel

★★★ 75% HOTEL

☎ 01721 720451 📄 01721 723510
Innerleithen Rd EH45 8BA
e-mail: reserve@parkpeebles.co.uk
dir: In town centre opposite filling station

PETS: **Bedrooms** unattended **Public areas** except restaurant & bar **Grounds Exercise area** 30yds **Other** dogs allowed in certain bedrooms only

This hotel offers pleasant, well-equipped bedrooms of various sizes - those in the original house are particularly spacious. Public areas enjoy views of the gardens and include a tartan-clad bar, a relaxing lounge and a spacious wood-panelled restaurant, open for lunch and early-bird suppers.

Rooms 24 **Facilities** STV Putt green Use of facilities at Peebles Hotel Hydro Xmas New Year Wi-fi **Conf** Class 15 Board 18 Thtr 30 Del from £50 to £160* **Services** Lift **Parking** 50

ST BOSWELLS

Dryburgh Abbey Hotel

★★★★ 73% ◎◎ COUNTRY HOUSE HOTEL

☎ 01835 822261 📠 01835 823945
TD6 0RQ
e-mail: enquiries@dryburgh.co.uk
web: www.dryburgh.co.uk
dir: B6356 signed Scott's View & Earlston.
Through Clintmains, 1.8m to hotel

PETS: Bedrooms unattended Charges Public
areas except restaurant Grounds Exercise area
Facilities food bowl water bowl Resident Pets:
Harry (Cocker Spaniel)

Sitting beside to the ancient ruins of Dryburgh
Abbey and the majestic River Tweed, this country
house hotel, dating from the mid 19th century,
offers comfortable public areas and an array
of bedrooms and suites.The award-winning
Tweed Restaurant, overlooking the river, offers
an 8-course dinner menu showcasing the chef's
dedication to producing modern Scottish cuisine.
The Abbey Bar offers food throughout the day.

Rooms 38 (31 fmly) (8 GF) S £63-£205;
D £126-£350 (incl. bkfst & dinner)*
Facilities FTV ⓒ Putt green Fishing ⤳ Sauna
Xmas New Year Wi-fi Conf Class 80 Board 60
Thtr 150 Del from £140 to £200* Services Lift
Parking 70 Notes LB Civ Wed 120

AYR

Savoy Park Hotel

★★★ 80% HOTEL

☎ 01292 266112 📠 01292 611488
16 Racecourse Rd KA7 2UT
e-mail: mail@savoypark.com
dir: From A77 follow A70 for 2m, through
Parkhouse Str, left into Beresford Terrace, 1st
right into Bellevue Rd

PETS: Bedrooms unattended Charges Public
areas Grounds xercise area 400mtrs Facilities
food (pre-bookable) food bowl water bowl

This well-established hotel retains many of its
traditional values including friendly, attentive
service. Public rooms feature impressive
panelled walls, ornate ceilings and open fires.
The restaurant is reminiscent of a Highland
shooting lodge and offers a wide ranging,
good-value menu to suit all tastes. The large
superior bedrooms retain a classical elegance
while others are smart and modern; all have well
equipped modern bathrooms.

Rooms 15 (3 fmly) S £50-£80; D £60-£120
(incl. bkfst)* Facilities FTV Xmas New Year Wi-fi
Child facilities Conf Class 40 Board 30 Thtr 50
Del from £80 to £120 Parking 60 Notes LB
Civ Wed 100

225

ABINGTON MOTORWAY SERVICE AREA (M74)

Days Inn Abington
BUDGET HOTEL

☎ 01864 502782 ▤ 01864 502759
ML12 6RG
e-mail: abington.hotel@welcomebreak.co.uk
web: www.welcomebreak.co.uk
dir: M74 junct 13, accessible from N'bound and S'bound carriageways

PETS: Bedrooms unattended Public areas must be kept on leads Grounds

This modern building offers accommodation in smart, spacious and well-equipped bedrooms, suitable for families and business travellers, and all with en suite bathrooms. Continental breakfast is available and other refreshments may be taken at the nearby family restaurant.

Rooms 52 (50 fmly) S £29-£59; D £39-£79*
Conf Board 10 Del from £69 to £99*

BIGGAR

Shieldhill Castle
★★★★ 70% ◉◉ COUNTRY HOUSE HOTEL

☎ 01899 220035 ▤ 01899 221092
Quothquan ML12 6NA
e-mail: enquiries@shieldhill.co.uk
web: www.shieldhill.co.uk
dir: A702 onto B7016 (Biggar to Carnwath road), after 2m left into Shieldhill Rd. Hotel 1.5m on right

PETS: Bedrooms unattended Charges Public areas Grounds Exercise area Resident Pet: Mutley (Springer/Cocker Spaniel cross)

The focus on food and wine are important at this imposing fortified country mansion that dates back almost 800 years. Public room are atmospheric and include the classical Chancellors' Restaurant, oak-panelled lounge and the Gun Room bar that offers its own menu. Bedrooms, many with feature baths, are spacious and comfortable. A friendly welcome is assured, even from the estate's own dog!

Rooms 26 (10 annexe) (10 GF) Facilities FTV ⚓
Cycling Clay shoot Hot air ballooning Falconry Laser & game bird shooting Xmas New Year Wi-fi Conf Class 200 Board 250 Thtr 500 Parking 50 Notes Civ Wed 200

STIRLING

Barceló Stirling Highland Hotel

★★★★ 75% HOTEL

☎ 01786 272727 📠 01786 272829
Spittal St FK8 1DU
e-mail: stirling@barcelo-hotels.co.uk
web: www.barcelo-hotels.co.uk
dir: A84 into Stirling. Follow Stirling Castle signs as far as Albert Hall. Left, left again, follow Castle signs

PETS: Bedrooms unattended Charges Public areas assist dogs only Exercise area 5 min walk Other prior notice required

Enjoying a location close to the castle and historic old town, this atmospheric hotel was previously the town's high school. Public rooms have been converted from the original classrooms and retain many interesting features. Bedrooms are more modern in style and comfortably equipped. Scholars Restaurant serves traditional and international dishes, and the Headmaster's Study is the ideal venue for enjoying a drink.

Rooms 96 (4 fmly) Facilities Spa STV 🐾 supervised Gym Squash Steam room Dance studio Beauty therapist Xmas New Year Wi-fi Conf Class 80 Board 60 Thtr 100 Del from £125* Services Lift Parking 96 Notes Civ Wed 100

STRATHYRE

Creagan House

★★★★★ ⊛⊛ RESTAURANT WITH ROOMS

☎ 01877 384638 📠 01877 384319
FK18 8ND
e-mail: eatandstay@creaganhouse.co.uk
web: www.creaganhouse.co.uk
dir: 0.25m N of Strathyre on A84

PETS: Bedrooms unattended Public areas Grounds Exercise area part of National Park accessible from house Facilities food bowl water bowl

Originally a farmhouse dating from the 17th century, Creagan House has operated as a restaurant with rooms for many years. The baronial-style dining room provides a wonderful setting for sympathetic cooking. Warm hospitality and attentive service are the highlights of any stay.

Rooms 5 en suite (1 fmly) (1 GF) S £70-£90; D £120-£140 Facilities FTV tea/coffee Dinner available Cen ht Wi-fi Conf Max 35 Thtr 35 Class 12 Board 35 Parking 26 Notes LB Closed 4-19 Nov, Xmas & 21 Jan-5 Mar RS Wed & Thu Closed

BALLOCH

Sunnyside

★★★ BED AND BREAKFAST

☎ 01389 750282 & 07717 397548
35 Main St G83 9JX
e-mail: enquiries@sunnysidebb.co.uk>aa
dir: From A82 take A811 then A813 for 1m, over
mini-rdbt 150mtrs on left

PETS: Bedrooms unattended Charges Public
areas Grounds Exercise area surrounding
countryside Facilities food (pre-bookable) food
bowl water bowl

Set in its own grounds well back from the road
by Loch Lomond, Sunnyside is an attractive,
traditional detached house, parts of which date
back to the 1830s. Bedrooms are attractively
decorated and provide comfortable modern
accommodation. Free Wi-fi is also available.
The dining room is located on the ground floor,
and is an appropriate setting for hearty Scottish
breakfasts.

Rooms 6 en suite (2 fmly) (1 GF) S £30-£45; D
£46-£56* Facilities tea/coffee Dinner available
Cen ht Wi-fi Parking 8

BRODICK

Kilmichael Country House

★★★ ⊛⊛ COUNTRY HOUSE HOTEL

☎ 01770 302219 🖹 01770 302068
Glen Cloy KA27 8BY
e-mail: enquiries@kilmichael.com
web: www.kilmichael.com
dir: From Brodick ferry terminal towards
Lochranza for 1m. Left at golf course, inland
between sports field & church, follow signs

PETS: Bedrooms unattended Charges Public
areas Grounds Exercise area adjacent Resident
Pets: Guiseppe (Dalmatian), chickens, ducks,
turkey, geese & peafowl

Reputed to be the oldest on the island, this
lovely house lies in attractive gardens in a quiet
glen less than five minutes' drive from the ferry
terminal. It has been lovingly restored to create
a stylish, elegant country house. There are two
inviting drawing rooms and a bright dining room,
serving award-winning contemporary cuisine. The
delightful bedrooms are furnished in classical
style; some are contained in a pretty courtyard
conversion.

Rooms 8 (3 annexe) (7 GF) S £76-£95;
D £128-£199 (incl. bkfst)* Facilities Wi-fi
Parking 14 Notes LB No children 12yrs Closed
Nov-Feb (ex for prior bookings)

SCARISTA

Scarista House
★★★★ ⑧⑧ RESTAURANT WITH ROOMS

☎ 01859 550238 📄 01859 550277
HS3 3HX
e-mail: timandpatricia@scaristahouse.com
dir: On A859, 15m S of Tarbert

ETS: Bedrooms unattended Public areas library
only Grounds Exercise area 200yds Facilities
food bowl water bowl Resident Pets: Molly
(Cavalier King Charles Spaniel), Misty (cat)

A former manse, Scarista House is a haven for
food lovers who seek to explore this magnificent
island. It enjoys breathtaking views of the
Atlantic and is just a short stroll from miles of
golden sandy beaches. The house is run in a
relaxed country-house manner by the friendly
hosts. Expect wellies in the hall and masses of
books and CDs in one of two lounges. Bedrooms
are cosy, and delicious set dinners and
memorable breakfasts are provided.

Rooms 3 en suite 2 annexe en suite (2 GF) S
£125-£140; D £175-£199* Facilities tea/coffee
Dinner available Direct Dial Cen ht Parking 12
Notes LB Closed Xmas, Jan & Feb No coaches
Civ Wed 40

STAFFIN

Flodigarry Country House
★★★ 78% ⑧ COUNTRY HOUSE HOTEL

☎ 01470 552203 📄 01470 552301
IV51 9HZ
e-mail: info@flodigarry.co.uk
web: www.flodigarry.co.uk
dir: Take A855 from Portree, approx 20m, through
Staffin. N to Flodigarry, signed on right

PETS: Bedrooms unattended Charges Public
areas Grounds Facilities (pre-bookable) Other
dogs allowed in Flora Macdonald cottage only

This hotel is located in woodlands on The
Quiraing in north-east Skye overlooking the sea
towards the Torridon Mountains. The dramatic
scenery is a real inspiration here, and this
charming house was once the home of the
Scotland's heroine, Flora MacDonald. Guests are
assured of real Highland hospitality and there
is an easy going atmosphere throughout. A full
range of activities is offered, with mountain
walks, fishing and boat trips proving to be the
most popular.

Rooms 18 (7 annexe) (3 fmly) (4 GF) S £80-£130;
D £80-£200 (incl. bkfst) Facilities FTV Xmas New
Year Wi-fi Parking 40 Notes LB Closed Nov-15
Dec & Jan Civ Wed 80

BEAUMARIS

Best Western Bulkeley Hotel
★★★ 77% HOTEL

☎ 01248 810415 ▤ 01248 810146
Castle St LL58 8AW
e-mail: reception@bulkeleyhotel.co.uk
web: www.bulkeleyhotel.co.uk
dir: From A55 junct 8a to Beaumaris. Hotel in town centre

PETS: **Bedrooms** unattended **Charges Public areas** lounge & bar only **Grounds Exercise area** 2 mins walk **Facilities** food bowl water bowl walks **Other** please phone for details of further facilities for dogs

A Grade I listed hotel built in 1832, the Bulkeley is just 100 yards from the 13th-century Beaumaris Castle in the centre of town; the friendly staff create a relaxed atmosphere. Many rooms, including 18 of the bedrooms, have fine panoramic views across the Menai Straits to the Snowdonian Mountains. The well-equipped bedrooms and suites, some with four-posters, are generally spacious, and have pretty furnishings. There is a choice of bars, a coffee shop, a restaurant and bistro.

Rooms 43 (5 fmly) S £60-£80; D £90-£140 (incl. bkfst)* **Facilities** New Year Wi-fi **Conf** Class 40 Board 25 Thtr 180 Del from £96 to £101* **Services** Lift **Parking** 25 **Notes** LB Civ Wed 140

CARDIFF

Barceló Cardiff Angel Hotel
★★★★ 70% HOTEL

☎ 029 2064 9200 ▤ 029 2039 6212
Castle St CF10 1SZ
e-mail: angel@barcelo-hotels-co.uk
web: www.barcelo-hotels.co.uk/hotels/wales/barcelo-cardiff-angel-hotel
dir: Opposite Cardiff Castle

PETS: **Bedrooms** unattended **Charges Public areas** except dining room

This well-established hotel is in the heart of the city overlooking the famous castle and almost opposite the Millennium Stadium. All bedrooms offer air conditioning and are appointed to a good standard. Public areas include an impressive lobby, a modern restaurant and a selection of conference rooms. There is limited parking at the rear of the hotel.

Rooms 102 (3 fmly) **Facilities** STV Xmas New Year Wi-fi **Conf** Class 120 Board 50 Thtr 300 Del from £110* **Services** Lift Air con **Parking** 60 **Notes** Civ Wed 200

CARDIFF

Ibis Cardiff
BUDGET HOTEL

☎ 029 2064 9250 🖷 029 2920 9260
Churchill Way CF10 2HA
e-mail: H2969@accor.com
web: www.ibishotel.com
dir: M4, then A48 2nd exit A4232. Follow signs
to City Centre on Newport Rd, left after railway
bridge, left after Queen St station

PETS: Bedrooms unattended Charges Public
areas except restaurant Exercise area 200mtrs

Modern, budget hotel offering comfortable
accommodation in bright and practical
bedrooms. Breakfast is self-service and dinner is
available in the restaurant.

Rooms 102 (19 GF) (7 smoking)

LLANELLI

Best Western Diplomat Hotel
★★★ 77% HOTEL

☎ 01554 756156 🖷 01554 751649
Felinfoel SA15 3PJ
e-mail: reservations@diplomat-hotel-wales.com
web: www.diplomat-hotel-wales.com
dir: M4 junct 48 onto A4138 then B4303, hotel
0.75m on right

PETS: Bedrooms unattended Charges Public
areas Grounds Exercise area Resident Pets:
Heidi & Duke (Alsatian/Collie cross)

This Victorian mansion, set in mature grounds,
has been extended over the years to provide
a comfortable and relaxing hotel. The well-
appointed bedrooms are located in the main
house and there is also a wing of comfortable
modern bedrooms. Public areas include
Trubshaw's Restaurant, a large function suite
and a modern leisure centre.

Rooms 50 (8 annexe) (2 fmly) (4 GF) S £55-£80;
D £70-£100 (incl. bkfst)* Facilities FTV ③
supervised Gym Sauna Steam room Sun
beds Hairdresser ♫ Xmas New Year Wi-fi
Conf Class 150 Board 100 Thtr 450 Del from £70
to £110 Services Lift Parking 250 Notes LB
Civ Wed 300

ABERYSTWYTH

Llety Ceiro Country House

★★★★ GUEST HOUSE

☎ 01970 821900 📠 01970 820966
Peggy Ln, Bow St, Llandre SY24 5AB
e-mail: marinehotel1@btconnect.com
dir: 4m NE of Aberystwyth. Off A487 onto B4353 for 300yds

PETS: **Bedrooms** unattended **Charges Public areas** except restaurant **Grounds Exercise area** 100yds **Facilities** food bowl water bowl

Located north of Aberystwyth, this house is well maintained throughout. Bedrooms are equipped with a range of thoughtful extras in addition to smart modern bathrooms. Morning coffees, afternoon teas and dinner are available in an attractive dining room, with a conservatory extension, and bicycle hire is also available.

Rooms 11 en suite (2 fmly) (3 GF) (1 smoking) **S** £35-£65; **D** £55-£95* **Facilities** FTV TVL tea/coffee Dinner available Direct Dial Cen ht Licensed Wi-fi Free use of facilities at sister hotel **Conf** Max 60 Thtr 60 Class 40 Board 40 **Parking** 21 **Notes** LB Civ Wed 65

EGLWYS FACH

Ynyshir Hall

★★★ ⊛⊛⊛ COUNTRY HOUSE HOTEL

☎ 01654 781209 & 781268 📠 01654 781366
SY20 8TA
e-mail: ynyshir@relaischateaux.com
web: www.ynyshir-hall.co.uk
dir: off A487, 5.5m S of Machynlleth, signed from main road

PETS: **Bedrooms** unattended **Charges Public areas Grounds Exercise area Facilities** food (pre-bookable) food bowl water bowl **Other** dogs allowed in ground-floor rooms only; outside kennel available **Resident Pet:** Oscar (Burmese Mountain Dog)

Set in beautifully landscaped grounds and surrounded by a RSBP reserve, Ynyshir Hall is a haven of calm. Lavishly styled bedrooms, each individually themed around a great painter, provide high standards of luxury and comfort. The lounge and bar have different moods, and both feature abundant fresh flowers. The dining room offers outstanding cooking using best ingredients with modern flair.

Rooms 9 (2 annexe) **D** £275-£405 (incl. bkfst)* **Facilities** ⌣ Xmas New Year **Conf** Class 20 Board 18 Thtr 25 Del from £245 to £350* **Parking** 20 **Notes** LB No children 9yrs Civ Wed 40

GWBERT-ON-SEA

The Cliff Hotel

★★★ 77% HOTEL

☎ 01239 613241 📄 01239 615391
SA43 1PP
e-mail: reservations@cliffhotel.com
dir: off A487 into Cardigan, take B4548 towards
Gwbert, 2m to hotel

PETS: Bedrooms unattended Charges Public
areas except restaurant & bars Grounds
Exercise area 20yds Other prior notice required

Set in 30 acres of grounds with a 9-hole golf
course, this hotel commands superb sea views
from its cliff-top location overlooking Cardigan
Bay. Bedrooms in the main building offer
excellent views and there is also a wing of 22
modern rooms. Public areas are spacious and
comprise a choice of bars, lounges and a fine
dining restaurant. The spa offers a wide range of
up-to-the-minute leisure facilities.

Rooms 70 (6 fmly) (5 GF) S £40-£75; D £75-£140
(incl. bkfst) Facilities Spa FTV ☜ ↖ ♨ 9 Fishing
Gym Xmas New Year Conf Class 150 Board 140
Thtr 250 Del from £85 to £120 Services Lift
Parking 100 Notes LB Civ Wed 200

LAMPETER

Best Western Falcondale Mansion

★★★ 86% ◉◉ COUNTRY HOUSE HOTEL

☎ 01570 422910 📄 01570 423559
SA48 7RX
e-mail: info@falcondalehotel.com
web: www.falcondalehotel.com
dir: 800yds W of High St (A475) or 1.5m NW of
Lampeter (A482)

PETS: Bedrooms unattended Charges Public
areas except restaurants & with other guests'
comfort in mind Grounds Facilities food (pre-
bookable) food bowl water bowl Resident Pets:
Pudgeley & Major (Cocker Spaniels) & Chloe (cat)

Built in the Italianate style, this charming
Victorian property is set in extensive grounds
and beautiful parkland. The individually-styled
bedrooms are generally spacious, well equipped
and tastefully decorated. Bars and lounges
are similarly well appointed with additional
facilities including a conservatory and function
room. Guests have a choice of either the Valley
Restaurant for fine dining or the less formal
Peterwells Brasserie.

Rooms 19 (2 fmly) S £100-£160; D £140-£180
(incl. bkfst)* Facilities FTV ⤹ Xmas New
Year Wi-fi Conf Class 30 Board 25 Thtr 60
Del from £132 to £164* Services Lift Parking 60
Notes LB Civ Wed 60

BETWS-Y-COED

Craig-y-Dderwen Riverside Hotel
★★★★ 71% ® COUNTRY HOUSE HOTEL

☎ 01690 710293 ▤ 01690 710362
LL24 0AS
e-mail: info@snowdoniahotel.com
web: www.snowdoniahotel.com
dir: A5 to town, cross Waterloo Bridge, take 1st left

PETS: Bedrooms unattended Charges Public areas except restaurant Grounds Exercise area 16 acres of fields Facilities food (pre-bookable) food bowl water bowl

This Victorian country-house hotel is set in well-maintained grounds alongside the River Conwy, at the end of a tree-lined drive. Very pleasant views can be enjoyed from many rooms, and two of the bedrooms have four-poster beds. There are comfortable lounges and the atmosphere throughout is tranquil and relaxing.

Rooms 16 (2 fmly) (1 GF) (3 smoking) S £75-£95; D £90-£170 (incl. bkfst)* Facilities STV FTV ⚓ Badminton Volleyball New Year Wi-fi Conf Class 25 Board 20 Thtr 50 Del from £110 to £205* Parking 50 Notes Closed 23-26 Dec & 2 Jan-1 Feb Civ Wed 50

COLWYN BAY

The Northwood
★★★ GUEST HOUSE

☎ 01492 549931
47 Rhos Rd, Rhos-on-Sea LL28 4RS
e-mail: welcome@thenorthwood.co.uk
web: www.thenorthwood.co.uk
dir: Exit A55 junct 22 (Old Colwyn), at T-junct right to next T-junct (facing sea). Left, past pier, opposite harbour turn left into Rhos Rd

PETS: Bedrooms unattended Charges Public areas except dining room & lounge Grounds Exercise area 10mtrs Facilities food (pre-bookable) food bowl water bowl Resident Pets: Sam (cat), Sticky & Fluffy (lovebirds)

A short walk from the seafront and shops, this constantly improving guest house has a warm and friendly atmosphere and welcomes back many regular guests. Bedrooms are furnished in modern style, and freshly prepared meals utilising fresh produce, with some home grown, can be enjoyed in the spacious dining room overlooking the pretty patio rear garden.

Rooms 11 rms (10 en suite) (1 pri facs) (3 fmly) (2 GF) S £27-£36; D £54-£72* Facilities TVL tea/coffee Dinner available Cen ht Licensed Wi-fi Conf Max 20 Class 20 Board 20 Parking 12 Notes LB

CONWY

The Groes Inn
★★★★★ ⍟ INN

☎ 01492 650545   📠 01492 650855
Tyn-y-Groes LL32 8TN
e-mail: enquiries@thegroes.com
web: www.groesinn.com
dir: A55, over Old Conwy Bridge, 1st left through
Castle Walls on B5106, Inn 2m on right

PETS: **Bedrooms** unattended **Charges Public
areas** in hall area only **Grounds Exercise area**
adjacent **Other** dogs allowed in two bedrooms
only **Resident Pets:** Buff (Wire Haired Fox Terrier)
& Hemi (Lurcher)

Located in the picturesque area this historic inn
dates from 1573 and was the first licensed house
in Wales. The lovely gardens create an immediate
welcome, which is matched by a friendly and
professional staff. Public areas are appointed
with flair. Spacious bedrooms, in renovated
outbuildings are equipped with a wealth of
thoughtful extras and many have balconies.

Rooms 14 en suite (1 fmly) (6 GF) S £85-£120;
D £105-£200* **Facilities** STV tea/coffee Dinner
available Direct Dial Cen ht Wi-fi **Conf** Max 20
Thtr 20 Class 20 Board 20 **Parking** 100 **Notes** LB
Closed Xmas

CONWY

The Old Rectory Country House
★★★★★ 🏠 GUEST ACCOMMODATION

☎ 01492 580611
Llanrwst Rd, Llansanffraid Glan Conwy
LL28 5LF
e-mail: info@oldrectorycountryhouse.co.uk
web: www.oldrectorycountryhouse.co.uk
dir: 0.5m S from A470/A55 junct on left, by
30mph sign

PETS: **Bedrooms** unattended **Charges Public
areas Grounds Exercise area** adjacent **Other**
dogs allowed in Coach House only **Restrictions**
no breed larger than a Labrador; no St Bernards,
Pyrenean Mountain Dogs, Newfoundlands or
Great Danes

This very welcoming accommodation has fine
views over the Conwy estuary and towards
Snowdonia. The elegant day rooms are luxurious
and afternoon tea is available in the lounge.
Bedrooms share the delightful views and are
thoughtfully furnished, while the genuine
hospitality creates a real home-from-home.

Rooms 3 en suite 2 annexe en suite (1 fmly) S
£79-£119; D £99-£159 **Facilities** STV FTV tea/
coffee Direct Dial Cen ht **Parking** 10 **Notes** LB No
Children 5yrs Closed 14 Dec-15 Jan

CONWY

Sychnant Pass Country House

★★★★★ ® GUEST ACCOMMODATION

☎ 01492 585486 📠 01492 585486
Sychnant Pass Rd LL32 8BJ
e-mail: info@sychnantpasscountryhouse.co.uk
web: www.sychnantpasscountryhouse.co.uk
dir: 1.75m W of Conwy. Off A547 Bangor Rd in
town onto Mount Pleasant & Sychnant Pass Rd,
1.75m on right near top of hill

PETS: **Bedrooms** unattended **Charges Public
areas** except restaurant & leisure area **Grounds
Exercise area Facilities** food (pre-bookable)
water bowl **Resident Pet:** Peter (cat)

Fine views are to be had from this Edwardian
house set in landscaped grounds. Bedrooms,
including suites and four-poster rooms, are
individually furnished and equipped with a range
of thoughtful extras. Lounges, warmed by open
fires in the chillier months, are comfortable and
inviting, and imaginative dinners and suppers
are served in the attractive dining room.

Rooms 12 en suite (3 fmly) (2 GF) S £75-£160; D
£95-£180* **Facilities** tea/coffee Dinner available
Cen ht Licensed Wi-fi 🕓 Sauna Solarium
Gymnasium **Parking** 30 **Notes** LB Closed 24-26
Dec & Jan Civ Wed 100

LLANRWST

Maenan Abbey

★★★ 78% HOTEL

☎ 01492 660247 📠 01492 660734
Maenan LL26 0UL
e-mail: reservations@manab.co.uk
dir: 3m N on A470

PETS: **Bedrooms** unattended **Charges Public
areas** except dining area & bar during food
service **Grounds Exercise area** surrounding area
Facilities food (pre-bookable) **Resident Pets:**
Poppy (Staffordshire cross), Harvey (Spaniel)

Set in its own spacious grounds, this privately
owned hotel was built as an abbey in 1850 on
the site of a 13th-century monastery. It is now
a popular venue for weddings as the grounds
and magnificent galleried staircase make an
ideal setting for photographs. Bedrooms include
a large suite and are equipped with modern
facilities. Meals are served in the bar and
restaurant.

Rooms 14 (3 fmly) (4 smoking) **Facilities** Fishing
Guided mountain walks Xmas New Year Wi-fi
Conf Class 30 Board 30 Thtr 50 **Parking** 60
Notes LB Civ Wed 55

TREFRIW

Hafod Country House
★★★★ GUEST ACCOMMODATION

☎ 01492 640029 📠 01492 641351
LL27 0RQ
e-mail: stay@hafod-house.co.uk
dir: On B5106 entering Trefriw from S, 2nd house
on right

PETS: **Bedrooms** unattended **Charges Public
areas Grounds Exercise area** 100yds **Facilities**
food (pre-bookable) food bowl water bowl
Other all bedrooms have a balcony with steps to
garden **Resident Pets:** Isla (Deerhound), Ricky
(Greyhound)

This former farmhouse is personally run and
friendly with a wealth of charm and character.
The tasteful bedrooms feature period furnishings
and thoughtful extras such as fresh fruit. There
is a comfortable sitting room and a cosy bar. The
fixed-price menu is imaginative and makes good
use of fresh, local produce while the breakfast
menu offers a wide choice.

Rooms 6 en suite S fr £30; D £57-£90*
Facilities tea/coffee Dinner available Direct Dial
Cen ht Licensed **Parking** 14 **Notes** LB No Children
11yrs RS Jan-Mar Mon & Tue no meals for non-
residents

LLANDYRNOG

Pentre Mawr Country House
★★★★★ 🛏 GUEST ACCOMMODATION

☎ 01824 790732 📠 01492 585486
LL16 4LA
e-mail: info@pentremawrcountryhouse.co.uk
dir: From Denbigh follow Bodfari/Llandyrnog
signs. Left at rdbt to Bodfari, in 50yds left onto
country lane, follow to Pentre Mawr on left

PETS: **Bedrooms** unattended **Charges Public
areas** except restaurant & pool areas **Grounds
Exercise area Facilities** food (pre-bookable)
water bowl **Resident Pets:** Mollie, Maisie & Millie
(Collies), Morris & Oscar (cats), 4 ponies

Expect a warm welcome from Graham and Bre
at this superb family country house set in nearly
200 acres of meadows, park and woodland. The
property has been in Graham's family for over
400 years. Bedrooms are individually decorated,
very spacious and thoughtfully equipped.
Breakfast is served in either the morning room
or on the Georgian terrace. Dinner is served in
the formal dining room. There is a salt water
swimming pool in the walled garden.

Rooms 5 en suite S £75-£130; D £95-£150*
Facilities tea/coffee Dinner available Cen ht
Licensed Wi-fi 🕂 🏊 🎣 Fishing **Parking** 8
Notes LB No Children 13yrs Closed Nov-Feb 🐾

MOLD

Beaufort Park Hotel

★★★ 74% HOTEL

☎ 01352 758646 📠 01352 757132
Alltami Rd, New Brighton CH7 6RQ
e-mail: info@beaufortparkhotel.co.uk
web: www.beaufortparkhotel.co.uk
dir: A55/A494. Through Alltami lights, over mini rdbt by petrol station towards Mold, A5119. Hotel 100yds on right

PETS: **Bedrooms** unattended **Charges Public areas** except restaurant **Grounds Facilities Restrictions** small, well behaved dogs only

This large, modern hotel is conveniently located a short drive from the North Wales Expressway and offers various styles of spacious accommodation. There are extensive public areas, and several meeting and function rooms are available. There is a wide choice of meals in the formal restaurant and in the popular Arches bar.

Rooms 106 (8 fmly) (32 GF) S £95; D £110 (incl. bkfst) **Facilities** FTV Squash ♫ Xmas New Year Wi-fi **Conf** Class 120 Board 120 Thtr 250 **Parking** 200 **Notes** LB Civ Wed 250

DOLGELLAU

Dolserau Hall

★★★ 81% ⊛ HOTEL

☎ 01341 422522 📠 01341 422400
LL40 2AG
e-mail: welcome@dolserau.co.uk
web: www.dolserau.co.uk
dir: 1.5m outside Dolgellau between A494 to Bala & A470 to Dinas Mawddy

PETS: **Bedrooms** unattended **Charges Public areas Grounds Exercise area** adjacent **Resident Pet:** Charlie (Golden Retriever)

This privately owned, friendly hotel lies in attractive grounds that extend to the river and are surrounded by green fields. Several comfortable lounges are provided and welcoming log fires are lit during cold weather. The smart bedrooms are spacious, well equipped and comfortable. A varied menu offers very competently prepared dishes.

Rooms 20 (5 annexe) (1 fmly) (3 GF) S £70-£88; D £140-£210 (incl. bkfst & dinner)* **Facilities** Fishing Xmas New Year **Services** Lift **Parking** 40 **Notes** No children 10yrs Closed Dec-Jan (ex Xmas & New Year)

FFESTINIOG

Ty Clwb

★★★★ BED AND BREAKFAST

☎ 01766 762658   📠 01766 762658
The Square LL41 4LS
e-mail: tyclwb@talk21.com
web: www.tyclwb.co.uk
dir: On B4391 in of Ffestiniog, opp church

PETS: Bedrooms unattended **Public areas** except dining room **Exercise area** 100yds **Resident Pets:** Ben (Lurcher/Old English Sheepdog cross), Casper (Border Collie)

Located opposite the historic church, this elegant house has been carefully modernised and is immaculately maintained throughout. Bedrooms are thoughtfully furnished and in addition to an attractive dining room, a spacious lounge with sun patio provides stunning views of the surrounding mountain range.

Rooms 3 en suite; D £54-£70 **Facilities** TVL tea/coffee Cen ht

LLANBEDR

Ty Mawr

★★ 71% SMALL HOTEL

☎ 01341 241440   📠 01341 241440
LL45 2NH
e-mail: tymawrhotel@onetel.com
web: www.tymawrhotel.org.uk
dir: From Barmouth A496 (Harlech road). In Llanbedr turn right after bridge, hotel 50yds on left, brown tourist signs on junct

PETS: Bedrooms unattended **Public areas** except restaurant **Grounds Exercise area** approx 200yds **Facilities** water bowl **Resident Pets:** Carlo (Welsh Sheepdog), Chelly (Border Collie), Tara (Sheepdog), Boyzie & Tallulah (rabbits)

Located in a picturesque village, this family-run hotel has a relaxed, friendly atmosphere. The attractive grounds opposite the River Artro provide a popular beer garden during fine weather. The attractive, rustically furnished bar offers a blackboard selection of food and a good choice of real ales. A more formal menu is available in the restaurant. Bedrooms are smart and brightly decorated.

Rooms 10 (2 fmly) S £35-£50; D £70-£80 (incl. bkfst)* **Facilities** STV **Conf** Class 25 **Parking** 30 **Notes** Closed 24-26 Dec

PORTHMADOG

Royal Sportsman Hotel

★★★ 77% ® HOTEL

☎ 01766 512015 📠 01766 512490
131 High St LL49 9HB
e-mail: enquiries@royalsportsman.co.uk
dir: By rdbt, at A497 & A487 junct

PETS: Bedrooms unattended Charges Public
areas except dining room Grounds Exercise area
countryside Facilities food (pre-bookable) food
bowl water bowl Resident Pet: Gelert (Sheepdog)

Ideally located in the centre of Porthmadog, this
former coaching inn dates from the Victorian era
and has been restored into a friendly, privately
owned and personally run hotel. Rooms are
tastefully decorated and well equipped, and some
are in an annexe close to the hotel. There is a
large comfortable lounge and a wide range of
meals is served in the bar or restaurant.

Rooms 28 (9 annexe) (7 fmly) (9 GF) S £55-£80;
D £84-£95 (incl. bkfst)* Facilities STV FTV Xmas
New Year Wi-fi Conf Class 50 Board 30 Thtr 50
Parking 17 Notes LB

ABERGAVENNY

Llansantffraed Court Hotel

★★★ 80% ®® COUNTRY HOUSE HOTEL

☎ 01873 840678 📠 01873 840674
Llanvihangel Gobion, Clytha NP7 9BA
e-mail: reception@llch.co.uk
web: www.llch.co.uk
dir: At A465/A40 Abergavenny junct take B4598
signed Usk (do not join A40). Continue towards
Raglan, hotel on left in 4.5m

PETS: Bedrooms unattended Charges Public
areas except dining area Grounds 20 acres
Facilities food bowl water bowl Other prior
notice required; 2 kennels available

In a commanding position and in its own
extensive grounds, this very impressive property,
now a privately owned country-house hotel, has
enviable views of the Brecon Beacons. Extensive
public areas include a relaxing lounge and a
spacious restaurant offering imaginative and
enjoyable dishes. Bedrooms are comfortably
furnished and have modern facilities.

Rooms 21 (1 fmly) S £86-£120; D £115-£175
(incl. bkfst) Facilities STV FTV ॐ Putt green
Fishing ॐ Clay pigeon shooting school
Wi-fi Conf Class 120 Board 100 Thtr 220
Del from £140 to £220 Services Lift Parking 250
Notes LB Civ Wed 150

ABERGAVENNY

Angel Hotel
★★★ 77% ◉ HOTEL

☎ 01873 857121   🖷 01873 858059
15 Cross St NP7 5EN
e-mail: mail@angelhotelabergavenny.com
web: www.angelhotelabergavenny.com
dir: Follow town centre signs from rdbt, S of
Abergavenny, past rail & bus stations. Turn left
along side of hotel

PETS: **Bedrooms** unattended **Charges Public
areas** except restaurant **Grounds Exercise area**
50mtrs **Facilities** water bowl

Once a coaching inn this has long been a popular
venue for both local people and visitors; the two
traditional function rooms and a ballroom are in
regular use. In addition there is a comfortable
lounge, a relaxed bar and a smart, award-
winning restaurant. In warmer weather there is a
central courtyard that is ideal for alfresco eating.
The bedrooms include a four-poster room and
some that are suitable for families.

Rooms 32 (2 fmly) **S** £65; **D** £85-£130 (incl.
bkfst)* **Facilities** ♫ Xmas New Year Wi-fi
Conf Class 120 **Board** 60 **Thtr** 200 **Parking** 30
Notes LB Closed 25 Dec RS 24, 26 & 27 Dec
Civ Wed 200

CHEPSTOW

Castle View
★★★ 64% HOTEL

☎ 01291 620349   🖷 01291 627397
16 Bridge St NP16 5EZ
e-mail: castleviewhotel@btconnect.com
dir: M48 junct 2, A466 for Wye Valley, at 1st rdbt
right onto A48 towards Gloucester. Follow 2nd
sign to town centre, then to Chepstow Castle,
hotel directly opposite

PETS: **Bedrooms** unattended **Charges ublic
areas** except restaurant **Grounds Exercise area**

This hotel was built around 300 years ago and
offers unrivalled views of Chepstow Castle.
Accommodation is comfortable - there are
family rooms, double-bedded rooms, and some
bedrooms that are situated in a separate
building; a good range of extras for guest comfort
is provided. There is a cosy bar area and a small
restaurant where home-cooked food using fresh,
local ingredients is offered.

Rooms 13 (4 annexe) (7 fmly) **S** £45-£60;
D £70-£85 (incl. bkfst) **Facilities** Xmas New Year
Wi-fi **Notes** LB

PORT TALBOT

Best Western Aberavon Beach Hotel

★★★ 75% HOTEL

☎ 01639 884949 📄 01639 897885

Neath SA12 6QP

e-mail: sales@aberavonbeach.com

web: www.aberavonbeach.com

dir: M4 junct 41/A48 & follow signs for Aberavon Beach & Hollywood Park

PETS: Bedrooms unattended **Charges Public areas** except restaurant **Grounds Exercise area** beach 100yds (restricted access May-Sep) **Facilities** water bowl **Other** dogs allowed unattended in bedrooms only if owners are on premises **Restrictions** no dangerous dogs (see page 5)

This friendly, purpose-built hotel enjoys a prominent position on the seafront overlooking Swansea Bay. Bedrooms, many with sea views, are comfortably appointed and thoughtfully equipped. Public areas include a leisure suite with swimming pool, open-plan bar and restaurant plus a choice of function rooms.

Rooms 52 (6 fmly) S £50-£120; D £60-£130 (incl. bkfst) **Facilities** FTV ⛲ All weather leisure centre Sauna ♬ Xmas New Year Wi-fi **Conf Class** 200 **Board** 100 **Thtr** 300 **Services** Lift **Parking** 150 **Notes** LB Civ Wed 300

FISHGUARD

Cartref Hotel

★★ 63% HOTEL

☎ 01348 872430 & 0781 330 5235

📄 01348 873664

15-19 High St SA65 9AW

e-mail: cartrefhotel@btconnect.com

web: www.cartrefhotel.co.uk

dir: On A40 in town centre

PETS: Bedrooms unattended **Charges Public areas** **Exercise area** 100mtrs **Facilities** food bowl water bowl **Resident Pet:** Tofie (Terrier)

Personally run by the proprietor, this friendly hotel offers convenient access to the town centre and ferry terminal. Bedrooms are well maintained and include some family rooms. There is also a cosy lounge bar and a welcoming restaurant that looks out onto the high street.

Rooms 10 (2 fmly) S £35-£41; D £60-£68 (incl. bkfst)* **Facilities** FTV **Parking** 4

MANORBIER

Castlemead Hotel

★★ 72% HOTEL

☎ 01834 871358 📠 01834 871358
SA70 7TA

e-mail: castlemeadhotel@aol.com
web: www.castlemeadhotel.com
dir: A4139 towards Pembroke, onto B4585 into village & follow signs to beach & castle. Hotel on left above beach

PETS: **Bedrooms** unattended **Public areas Grounds Exercise area** beach 500yds **Resident Pets:** Rosie (Border Collie), Max & Polly (cats)

Benefiting from a superb location with spectacular views of the bay, the Norman church and Manorbier Castle, this family-run hotel is friendly and welcoming. Bedrooms which include some in a converted former coach house, are generally quite spacious and have modern facilities. Public areas include a sea-view restaurant, bar and residents' lounge, as well as an extensive garden.

Rooms 8 (3 annexe) (2 fmly) (3 GF) S fr £45; D fr £86 (incl. bkfst) **Facilities** FTV Wi-fi **Parking** 20 **Notes** LB Closed Dec-Feb RS Nov

ST DAVID'S

Warpool Court Hotel

★★★ 79% @@ COUNTRY HOUSE HOTEL

☎ 01437 720300 📠 01437 720676
SA62 6BN

e-mail: info@warpoolcourthotel.com
web: www.warpoolcourthotel.com
dir: At Cross Square left by The Bishops Restaurant (Goat St). Pass Farmers Arms pub, after 400mtrs left, follow hotel signs, entrance on right

PETS: **Bedrooms** unattended **Charges Public areas Grounds Exercise area Facilities** water bowl

Originally the cathedral choir school, this hotel is set in landscaped gardens looking out to sea and is within easy walking distance of the Pembrokeshire Coastal Path. The lounges are spacious and comfortable, and the bedrooms are well furnished and equipped with modern facilities. The restaurant offers delightful cuisine.

Rooms 21 (3 fmly) S £125; D £150-£350 (incl. bkfst)* **Facilities** ✪ ✦ ✦ Table tennis Pool table Xmas New Year Wi-fi **Conf** Class 25 Board 25 Thtr 40 **Parking** 100 **Notes** LB Closed Jan Civ Wed 120

TENBY

Clarence House

★★ 62% HOTEL

☎ 01834 844371 🖹 01834 844372
Esplanade SA70 7DU
e-mail: clarencehotel@freeuk.com
dir: Off South Parade by town walls onto St
Florence Parade & Esplanade

PETS: Bedrooms unattended Charges Public
areas except restaurant Grounds Exercise area
beach 5 min walk

Owned by the same family for over 50 years, this
hotel has superb views from its elevated position.
Many of the bedrooms have sea views and all
are comfortably furnished. The bar leads to a
sheltered rose garden or a number of lounges.
Entertainment is provided in high season, and
this establishment is particularly popular with
coach tour parties.

Rooms 76 (6 fmly) S £27-£37; D £54-£74 (incl.
bkfst)* Facilities ♫ Services Lift Notes Closed
18-28 Dec

WOLF'S CASTLE

Wolfscastle Country Hotel

★★★ 78% ⊛ COUNTRY HOUSE HOTEL

☎ 01437 741688 & 741225 🖹 01437 741383
SA62 5LZ
e-mail: enquiries@wolfscastle.com
web: www.wolfscastle.com
dir: On A40 in village at top of hill. 6m N of
Haverfordwest

PETS: Bedrooms unattended Charges Public
areas Grounds Exercise area 200mtrs Other
dogs not allowed in executive bedrooms

This large stone house, a former vicarage, dates
back to the mid-19th century and is now a
friendly, privately owned and personally run hotel.
It provides stylish, modern, well-maintained and
well-equipped bedrooms. There is a pleasant bar
and an attractive restaurant, which has a well
deserved reputation for its food.

Rooms 20 (2 fmly) Facilities FTV New Year Wi-fi
Conf Class 100 Board 30 Thtr 100 Del from £125
to £210* Parking 60 Notes Closed 24-26 Dec
Civ Wed 70

BRECON

The Felin Fach Griffin
★★★★ ◉◉ INN

☎ 01874 620111
Felin Fach LD3 0UB
e-mail: enquiries@eatdrinksleep.ltd.uk
dir: 4m NE of Brecon on A470

PETS: Bedrooms unattended Public areas except
dining room Grounds Exercise area Facilities
food bowl water bowl Resident Pets: Max (Kelpie
Collie), Gizmo (Chihuahua)

This delightful inn stands in an extensive garden
at the northern end of the village of Felin Fach.
The public areas have a wealth of rustic charm
and provide the setting for the excellent food that
is served. The bedrooms are carefully appointed
and have modern equipment and facilities. The
service and hospitality are commendable here.

Rooms 7 en suite (1 fmly) S £65-£85; D
£115-£140* Facilities tea/coffee Dinner
available Direct Dial Cen ht ⏳ Conf Max 15
Board 15 Parking 61 Notes LB Closed 25-26 Dec
No coaches

BRECON

Borderers
★★★ GUEST ACCOMMODATION

☎ 01874 623559
47 The Watton LD3 7EG
e-mail: info@borderers.com
web: www.borderers.com
dir: 200yds SE of town centre on B4601, opposite
church

PETS: Bedrooms unattended Public areas
Grounds Exercise area 100mtrs Facilities food
bowl water bowl Resident Pets: Ella (Black
Labrador), Breagh (Chocolate Labrador)

This guest house was originally a drovers' inn
in the 17th century. The courtyard, now a car
park, is surrounded by many of the bedrooms,
and pretty hanging baskets are seen everywhere.
The bedrooms are attractively decorated with
rich floral fabrics. A room with easier access is
available.

Rooms 4 rms (3 en suite) (1 pri facs) 5 annexe en
suite (2 fmly) (4 GF) Facilities tea/coffee Cen ht
Wi-fi Parking 6

BUILTH WELLS

Caer Beris Manor

★★★ 77% COUNTRY HOUSE HOTEL

☎ 01982 552601 📄 01982 552586
LD2 3NP
e-mail: caerberis@btconnect.com
web: www.caerberis.com
dir: From town centre follow A483/Llandovery
signs. Hotel on left

PETS: Bedrooms unattended Charges Public
areas except main restaurant Grounds Exercise
area

Guests can expect a relaxing stay at this friendly
and privately owned hotel that has extensive
landscaped grounds. Bedrooms are individually
decorated and furnished to retain an atmosphere
of a bygone era. The spacious and comfortable
lounge and a lounge bar continue this theme,
and there's an elegant restaurant, complete with
16th-century panelling.

Rooms 23 (1 fmly) (3 GF) S fr £69.95;
D fr £119.95 Facilities FTV Fishing 🥄
Clay pigeon shooting Xmas New Year Wi-fi
Conf Class 75 Board 50 Thtr 100 Del from £79.95
to £115.95 Parking 100 Notes LB Civ Wed 200

CRICKHOWELL

Bear Hotel

★★★ 77% ® HOTEL

☎ 01873 810408 📄 01873 811696
NP8 1BW
e-mail: bearhotel@aol.com
dir: On A40 between Abergavenny & Brecon

PETS: Bedrooms (unattended Public areas
except restaurant Grounds Exercise area 350yds
Facilities food bowl water bowl Other freshly
cooked chicked offered to all visiting dogs
Resident Pet: Magic (cat)

A favourite with locals as well as visitors, the
character and friendliness of this 15th-century
coaching inn are renowned. The bedrooms come
in a variety of sizes and standards including
some with four-posters. The bar and restaurant
are furnished in keeping with the style of the
building and provide comfortable areas in which
to enjoy some of the very popular dishes that use
the finest locally-sourced ingredients.

Rooms 34 (13 annexe) (6 fmly) (6 GF)
S £70-£117; D £86-£153 (incl. bkfst)
Facilities STV FTV Wi-fi Conf Class 20 Board 20
Thtr 40 Del from £137 to £143 Parking 45
Notes LB No children 6yrs RS 25 Dec

CRICKHOWELL

Manor Hotel
★★★ 75% ® HOTEL

☎ 01873 810212   📄 01873 811938
Brecon Rd NP8 1SE
e-mail: info@manorhotel.co.uk
web: www.manorhotel.co.uk
dir: On A40, Crickhowell/Brecon, 0.5m from Crickhowell

PETS: **Bedrooms** unattended **Charges Public areas** except restaurant **Grounds Exercise area** adjoining footpaths **Other** dogs allowed in certain bedrooms only **Resident Pets:** Honey & Henry (Golden Retrievers), Cerys (Welsh Cob)

This impressive manor house, set in a stunning location, was the birthplace of Sir George Everest. The bedrooms and public areas are elegant, and there are extensive leisure facilities. The restaurant, with panoramic views, is the setting for exciting modern cooking.

Rooms 22 (1 fmly) **Facilities** STV FTV ⊙ Gym Fitness assessment Sunbed Xmas New Year Wi-fi **Conf** Class 250 Board 150 Thtr 300 Del from £125 to £145 **Parking** 200 **Notes** Civ Wed 150

LLANDRINDOD WELLS

The Metropole
★★★ 82% ® HOTEL

☎ 01597 823700   📄 01597 824828
Temple St LD1 5DY
e-mail: info@metropole.co.uk
web: www.metropole.co.uk
dir: On A483 in town centre

PETS: **Bedrooms** unattended **Charges Public areas** except restaurants & food outlets **Grounds Exercise area** park adjacent to hotel

The centre of this famous spa town is dominated by this large Victorian hotel, which has been personally run by the same family for well over 100 years. The lobby leads to Spencers Bar and Brasserie and to the comfortable and elegantly styled lounge. Bedrooms vary in style, but all are quite spacious and well equipped. Facilities include an extensive range of conference and function rooms, as well as the leisure centre.

Rooms 120 (11 fmly) **S** £94-£96; **D** £120-£150 (incl. bkfst) **Facilities** Spa ⊙ Gym Beauty & holistic treatments Sauna Steam room Xmas New Year Wi-fi **Conf** Class 200 Board 80 Thtr 300 Del from £120 to £125 **Services** Lift **Parking** 150 **Notes** LB Civ Wed 300

LLANWDDYN

Lake Vyrnwy Hotel

★★★★ 76% ® COUNTRY HOUSE HOTEL

☎ 01691 870692 📠 01691 870259
Lake Vyrnwy SY10 0LY
e-mail: info@lakevyrnwyhotel.co.uk
web: www.lakevyrnwyhotel.co.uk
dir: On A4393, 200yds past dam turn sharp right

PETS: **Bedrooms** unattended **Charges Public areas Grounds Exercise area** countryside walks **Other** dogs allowed in designated bedrooms only; heated kennels available **Resident Pets:** 2 Labradors

This elegant Victorian country-house hotel lies in 26,000 acres of woodland above Lake Vyrnwy. Sympathetically refurbished during the past few years, it provides a wide range of bedrooms, most with superb views and many with four-poster beds and balconies. Extensive public rooms retain many period features and more informal dining is available in the popular Tower Tavern. Relaxing and rejuvenating treatments are a feature of the stylish health spa.

Rooms 52 (4 fmly) **Facilities Spa** STV FTV ॐ Fishing Gym Archery Birdwatching Canoeing Kayaking Clay shooting Sailing Fly fishing Cycling Xmas New Year Wi-fi **Conf** Class 80 Board 60 Thtr 200 Del from £145 to £165 **Services** Lift **Parking** 70 **Notes** Civ Wed 200

MONTGOMERY

Dragon Hotel

★★ 79% ® HOTEL

☎ 01686 668359 📠 0870 011 8227
SY15 6PA
e-mail: reception@dragonhotel.com
web: www.dragonhotel.com
dir: Behind town hall

PETS: **Bedrooms** unattended **Charges Public areas** except dining areas **Grounds Exercise area** countryside nearby

This fine 17th-century coaching inn stands in the centre of Montgomery. Beams and timbers from the nearby castle, which was destroyed by Cromwell, are visible in the lounge and bar. A wide choice of soundly prepared, wholesome food is available in both the restaurant and bar. Bedrooms are well equipped and family rooms are available.

Rooms 20 (6 fmly) (2 smoking) **S** £56-£66; **D** £94.50-£104.50 (incl. bkfst)* **Facilities** ॐ ♫ Xmas New Year Wi-fi **Conf** Class 30 Board 25 Thtr 40 Del from £86 to £125* **Parking** 21 **Notes** LB

PONTYPRIDD

Llechwen Hall Hotel

★★★ 73% ❀ COUNTRY HOUSE HOTEL

☎ 01443 742050 & 743020 📄 01443 742189
Llanfabon CF37 4HP
e-mail: steph@llechwen.co.uk
dir: A470 N towards Merthyr Tydfil. At large rdbt
take 3rd exit. At mini rdbt take 3rd exit, hotel
signed 0.5m on left

PETS: Bedrooms unattended Public areas
Grounds Exercise area 300mtrs

Set on top of a hill with a stunning approach,
this country house hotel has served many
purposes in its 200-year-old history including
a private school and a magistrates' court. The
spacious, individually decorated bedrooms are
well equipped; some are situated in the separate
coach house nearby. There are ground-floor,
twin, double and family bedrooms on offer. The
Victorian-style public areas are attractively
appointed and the hotel is a popular venue for
weddings.

Rooms 20 (8 annexe) (6 fmly) (4 GF)
Facilities FTV New Year Wi-fi Conf Class 40
Board 40 Thtr 80 Parking 150 Notes Closed
24-30 Dec Civ Wed 80

SWANSEA

Ramada Swansea

★★★ 77% HOTEL

☎ 01792 310330 📄 01792 797535
Phoenix Way, Swansea Enterprise Park
SA7 9EG
e-mail: sales.swansea@ramadajarvis.co.uk
web: www.ramadajarvis.co.uk
dir: M4 junct 44, A48 (Llansamlet), left at 3rd
lights, right at 1st mini rdbt, left into Phoenix
Way at 2nd rdbt. Hotel 800mtrs on right

PETS: Bedrooms unattended Charges Public
areas Grounds

This large, modern hotel is conveniently situated
on the outskirts of the city with easy access to
the M4. Bedrooms are comfortably appointed for
both business and leisure guests. Public areas
include the Arts Restaurant, Arts Bar and elegant
lounges. 24-hour room service is also available.

Rooms 119 (12 fmly) (50 GF) (10 smoking)
S £49-£140; D £59-£160 (incl. bkfst)*
Facilities STV FTV ❄ supervised Gym Sauna
New Year Wi-fi Conf Class 80 Board 60 Thtr 200
Del from £99 to £149 Parking 180 Notes LB
Civ Wed 120

BARRY

Egerton Grey Country House
★★★★ 81% ◉ COUNTRY HOUSE HOTEL

☎ 01446 711666 📠 01446 711690
Porthkerry CF62 3BZ
e-mail: info@egertongrey.co.uk
web: www.egertongrey.co.uk
dir: M4 junct 33 follow airport signs, left at rdbt for Porthkerry, 500yds left down lane between thatched cottages

PETS: Bedrooms unattended Charges Public areas conservatory only Grounds Exercise area country park & seaside nearby Facilities food (pre-bookable) food bowl water bowl Resident Pets: Louis (Cavalier King Charles Spaniel)

This former rectory enjoys a peaceful setting and views over delightful countryside with distant glimpses of the sea. The bedrooms are spacious and individually furnished. Public areas offer charm and elegance, and include an airy lounge and restaurant, which has been sympathetically converted from the billiards room.

Rooms 10 (4 fmly) S £100-£150; D £140-£180 (incl. bkfst)* Facilities FTV Putt green ⛳ Xmas New Year Wi-fi Conf Class 30 Board 22 Thtr 30 Del from £170 to £190* Parking 40 Notes LB Civ Wed 40

LLANARMON DYFFRYN CEIRIOG

West Arms
★★★★ ◉◉ INN

☎ 01691 600665 & 600612
📠 01691 600622
LL20 7LD
e-mail: gowestarms@aol.com
dir: Off A483/A5 at Chirk, take B4500 to Ceiriog Valley

PETS: Bedrooms Charges Public areas except restaurant Grounds Exercise area 300yds Facilities water bowl Other kennels with hay available Resident Pet: Marmite (Black Labrador)

Set in the beautiful Ceiriog Valley, this delightful 17th-century inn has a wealth of charm and character. There is a comfortable lounge, a room for private dining and two bars, as well as an elegant, award-winning restaurant offering a set-price menu of imaginative dishes, utilising quality local produce. The attractive bedrooms have a mixture of modern and period furnishings.

Rooms 15 en suite (2 fmly) (3 GF) Facilities tea/coffee Direct Dial Wi-fi Fishing Parking 22 Notes Civ Wed 50

AGHADOWEY

Brown Trout Golf & Country Inn

★★ 76% HOTEL

☎ 028 7086 8209 📠 028 7086 8878
209 Agivey Rd BT51 4AD
e-mail: jane@browntroutinn.com
dir: At junct of A54 & B66 junct on road to
Coleraine

PETS: Bedrooms unattended Charges Public
areas except restaurant Grounds Exercise
area Resident Pets: Muffin & Lucy (Chocolate
Labradors)

Set alongside the Agivey River and featuring
its own 9-hole golf course, this welcoming inn
offers a choice of spacious accommodation.
Comfortably furnished bedrooms are situated
around a courtyard area whilst the cottage suites
also have lounge areas. Home-cooked meals
are served in the restaurant and lighter fare is
available in the charming lounge bar which has
entertainment at weekends.

Rooms 15 (11 fmly) S £60-£75; D £70-£110
(incl. bkfst)* Facilities STV FTV ♨ 9 Putt green
Fishing Gym Game fishing ♫ Xmas New Year
Wi-fi Conf Class 24 Board 28 Thtr 40 Parking 80
Notes LB

BLARNEY

Blarney Golf Resort

★★★★ 76% ◉ HOTEL

☎ 021 4384477 📠 021 4516453
Tower
e-mail: reservations@blarneygolfresort.com
dir: Exit N20 for Blarney, 4km to Tower, turn right
onto Old Kerry Road. Hotel 2km on right.

PETS: Bedrooms unattended Charges Public
areas Grounds Exercise area Facilities food
food bowl water bowl Other dogs are required to
be muzzled

Set amid a John Daly designed golf course on the
outskirts of the village of Tower, this hotel offers
a range of well-equipped comfortable bedrooms.
Excellent standards of cuisine are on offer in the
Inniscarra Restaurant, with more casual eating
available throughout the afternoon in Cormac's
bar. The hotel also features a Sentosa Spa.

Rooms 117 (56 annexe) (56 fmly) (30 GF)
Facilities Spa FTV ☜ supervised ♨ 18 Putt green
Gym Steam room Sauna ♫ Xmas New Year Wi-fi
Conf Class 150 Board 40 Thtr 300 Services Lift
Air con Parking 250 Notes LB

RATHMULLAN

Rathmullan House

★★★★ 79% ⑳⑳ COUNTRY HOUSE HOTEL

☎ 074 9158188 🖹 074 9158200
e-mail: info@rathmullanhouse.com
dir: From Letterkenny, then Ramelton then
Rathmullan R243. Left at Mace shop, through
village, hotel gates on right

PETS: **Bedrooms** unattended **Charges Public
areas Grounds Exercise area** 500yds **Facilities**
food (pre-bookable) food bowl water bowl
Restrictions max height of dog 80cm; no Pit Bull
Terriers **Resident Pets:** Suzy (Labrador) & Odie
(Jack Russell)

This fine 18th-century property has been
operating as a hotel for the last 40 years under
the stewardship of the Wheeler family. Guests
are welcome to wander around the well-planted
grounds and the walled garden, from where
much of the ingredients for the Weeping Elm
Restaurant are grown. The many lounges are
relaxing and comfortable, while many of the
bedrooms benefit from balconies and patio areas.

Rooms 34 (4 fmly) (9 GF) S €80-€155;
D €160-€240 (incl. bkfst)* **Facilities Spa** ⓩ
🏊 🐾 New Year Wi-fi **Conf** Class 90 Board 40
Thtr 135 Del from €150 to €195 **Parking** 80
Notes LB Closed 11 Jan-5 Feb RS 15 Nov-12 Mar
Civ Wed 135

DUBLIN

Glenshandan Lodge

★★★★ GUEST ACCOMMODATION

☎ 01 8408838 🖹 01 8408838
Dublin Rd, Swords
e-mail: glenshandan@eircom.net
dir: Beside Statoil on airport side of Swords
Main St

PETS: **Bedrooms** unattended **Charges Public
areas** except restaurant & lounge **Grounds
Exercise area** 20mtrs **Resident Pets:** 2 Boxer
dogs

Family and dog-friendly house with hospitable
owners and good facilities including e-mail
access. Bedrooms are comfortable and one room
has easier access. Secure parking available.
Close to pubs, restaurants, golf, airport and the
Kennel Club.

Rooms 9 en suite (5 fmly) (5 GF) **Facilities** TVL
tea/coffee Cen ht Wi-fi **Conf** Max 20 **Parking** 10
Notes Closed Xmas/New Year

CASHEL

Cashel House Hotel

★★★ ◉◉ COUNTRY HOUSE HOTEL

☎ 095 31001   📄 095 31077
e-mail: res@cashel-house-hotel.com
web: www.cashel-house-hotel.com
dir: S off N59, 1.5km W of Recess, well signed

PETS: Bedrooms unattended **Charges Public areas** except food areas **Grounds Exercise area Other** 2 stables suitable for bigger dogs & gun dogs **Resident Pets:** cats, horses

Cashel House is a mid-19th century property, standing at the head of Cashel Bay, in the heart of Connemara. Quietly secluded in award-winning gardens with woodland walks. Attentive service comes with the perfect balance of friendliness and professionalism from McEvilly family and their staff. The comfortable lounges have turf fires and antique furnishings. The restaurant offers local produce such as the famous Connemara lamb, and fish from the nearby coast.

Rooms 29 (4 fmly) (6 GF) (4 smoking)
S €90-€135; D €190-€270 (incl. bkfst)
Facilities STV FTV 🏊 Garden school Xmas New Year Wi-fi Parking 40 Notes LB Civ Wed 80

RECESS (SRAITH SALACH)

Lough Inagh Lodge

★★★ ◉ COUNTRY HOUSE HOTEL

☎ 095 34706   & 34694   📄 095 34708
Inagh Valley
e-mail: inagh@iol.ie
dir: From Recess take R344 towards Kylemore

PETS: Bedrooms unattended **Public areas** except at food service **Grounds Exercise area** countryside walks nearby **Facilities** food bowl water bowl **Other** please phone for details of further facilities for dogs **Resident Pets:** Rex (Cocker Spaniel), Sasha (cat)

This 19th-century, former fishing lodge is akin to a family home where guests are encouraged to relax and enjoy the peace. It is situated between the Connemara Mountains and fronted by a good fishing lake. Bedrooms are smartly decorated and comfortable, there is a choice of lounges with turf fires and a cosy traditional bar. The delightful restaurant specialises in dishes of the local lamb and lake caught fish.

Rooms 13 (1 fmly) (4 GF) Facilities Fishing Hill walking Fly fishing Cycling Conf Class 20 Board 20 Thtr 20 Services Air con Parking 16 Notes Closed mid Dec-mid Mar

GLENBEIGH

Towers Hotel
★★★ 64% HOTEL

☎ 066 9768212 📄 066 9768260
e-mail: towershotel@eircom.net

PETS: Bedrooms unattended Charges Public
areas Grounds Exercise area beach 3km

Located on the northern side of the Ring of Kerry,
this long established, family run hotel is full of
character and charm. The traditional pub is very
much the social centre of the village, and the
restaurant has a reputation for the quality of its
seafood.

Rooms 34

KILLARNEY

Randles Court Hotel
★★★★ 81% HOTEL

☎ 064 6635333 📄 064 6639301
Muckross Rd
e-mail: info@randlescourt.com
dir: N22 towards Muckross, turn right at T-junct
on right. From N72 take 3rd exit on 1st rdbt into
town & follow signs for Muckross, hotel on left

PETS: Bedrooms unattended Charges Public
areas except restaurants & bars Grounds
Exercise area 500mtrs Facilities food (pre-
bookable) food bowl water bowl

Close to all the town's attractions, this is a
friendly family-run hotel with an emphasis
on customer care. Bedrooms are particularly
comfortable. Guests can enjoy a relaxing drink
in the cosy bar then dine in the chic Checkers
bistro restaurant where good food is served in
the evenings. A swimming pool and other leisure
facilities are available.

Rooms 78 (4 fmly) S €60-€150; D €85-€170
(incl. bkfst) Facilities STV ⓢ supervised Sauna
Steam room Hydrotherapy suite New Year Wi-fi
Conf Class 50 Board 40 Thtr 90 Services Lift
Parking 110 Notes LB Closed 22-27 Dec
Civ Wed 140

BALLINA

The Ice House
★★★★ 76% ® HOTEL

☎ 096 23500 🖹 096 23598
The Quay
e-mail: chill@theicehouse.ie
dir: On Sligo road turn right at Judge's Garage
into Riverside Estate. Right at T-junct onto Quay
Rd. Hotel on left

PETS: Bedrooms unattended Charges Public
areas except restaurant & lounge Exercise area
riverside walk Facilities food food bowl water
bowl Restrictions small - medium size dogs only

With a fascinating history, this property is a
stunning mix of old and new. The contemporary
decor features lots of wood, steel and glass
creating a very light and airy interior. The stylish
bedrooms include suites that have river views
from their balconies. An interesting menu is
offered at dinner in the vaulted Pier Restaurant,
once an ice store, with lighter fare offered during
the day in the bright riverside bar.

Rooms 32 (7 fmly) (10 GF) S €135-€195;
D €135-€250 (incl. bkfst)* Facilities Spa STV
Laconium Steam room New Year Wi-fi Child
facilities Conf Class 35 Board 30 Thtr 70
Services Lift Parking 32 Notes LB Closed 25-26
Dec Civ Wed 130

NENAGH

Ashley Park House
★★★★ BED AND BREAKFAST

☎ 067 38223 & 38013 🖹 067 38013
e-mail: margaret@ashleypark.com
web: www.ashleypark.com
dir: 6.5km N of Nenagh. Off N52 across lake,
signed on left & left under arch

PETS: Bedrooms unattended Public areas
Grounds Exercise area 20yds Facilities water
bowl Resident Pets: horses, ducks, peacocks,
hens, lambs in spring

The attractive, colonial style farmhouse was built
in 1770. Set in gardens that run down to Lake
Ourna, it has spacious bedrooms with quality
antique furnishings. Breakfast is served in the
dining room overlooking the lake, and dinner is
available by arrangement. There is a delightful
walled garden, and a boat for the fishing on the
lake is available.

Rooms 5 en suite (3 fmly) Facilities TVL tea/
coffee Dinner available Cen ht Licensed Wi-fi
Golf 18 Fishing Rowing boat on lake Conf Max 30
Board 30 Parking 30 Notes ☺

CAMPILE

Kilmokea Country Manor & Gardens

★★★★★ GUEST ACCOMMODATION

☎ 051 388109   📠 051 388776
Great Island
e-mail: kilmokea@eircom.net
dir: R733 from New Ross to Campile, right before village for Great Island & Kilmokea Gardens

PETS: Bedrooms unattended Charges Public areas except restaurant, lounge & conservatory Grounds Exercise area orchard & fields Facilities food (pre-bookable) food bowl water bowl Other kennels in courtyard; please phone for details of further facilities for dogs Resident Pets: Jasmin (Labrador), Rosa (Springer Spaniel), Jackie (horse), chickens, peacocks, ducks

An 18th-century rectory located in wooded gardens. Comfortable bedrooms and public rooms are richly furnished, and a country-house style dinner is served nightly (booking essential). Take breakfast in the conservatory and tea overlooking the beautiful gardens.

Rooms 4 en suite 2 annexe en suite (1 fmly) (2 GF) S €75-€180; D €180-€300 Facilities STV TVL tea/coffee Dinner available Direct Dial Cen ht Licensed Wi-fi 🕙 🏊 🏄 Fishing Riding Sauna Gym Conf Max 75 Thtr 40 Class 30 Board 25 Parking 23 Notes LB RS Nov-end Jan

MACREDDIN

BrookLodge & Wells Spa

★★★★ 86% ֍֍ HOTEL

☎ 0402 36444   📠 0402 36580
e-mail: info@brooklodge.com
web: www.brooklodge.com
dir: N11 to Rathnew, R752 to Rathdrum, R753 to Aughrim follow signs to Macreddin Village

PETS: Bedrooms unattended Public areas small dogs only Grounds Exercise area Resident Pets: Rudi, Lilly & Sam (Golden Retrievers)

A luxury country-house hotel complex, in a village setting, which includes Acton's pub, Orchard Café and retail outlets. Bedrooms in the original house are very comfortable, and mezzanine suites are situated in the landscaped grounds. Now available is Brook Hall with ground-floor and first floor bedrooms overlooking the 18th green of the golf course. The award-winning Strawberry Tree Restaurant is a truly romantic setting, specialising in organic and wild foods. The Wells Spa Centre offers extensive treatments and leisure facilities.

Rooms 90 (32 annexe) (27 fmly) (4 GF) Facilities Spa STV FTV 🕙 ⌇ ⚓ 18 Putt green Gym Archery Clay pigeon shooting Falconry Off road driving Xmas New Year Wi-fi Conf Class 120 Board 40 Thtr 300 Services Lift Parking 200 Notes Civ Wed 180